DUQUESNE STUDIES

Philosophical Series

13

SCIENCE AND TECHNOLOGY

DUQUESNE STUDIES

Philosophical Series

13

SCIENCE AND TECHNOLOGY

by

ANDREW G. VAN MELSEN, D.Sc.

Bradford Junior College Library
Bradford, Massachusetts

DUQUESNE UNIVERSITY PRESS, Pittsburgh, Pa.
Editions E. Nauwelaerts, Louvain, Belgium
1961

DUQUESNE STUDIES
Philosophical Series

Andrew G. van Melsen, D.Sc., D.Ed., and Henry J. Koren, C.S.Sp., S.T.D., editors.

Volume One—*Andrew G. van Melsen,* From Atomos to Atom. Pp. XII and 240. Price: paper $3.50, cloth $4.25. Published also in Dutch, German, Spanish, and Italian.

Volume Two—*Andrew G. van Melsen,* The Philosophy of Nature. Pp. XII and 263. Price: paper $3.75, cloth $4.50. Published also in Italian and Dutch. Polish edition in preparation. Second edition, third impression.

Volume Three—*P. Henry van Laer,* Philosophico-Scientific Problems. Out of print.

Volume Four—*Cajetan's* The Analogy of Names and The Concept of Being. Pp. X and 93. Second edition. Price: $2.25, cloth.

Volume Five—*Louis de Raeymaeker and others,* Truth and Freedom. Pp. VII and 132. Second impression. Price: $3.00, cloth. Published also in French.

Volume Six—*P. Henry van Laer,* The Philosophy of Science. Part One: Science in General. Pp. XVII and 164. Price: paper $3.00, cloth $3.75.

Volume Seven—*Stephan Strasser,* The Soul in Metaphysical and Empirical Psychology. Pp. X and 275. Price: paper $4.25, cloth $5.00. Published also in German, Dutch, and French.

Volume Eight—*Albert Dondeyne,* Contemporary European Thought and Christian Faith. Pp. XI and 211. Price: paper $5.00, cloth $5.75. Published also in French.

Volume Nine—*Maxwell J. Charlesworth,* Philosophy and Linguistic Analysis. Pp. XIII and 234. Price: paper $4.75, cloth $5.50.

Volume Ten—*Remy C. Kwant,* Philosophy of Labor. Pp. XI and 163. Price: paper $4.50, cloth $5.25.

Volume Eleven—*Remy C. Kwant,* Encounter. Pp. VIII and 85. Price: paper $2.50, cloth $3.25. Published also in Dutch.

Volume Twelve—*William A. Luijpen,* Existential Phenomenology. Pp. XIII and 355. Price: paper $6.00, cloth $6.75. Published also in Dutch.

Volume Thirteen—*Andrew G. van Melsen,* Science and Technology. Pp. X and 373. Price: paper $6.20, cloth $6.95. Published also in Dutch.

Library of Congress Catalog Card Number: 61-10975

All rights reserved
©1961, by Duquesne University

Printed in the United States of America by
The Ad Press, Ltd., New York, N. Y.

501
M

TABLE OF CONTENTS

35291

PART TWO

THE INFLUENCE OF PHYSICAL SCIENCE UPON CULTURE

INTRODUCTION

No one can claim to understand modern man without having a clear idea of something which constitutes one of man's principal occupations in our time, viz., physical science and technology. A reflection on this occupation, therefore, is necessary to understand contemporary man, but its value is not limited only to the understanding of man *in our time*. For the form in which man reveals himself in our days is not just one of the many pertaining to the history of mankind, in which the philosopher is especially interested because he happens to be a contemporary of this man. In an historical perspective there is also something of man's very essence that reveals itself in the form of modern man, whose life is so strongly dominated by physical science and technology, whose science manifests so many undreamt-of possibilities of knowledge and power. In what man now *is* and can do we find the realization or fulfilment of what he formerly was or wanted to be, just as it also makes us conjecture the future forms man will assume.

This realization, however, appears to differ considerably in many respects from what his original purpose gave reason to expect. Is it because the purpose itself implied these unsuspected possibilities or did man later become unfaithful to his former ideal?

This question becomes urgent when we pay attention to contemporary physical science. This science was born from the thinking of the ancient Greeks who sought to understand the cosmos and man's place in this cosmos. Greek thought was primarily theoretical in purpose, i.e., it aimed at pure knowledge without any selfish intention, at knowledge for the sake of knowledge. Although the Greeks knew, of course, about knowledge for utilitarian purposes, they explicitly considered such knowledge to be of an inferior grade. Utilitarian knowledge remained on a secondary and subordinate level.

Is Modern Science a Deviation of the Classical Ideal? Modern physical science gradually developed, in a way which we will discuss later, from the thinking of the ancient Greeks, which was mainly of a philosophical nature. Our present purpose is only to show that the physical science of subsequent times gradually began to exhibit an inspiration that was quite different from the Greek science from

1

which it had come forth. From being pure *theoria,* intellectual vision, science seems to have become primarily *praxis,* the guidance of action. Nowadays the meaning of physical science seems to lie especially in the possibilities it offers to man in his way of acting and of producing things. Science seems to have been drawn completely into the sphere of practicality and usefulness. Thus the development of science has taken place along lines which differ considerably from what its incipient stage appeared to suggest or even explicitly held up as the ideal to be pursued.

Does this evolution of science point to an apostasy from the authentic human ideal of science or is it the effect of an internal development in the scope of man's quest for scientific knowledge—a scope that was always inherent in any such quest, but remained hidden until modern times? To reply to this question, we must ask ourselves whether we may simply and unqualifiedly speak about man, about science, about the scope and meaning of science. We have to keep in mind that it is not possible to present a picture of man that does not take into account the way in which this picture historically manifests and modifies itself. Likewise, we may not speak of science and its ideals unqualifiedly, without historical perspective. Perhaps also the neglect of this historical perspective is one of the reasons why our culture is in a state of crisis.

For instance, an often-heard complaint about our universities is that they have become mere training schools for the various professions. The subject gives rise to many discussions. All kinds of efforts are made to modify this situation through so-called "core courses" or other means. But we must ask: are these efforts realistic and honest? Are they not inspired by a scientific ideal that is antiquated and superseded by the evolution of science itself? The question is not at all rhetorical, but demands a serious inquiry. It may very well be true that the crisis of the universities does really arise, at least in part, from the desire to hold fast in theory to a conception of science which was abandoned long ago in the actual practice of science, even as it is pursued in the universities. For the study of science has undergone a change which the Greeks did not foresee and which they could never have even thought of.

Devoting oneself to science is an adventure of the mind whose issue can never be predicted. This assertion applies to the pathway of every science in particular, to every concrete scientific investigation—they are by definition a venture into the unkown. It applies also to the course taken by the whole of science, considered as a human activity. Its ultimate result cannot be foretold. Knowledge for its own sake, the ancient Greek adventure, undertaken for wholly unselfish motives, has *de facto* developed into a science of the utmost servility, a science which is subservient to the development of human life in a way that would have been considered impossible in former times.

Is Modern Science an Effort to Deify or Secularize Man? On the other hand, it may also be true that the supposed discrepancy between the traditional theoretical ideal of science and the way in which science is actually pursued is not the only explanation of the crisis affecting our modern civilization. It could very well be true that our cultural forefathers clearly foresaw the general tendencies of our contemporary pursuit of science and that they called attention to it as an apostasy from the authentic ideal of science. In that case there would really be solid reasons for concern over the progressive predominance of science and technology in our cultural world. The myth of Prometheus narrates how man learned to use fire—one of the oldest technical inventions—by stealing it from the gods. Are not science and technology inspired by a similar desire of man to transgress his appointed realm and to claim for himself prerogatives belonging to God alone? The old myth shows at least that the Greeks, our cultural ancestors, knew what was appointed to man as well as man's capacity to deny and transgress these limits. May one not see in the creative urge of technology and in the passionate desire of modern man to make the world more livable, a kind of secularization of the Christian idea of Redemption—a redemption to be attained by man's own power, not in heaven but on earth? It seems that this idea is the driving force of contemporary science.

At least, it is certain that the modern forms of science are characterized by the enormous influence which they exercise upon man's life. They permeate society to such an extent that the entire social order is made dependent upon science. The evolution of science and technology has dislodged even what seemed to be most solidly anchored. Both literally and figuratively it has changed the face of the earth. No one knows where it will end—if ever it will come to an end. What inspires this ceaseless drive to renovate everything, to leave nothing as it is? Is it animated by the same human desire which in former times gave rise to pure science? In other words, is modern science which is so useful for life the logical continuation of the old ideal of science or is it a deviation from this ideal, or perhaps something entirely new? To many it is quite apparent that it is a deviation. One has only to think here of the feeling so often expressed that education in the professional under-graduate schools of a university pays little more than lip service to the broadening of the student's mind, that such schools do not really belong in a universtiy and serve only a utilitarian purpose.

The Danger of Man's Subservience to Science. Meanwhile it is certainly not only the tenacious clinging to the cultural and scientific ideals of the past which makes many dislike modern science and technology. Science and technology themselves contribute to it, for they have a peculiar nature. It is characteristic of them that they themselves do not give us any idea of the revolution which they cause. They exercise their influence, as it were, unwittingly, just as, as sciences, they do not have any idea of what exactly they are. For the question of what exactly physical science is, is not a ques-tion which can be raised within physical science itself. It cannot be solved through the intellectual apparatus of this science. Like-wise, reflection upon technical science and technical activity does not belong to technology itself. Accordingly, the above-mentioned concern about the predominance of science and technology finds its source, we think, at least partly, in this typically positive character of these human activities. Thinkers fear that in the pursuit of science and technology man is carried away by something which he himself has set into motion but over which he cannot retain his spiritual control. Because of the positive character of science and technology, there is indeed a possibility that, in pursuing them, man will plunge into them without clearly knowing what he is doing.

This possibility indicates the real danger that, instead of being authentically human activities, science and technology make man degenerate into a kind of passivity, a being-lived rather than living, which drags the whole of society and the social order into a fatal spiral. For, the more life becomes based on science and technology, the more these two will demand of man. Education, for instance, becomes more and more attuned to these forms of knowledge. Uni-versities, which in former times were centers of culture, are in danger of becoming training schools of scientific human robots, pro-grammed in such a way that they will create always newer and more perfect technical products. The ultimate will be that these human robots make themselves superfluous by creating real, more perfect, robots which can take over the whole business. All this, of course, may sound somewhat exaggerated. Nevertheless, it is rather striking that contemporary novels about the future paint exactly such a vision. We may mention, for instance, Aldous Huxley, *Brave New World,* and George Orwell, *1984.*

Fear and Awe of Science. Above we have indicated that there is a realistic ground for the concern expressed by so many thinkers. Physical science and technology have indeed a peculiar character because they are non-reflective. Of course, this does not condemn them, but merely indicates that alongside these sciences there must be other intellectual activities in which man reflects upon physical science and technology. In this reflection man must consider his activities in the realm of these sciences in the light of his whole being. On the other hand, so far as this reflection is concerned, if it is to be an authentic reflection upon man as he *is,* then it may not omit to take into consideration the human activities whch we call the pursuit of science and technology.

Unfortunately, it is a fact that the traditional cultural circles, which have always seen the source of genuine humanity in reflection upon man's being and in living the full human life, usually assume a mental attitude which rejects science and technology, although they are sometimes forced to pay lip service to the inevitable. In their view, modern man's pursuit of science and technology is an expression of a materialistic frame of mind, a preference for matter above mind. They view this preference as very dangerous because it subordinates man's intellectual nature to the satisfaction of material desires.

All this shows that our time is marked by a clear ambivalence with respect to physical science and its accomplishments. They are feared and desired at the same time. People realize intuitively that, by dominating nature, science has opened up such tremendous possibilities of living a human life that man may not discard them without renouncing his appointed human task. For it is in man that the supremacy of mind over matter must show itself both in the realm of knowledge and in that of action and production. On the one hand, therefore, science and technology lie fully in the line of man's being, they make man more man, they are necessary factors in man's progressive "humanization." On the other hand, thinkers fear that science and technology will lead to "dehumanization," because man is made subservient to the deterministic operations of a technical order. Man is creating something which he is no longer capable of controlling. Instead of dominating the technical order, he is dominated by it.

Science and Culture. The last-named danger—for a danger it is— is seen especially by so-called traditional cultural circles. Or rather, it is more felt than seen by them, for frequently they lack a good understanding of science and technology. This understanding is lacking also in those who pursue science and technology, but in a different fashion. The specialists in these branches of knowledge are, of course, thoroughly familiar with the theories and methods of the physical sciences, but this familiarity does not guarantee at all that they understand the place which must be assigned to scientific knowledge and technological power in the totality of man's existence. For possessing the concepts proper to physical science is not the same as having a concept of what physical science is, because this concept cannot be expressed in terms of the notions that are proper to physical science.

This lack of understanding of what physical science and technology are in those who pursue science and technology as well as in the students of the humanities leads to great uncertainty in our culture. Whether we want it or not, technical civilization cannot be discarded from contemporary culture. If we want to understand this culture, then we must include this civilization in our vision of culture. Likewise, we cannot understand man without understanding contemporary man who devotes, and has to devote, so much time to the pursuit of science and technology.

Purpose of this Book. These considerations sufficiently indicate the scope of this book. It intends to provide an understanding of physical science and technology and of their fundamental meaning for human existence. In the first part we will examine the nature of the knowledge attained in the physical sciences. This investigation will show that this knowledge is intrinsically connected with technological power. Making use of the insights acquired in the first part, we will investigate in the second part the influence both exercise upon culture and the place that should be assigned to them within the frame of this culture. Considerable attention will be devoted to the question as to which of the many deprecated results attributed to the influence of science and technology are essential and non-essential, i.e., flow necessarily or not necessarily from the nature of these sciences.

PART ONE

THE NATURE OF PHYSICAL SCIENCE

CHAPTER ONE

THE NON-REFLECTIVE CHARACTER
OF PHYSICAL SCIENCE

1. *The Difference Between Philosophy and Physical Science*

Unanimity Within Physical Science. As soon as an effort is made to determine the nature of physical science, we are struck by a curious discrepancy between the fundamental unanimity which physicists and chemists display in the pursuit of their science and the great division that reigns when a reply has to be given to the question of what exactly physical science is. *In principle,* physical and chemical circles are in full agreement as to what may be considered to be actually a scientific explanation of a given complex of phenomena. Likewise, they agree about numerous laws as well as about the results and the scope of all kinds of experiments.

All this is true, of course, only *in principle.* In any living science there are, alongside the unanimously accepted theories and explanations, *de facto* also a large number of hypotheses awaiting further verification or falsification. More important, however, than all actual differences of opinion is the fact that the scientists agree in principle about the ways and means by which these disputed points and uncertainties are to be solved in the future.

Accordingly, in physical science there is, at least in practice, agreement about the scientific *method* to be followed. By virtue of this unanimously accepted method, the physicist knows exactly what belongs to his science and what not. Hence he knows also what the object is of his science. Because the method is definitely laid down, there exists something like a body of physical statements that have been definitely established, so that everyone pursuing the physical sciences may confidently base himself on these statements in his contributions to the development of these sciences. This permanent body of statements contains, e.g., classical mechanics, optics, and electrodynamics. Their contents have been embodied in the instruments used in scientific research. We may refer here, for instance, to the use of the balance, of the microscope, and of all kinds of electric apparatus. Everyone uses these instruments without the slightest hesitation, even when he intends to show that the classical theories are imperfect.[1]

No Unanimity About Physical Science. A wholly different picture presents itself when our attention is not directed to the actual pursuit of the method proper to the physical sciences or to the body of its established laws, but to questions which in one way or another refer to these sciences as human activities. Such a question is, e.g., what exactly is a physical theory? Does it penetrate into the essence of the material reality which we study, in such a way that our mind mirrors, as it were, that which constitutes the essence of this reality? If the question is answered in the affirmative, material reality would be built of atoms in exactly the same way as our theories and models represent it. In other words, if our senses were more perfect instruments of perception than they actually are, we would be able to perceive the atomic structures directly with our eyes, although at present we are limited to mere intellectual conclusions regarding their existence on the basis of our indirect means of perception.

However, the reply to the question of what exactly a physical theory is may also be quite different from the preceding affirmative answer. According to a view held by many, a theory of the physical sciences is nothing else than a human device for summarizing our many experiences in such a way that they can be remembered in an easy and systematic fashion. Instead of obliging us to remember all the experiences one by one, a physical theory makes it possible for us to deduce them from an ingenious classification system which is logically well-organized and therefore presents a quick survey of the whole.

The difference between the two replies makes itself felt very strikingly when we apply them to the above-mentioned case of the atomic structure. According to the first reply, which we may briefly call the realistic view, the perceptible phenomena must be considered to be effects of a really existing atomic structure which itself, however, is not directly perceptible. Because we understand this real structure, we can also understand the perceptible workings of this structure as its effects. According to the second reply, which may be briefly called the positivistic view, the atomic structure is merely an

---

[1]Thus it should be clear that the classical theories are never completely superseded by others. What newer theories contradict is, strictly speaking, not so much the classical theory itself as certain extrapolations of this theory beyond the realm for which it has been actually established.

intellectual device in which we arrange the many perceptible phenomena in such a way that we can deduce them logically from this device. As far as reality is concerned, however, this intellectual device is, in principle, not capable of telling us anything.

Consequences for the Evaluation of Science. The difference in views about the nature of physical theory which manifests itself in the above-mentioned replies obviously has consequences for the evaluation of science. The first reply will attribute a high value to science, regardless of the practical applications to which it gives rise. Science, this view holds, makes man understand nature, and this suffices to enrich man, for thus he takes possession of nature which first appeared strange to him. Since science enriches the mind, it has value in itself. Any possible practical usefulness of science is merely an added benefit.

The second reply, on the other hand, does not consider the classifying power of science to be a value in itself. It attributes value to this power only insofar as it enables man to maintain himself more easily in the world around him because it makes it possible for him to anticipate the workings of nature.

Of course, both replies leave room for many differentiations and qualifications. We do not want to mention them here for the simple reason that these differentiations are irrelevant to our present problem. The only point which matters here is that the controversy in question is not a controversy within the realm of physical science: it cannot be expressed in terms of physical concepts and consequently cannot be solved through the methods of the physical sciences. This controversy delves deeper than the level on which physical concepts operate. It leaves also untouched the whole apparatus of physical concepts. Let us illustrate the point by means of an example.

Before the ionic theory, classical chemistry conceived atoms as immutable, so that all chemical phenomena had to be explained by means of modifications in atomic configurations. However, certain phenomena could not be explained in this way; hence theoretical chemistry abandoned the idea of immutable atoms and assumed that atoms could be charged with positive or negative electricity. Thus an existing theory was modified on the basis of certain experimental data. The important point here is that, as far as the above-mentioned controversy is concerned, it is wholly irrelevant whether one accepts the immutable chemical atoms of the old theory or the changeable atoms of a new theory.

The realistic interpretation, as a realistic interpretation, did not at all have to change its standpoint. The modification of the chemical theory simply meant, insofar as the realistic view was concerned, that in this concrete point chemistry had presented an imperfect picture of the atomic structures as they existed. This was nothing new, for the realists knew in general that the picture was imperfect because the chemical theory fell short of explaining everything. Likewise, the positivistic interpretation did not have to be modified. It was forced to design a new intellectual device to summarize everything on the basis of the new data, but its adherents knew already that any such device is merely provisional.

In other words, whether we think in terms of atoms or in terms of atoms and ions may be extremely important from the chemical viewpoint, but it is not important insofar as the controversy about the *general* interpretation of physical theory as such is concerned. For in the judgment *about* the physical theory the concepts of atoms, molecules, ions, energy, etc. play no role. All roles here are assigned to concepts such as *reality* and *knowledge*. If anyone wants to affirm or deny that man's cognitive powers are capable of knowing reality as it is, he cannot express his judgment in the language of physical science. What is needed here is a different language, another set of concepts, because the judgment in question lies on a different level— the level which is traditionally called "philosophical."

To prevent any misunderstanding, we must point out that these remarks do not at all imply that the evolution of physical science could not become a reason for modifying our philosophical interpretation of this science and lead to a different idea of what physical science is. The contrary is true. All we wanted to do was to make it clear that such a modification is not accomplished within physical science itself but in man's reflection upon this science. It goes without saying that a radical development of physical science offers an urgent reason for further reflection. This reflection, however, lies on another level than physical science itself.

The Non-Reflective Character of Physical Science. This last remark throws some light on the puzzling fact, mentioned at the beginning of this section—namely, that human beings are apparently capable of unanimously pursuing physical science without agreeing as to what exactly physical science is. For the pursuit of this science it appears to be sufficient to have knowledge of its practical method.

A more profound insight into its essence does not seem to be required. Apparently, simply to make use of certain methods in the acquisition of knowledge and thus to satisfy man's desire of an understanding of the physical data which will enable him to utilize them is more congenial to man's cognitive capacities than is reflection upon the more profound foundation of all this.

Such a conclusion appears to follow inevitably from the difference in unanimity mentioned above. This difference finds its explanation in the fact that there is question of two different levels of knowledge. They do not lie on the same line. Unanimity *within* physical science does not necessarily prolongate itself as unanimity in evaluating physical science as a human activity. What reveals itself here is a difference in cognitive grasp, a difference to which witness is borne by the entire history of the physical sciences as contrasted with that of philosophy. Because of this difference in cognitive grasp, it does not surprise us to see in the history of philosophy that after the rise of physical science efforts have been made constantly to declare all philosophical reflection meaningless, because such reflection is supposed to be beyond the capacities of man. Yet this idea is not so modern as it may seem, for even in ancient times Aristotle considered philosophy to be superhuman, i.e., "divine." Nevertheless, the desire to eliminate philosophy, obvious as it may be, cannot be carried out, for such an elimination itself is a philosophical undertaking. It is not without reason that positivism, which wants to perform this elimination in the most radical way, is a philosophical and not a scientific system.

Accordingly, we find the first characteristic of physical science in its non-reflective character. The absence of this reflectivity is not a property pertaining to every form of science. The case of philosophy illustrates this point. For philosophy investigates not only the character proper to physical science but also its own nature. While the question of what physical science is itself does not belong to the domain of physical science and therefore can neither be formulated nor answered in terms of this science, the question of what philosophy is itself is a philosophical question.

This characteristic difference between physical science and philosophy reveals itself also in the way in which we learn to pursue these sciences. We do not study physical science by reflecting upon it but by actually pursuing it. The best introduction to this pursuit is to point to certain phenomena which occur spontaneously in nature, e.g., the freezing of water and the melting of ice, and to ask a few questions about these phenomena. In this way attention is drawn to possible connections, which can be further illustrated by means of a few simple experiments. Thus the student is given a feeling for the way in which physical science raises its problems and for the method through which they are solved. Every chemist and physicist has been introduced to his science in this fashion and acquired an infallible instinct for distinguishing the problems, methods, and theories of physical science from those that are non-physical.

Of course, this practical and instinctive knowledge does not always protect the physicist or the chemist against illicit extrapolations beyond the realm of his specialty, but as a rule he is aware of it when he goes beyond the confines of his realm. In his extrapolations he justifies his procedure on the assumption that the method which has been so successful in his own science can very likely, with the necessary changes, be applied also in other realms and lead there to results similar to the successes of physical science.

Accordingly, the physicist and the chemist learn what physical science is or is not from their practical experience in pursuing this science and not through a philosophical introduction to physical science. Such an introduction would have been of little use to him. Moreover, strictly speaking, an introduction of this nature is not possible. It would have to consist in a reflection upon physical science, and therefore presupposes that this science is somehow known. For philosophy is essentially reflective. Philosophy consists in thinking in an orderly fashion about what is already present in us in a spontaneous way. For instance, a philosophical analysis of human knowledge, of the way in which we form our concepts, judge things, and reason about them presupposes that in our spontaneous intellectual life we have already actually formed all kinds of concepts, made many judgments, and indulged in reasoning.

The Difference Between Philosophy and Physical Science. This difference may be expressed also in the following way. Both philosophy and physical science are essentially fastened to our spontaneous cognitive life. Physical science cultivates this life by systematically directing attention to a certain realm of phenomena, while philosophy fosters it by concentrating attention upon spontaneous cognitive life itself and its implications. In our cognitive life we touch, as it were, our own activity from within. Thus an introduction to physical science satisfies its purpose when it manages to draw the student's attention to the realm of its interest and to teach him how to explore this realm. The introduction is successful if, and only if, it leads to the actual pursuit of physical science. Reflection upon the more profound meaning of the activity exercised in physical science, as such, lies beyond its scope.

An introduction to philosophy, on the other hand, can never be intended for the purpose of letting someone pursue philosophy in a practical way without any insight into the more profound meaning of philosophical reflection, because this insight is precisely what is intended by philosophy. What philosophy aims at is reflection upon man's integral activity. If philosophical reflection pertains to this activity, then it follows that this reflection belongs to the object of philosophical thinking. It is precisely this which gives philosophy its own peculiar character. Physical science may freely allow itself to make use of everything which is spontaneously present in our cognitive life, but philosophy cannot permit itself such a liberty. Physical science does not have to ask what knowledge is or what concepts, judgments, etc. are. It may simply start from the fact that man *de facto* is a cognitive being, that he forms concepts, and pronounces judgments. By its very nature, philosophy cannot do the same, but has to make a problem of man's power to form concepts and judgments.

These considerations lead us easily to the conclusion that the pursuit of the physical sciences is more immediately connected with man's spontaneous cognitive life than is the pursuit of philosophy. This point would explain also the striking difference in unanimity between physical science and philosophy, which was spoken of above.

In favor of such a more direct contact with man's spontaneous cognitive life is also the fact that physical science reveals itself practically useful. When physical science reflects, its *re*-consideration is at the same time a *pre*-consideration. For the reflection of physical science is fruitful for the subsequent activity of the physicist, for the way in which he will devise new experiments. Accordingly, in the reflection of the physical sciences the situation is similar to that of our spontaneous cognitive life, in which our knowledge directs our activity and the results of our activity supplies us with new cognitive data.[2]

---

[2]Cf. Remy C. Kwant, *Philosophy of Labor,* Pittsburgh, 1960, Ch. 2.

The more immediate connection of physical science with man's spontaneous cognition and activity seems to contain also a justification for a more or less spontaneous feeling many scientists have—namely, that it is best to stay away from philosophical speculations, because they are a dead-end street. As we have seen above, not a few philosophers endorse this spontaneous feeling—which is quite a *tour de force*.

Objections. Nevertheless, certain objections can be raised against our conclusion. They do not simply neutralize it, but considerably reduce its scope. First of all, one could say that the spontaneity of physical science is rather relative, witness the fact that it arose only in a very restricted cultural circle. Physical science, in the modern sense of the term, originated in Western Europe, which itself was strongly influenced by Greek thought.

A second remarkable fact is that Greek thought was primarily of a philosophical orientation. Historically speaking, therefore, philosophical reflection preceded physical science. Of course, to a greater or lesser degree knowledge of nature may be found in all cultural milieus in connection with certain technical abilities. But physical science originated only where this knowledge was guided by a profound philosophical reflection of the Greek type. Accordingly, it is undeniable that philosophical reflection has played an important role in the historical rise of physical science. Thus we may ask: Is it really true that physical science is as little reflective as was suggested above? The form which the reply to this question must assume reveals itself when we acquire an idea about the contribution which Greek philosophical thought has made to the origin of physical science.

2. *The Importance of Greek Thought for Physical Science*

The history of nearly all physical sciences goes back to Greek thinkers. Astronomy was brilliantly represented by Ptolemy, biology by Aristotle, mechanics by Archimedes, medicine by Hippocrates. Mathematics, which is a very important auxiliary science of physics, had equally important representatives in Pythagoras and Euclid. True, in some cases the achievements of these initiators did not go very far beyond what had been accomplished or discovered in other cultural surroundings than those of the Greeks. There is, however, another point, which is at least just as important as the actual beginning of these sciences—namely, the intellectual climate created by the Greek philosophers. Among the Greeks these sciences found a climate that was favorable to their development. The great merit of the Greeks lies in the cultivation of a scientific attitude, i.e., an attitude containing a particular view about the possibilities of human knowledge and about the structure of nature. This particular view is the condition of all rational science. Let us illustrate the matter by means of an example.

Parmenides. No immediate importance with respect to the origin of physical science can be attached to Parmenides, a thinker of the fifth century B.C. At least, we do not know anything about any personal contribution of this philosopher. Nevertheless, his thinking was of the greatest stimulating importance, because he was clearly aware of the cognitive power possessed by the human intellect: "Only that can exist which can be understood." Guided by this principle, Parmenides through subtle arguments came to the conclusion that reality must be one and immutable, despite the apparent testimony of the senses to the contrary. This same testimony, however, led his contemporary Heraclitus to the assertion that everything is mutable and that nothing remains.

At first sight, Parmenides' thesis does not at all seem favorable for the rise of physical science. No matter how high the value is which belongs to rational thinking in the physical sciences, this thinking can be fruitful only if it takes places in intimate contact with what is given by the senses. Nevertheless, a closer consideration of Parmenides' thesis about the unity and immutability of being reveals its profound meaning for physical science.

If the plurality and manifoldness of the empirical data are ever to lead to science, then they will have to be reduced somehow to immutable unity. We see this clearly illustrated in the laws of conservation. A law of conservation, whether it applies to the conservation of impetus, of energy, of mass or, in its most modern version, to that of mass and energy taken together, always expresses that in matter there is something immutable which remains equal to itself in its manifold forms and operations throughout all changes. Thus it expresses immutability, as well as unity. For, as is so splendidly illustrated by the development of the law of conservation of energy in the nineteenth and the twentieth centuries, every law of conservation tends to universality and therefore to unity. The whole line of scientific thinking which reveals itself in this development derives its inspiration from Parmenides' idea, even though the physical theorists in question had never heard about him or made his ideas explicitly their own. For Parmenides' idea had become part and parcel of the intellectual attitude which subsequent western science owed to the Greeks and which everyone who pursues physical science implicitly accepts when he is introduced to this science.

Democritus. The illustration taken from the doctrine of Parmenides could, of course, be taken also from the thinking of other Greeks. A few of these thinkers we simply cannot omit entirely. For if Greek thought had given us only Parmenides, there could hardly have been question of giving rise to physical science. Physical science has to bridge the gap between thought and sense perception, and the distance between these two remains too large in Parmenides to lead immediately to science.

Nevertheless, how fruitful Parmenides' thought was appears from the fact that the man who comes first to mind when there is question of philosophical influences upon physical science developed his doctrine entirely along the pattern of Parmenides' theses. We mean Democritus, the spiritual father of atomism, in whose theory Parmenides' ideas about the unity and immutability of being are fundamental. Democritus' atoms are all qualitatively the same and they are immutable. But he manages to assign a place to the mutability and plurality revealed in sense perception by accepting local and configurative differences as well as quantitative differences between various atoms. What was the reason why Democritus sought this escape from Parmenides' dilemma? No other than the fact that local changes and quantitative differences are mathematically intelligible. Consequently, this kind of change and plurality were intellectually acceptable to him.

Parmenides had thought that any plurality and mutability were against the demand of intelligibility. For Democritus, however, this reason was no longer fully tenable. Although he continued to accept the laws of thought formulated by Parmenides, he elaborated them in a more subtle and fruitful way. Precisely because this elaboration introduced mathematics as a matter of principle, it was of the greatest significance for the development of thinking on the level of physical science. We may add here that, even before Democritus, Pythagoras had already pointed to the importance of mathematics in the explanation of nature, and that Plato soon was to underscore the same point very energetically.

Aristotle. No matter how daring these views were, they remained too much out of touch with experience. If all kinds of phenomena have actually to be reduced to unity and thus explained in the way proposed by Parmenides and Democritus, it is necessary that they be accurately known also in their diversity. Only then will a rational unifying schema be really fruitful, only then will there really be question of physical science. It was the great merit of Aristotle to point to the decisive value of experience with respect to human knowledge. This did not induce him to minimize the role of rational thought, as should be evident from the fact that he is known as the father of logic as well as of the general methodology of science.

For Aristotle's empirical and rational intellect Democritus' effort to make mutability and plurality intelligible was too narrowly conceived: it failed to do justice to the manifoldness and mutability of reality which we actually experience. For this reason he endeavored to provide a basis for a more radical changeability and plurality by means of his matter-form theory, in such a way that material reality would include in its most intimate essence both unity and plurality, both immutability and the possibility of change. However, we cannot enter here into details concerning this point.[3]

What has been said here should be sufficient to make it clear that Greek thinkers struggled to reach a vision of nature capable of letting physical science grow up and flourish. For we find in it everything that is wanted and that now has entered into the permanent endowment of physical science—namely, the realization that a science of nature is possible, the conviction that this science must assume a mathematical structure, and the demand that it be based upon empirical investigation.

A question which arises here spontaneously is why, if it is true that the Greek view contained the germ of physical science, it had to last till 1600 A.D.—two thousand years—before physical science, in the modern sense of the term, actually did develop. This is a very interesting question which, however, can be properly considered only later when we will have seen more about the character of physical science. At present, we will have to restrict ourselves to the following remark. Although in principle the correct intellectual attitude which could make physical science flourish was present, it was precisely the empirical character of this science which prevented it from actually reaching an advanced state of growth and development.

[3]Cf. Andrew G. van Melsen, *From Atomos to Atom,* Pittsburgh, 1952, Ch. I.

The Non-Reflective Character of Physical Science and its Dependence upon Greek Philosophy. There is, however, another question which can be considered here—namely, the question which led us to pay attention to the value of Greek philosophy. We asked how the proclaimed non-reflective character of physical science can be reconciled with its actual dependence upon Greek philosophy.

The reply is really rather simple. It is true that philosophical reflection was necessary for the acquisition of a scientific attitude of mind, which is one of the indispensable elements of physical science. However, once this science has been established and the method proper to it has been found, the required attitude of mind becomes part and parcel of the method of physical science. Accordingly, anyone who is introduced to the scientific method receives implicitly the attitude in question and together with it the vision of man and nature which it contains and upon which physical science is based. It does not matter whether or not the scientist is explicitly aware of this attitude and of the vision implied in it. The only important point is that he spontaneously assumes this attitude, and this is something that happens almost automatically when he uses the scientific method correctly.

At present philosophical reflection is no longer a necessary condition for the use of the scientific method, because this method has found a clear expression in the way physical science is pursued. The method has, as it were, become second nature to the scientist. Thus the wealth of Greek thought is incorporated into the method of the physical sciences, which has become a permanent acquisition of our culture. Hence it is not surprising that, as was pointed out above and as we will see more in detail later, all the great themes of Greek thought are encountered when we consider the presuppositions of the scientific method. The physicist does not realize all this, or rather, he does not have to realize all this to be able to use the method correctly. If, however, he wants to reflect upon the nature of the knowledge obtained through physical science, upon the influence which this knowledge exercises upon intellectual life in its entirety, and upon the influence of technology, which is guided by physical science, upon society, he may, of course, not leave these presuppositions out of consideration. For they are the heart of everything that goes on in physical science.

To throw more light upon the general character of these presuppositions and their function, we will terminate this chapter, which is devoted to the non-reflective nature of physical science, by considering the philosophical presuppositions of this science somewhat more in detail. This consideration, moreover, will be useful to prevent a few misunderstandings that could easily occur.

3. *The Presuppositions of Physical Science*

Are there Any Permanent Principles in Physical Science? The presuppositions of physical science could be called its fundamental principles, in the sense that they are the principles which constitute this type of knowledge as physical science. Immediately, however, there is a difficulty. Does physical science really have principles which as immutable presuppositions are its foundation? Is it not rather characteristic of physical science that it always is and has to be subject to revision, so that it does not have any immutable principles? The great lesson, so it may seem, which the history of physical science teaches is precisely that in physics anything is always liable to be revised in the light of new discoveries.

To express it differently, is not the only presupposition of physical science not to have any presuppositions? Are not all so-called immutable principles always the result of a petrifaction in which certain habitual thought patterns of prescientific thinking or of the physical thinking proper to a period become so deeply ingrained in us that we consider it unthinkable that these principles could ever be modified? One has only to think here of the mechanistic principles, upon which classical physics was based, to find a ready example.

We may add here that precisely this kind of philosophical principle is hardest hit by the development of the physical sciences. Classical mechanics, for instance, continues to be valid, even after the rise of quantum mechanics, as a simplified case of the new mechanics, but now applies only to a limited field of phenomena. But this restriction shows beyond any doubt that modern science has abandoned the essentially philosophical principle of mechanism, which held that material reality ultimately *had to* consist of moving, indestructible and immutable particles. Accordingly, what has been hit hardest by the development of science is not so much the classical theory itself as the fundamental principle of mechanism, which was so evident to past generations of physicists.

Fundamental Principles of the Whole of Physical Science. Thus it seems that the tendency to hold fast to such so-called philosophical principles or presuppositions is due to a kind of conservatism. Its victims are not only philosophers, who *ex professo* look for immutable principles, but from time to time also scientists themselves, and not necessarily only the second-rate variety. We may refer here, e.g., to the reproaches which most present-day specialists in quantum mechanics address to Albert Einstein, who personally in several respects was one of the founders of modern physics. Einstein himself, moreover, wondered whether his attachment to classical ideas did not arise from "the metaphysical original sin" which always wants to absolutize the relative.[4]

Accordingly, we must face the crucial question whether or not all so-called presuppositions or philosophical principles of physical science are not ultimately absolutized formulae of non-absolute principles. We mean principles which for a certain time supported and aided physical science, until their inspiring force assumed the character of a brake, so that they had to be discarded. If this is true, we would have to admit also that the Greek philosophical principles which, as we mentioned, made physical science possible, have no absolute value but are merely relative.

History makes it abundantly clear that Greek thought contained many principles which merely served to help physical science to get started and then had rendered every service of which they were capable. The same is true also of Arabian, medieval, and seventeenth century thought—the historical line along which physical science gradually developed. Such a principle is, e.g., that of mechanicism, which may be found in Democritus and which was of the greatest importance for seventeenth century physical science.

However, in speaking about the presuppositions of physical science, we did not have in mind this kind of principles but another, more fundamental type—namely, principles which are the basis of physical science as such and not merely of any particular phase or theory. It is these fundamental presuppositions which, precisely because they are not limited to any particular phase, dominate the *entire* development of physical science. That there are such principles which guide the whole of physical science in its development becomes clear when we ask ourselves which physical situations lead unanimously to the abandonment or the revision of classical ideas.

The reply is well-known. Ideas are abandoned or changed when the progress of experience demands it. Although the answer may be

---

[4]P. A. Schilpp (ed.), *Albert Einstein, Philosopher-Scientist,* New York, 2nd ed., 1951, p. 673.

formulated in such a brief way, in reality, as we will see later, the process leading to a revision or abandonment is rather complicated. Nevertheless, analysis of this process shows that the decisive factor is always experience as it is embodied in experimental verification. Planck, Einstein, and Bohr introduced their new theories because the classical theory no longer agreed with experience. Likewise, it was disagreement with experience which led the past masters of classical physical science, such as Galileo, Newton, Huygens, Lavoisier, and Dalton, to reject the theories that were current in their time.

Accordingly, the evolution of physical science follows a very definite line, even with respect to discarding or relativizing cherished ideas. No matter how radical this evolution may sometimes seem to be —"Heaven knows what seeming nonsense may not tomorrow be demonstrated truth"[5]—physical science will always continue to propose these truths of tomorrow by following the same methodic demands which have led it in the past—namely, experimental verification and a strictly logical superstructure. It holds fast unconditionally to these demands, and has to do so under penalty of committing suicide as physical science.

It is this kind of principles which interests the philosopher who reflects upon the nature of physical science. These principles are embedded in the very method of physical science and thus determine this science. They portray a particular intellectual attitude and this attitude contains a certain view regarding the possibilities of human knowledge and regarding the fundamental structure of material reality.

The Fundamental Structure of Matter. When in connection with the presuppositions of physical science we speak about the fundamental structure of material reality, one should realize that, of course, we are not thinking of the structures presented to us by physical theories. The structures of such theories, e.g., the atomic structure, are the *results* attained by scientific research and, consequently, not at all presuppositions. When there is question of presuppositions, we are concerned with those structures which make matter in general accessible to experimental investigation. Such a structure is, e.g., the species-individual structure, which expresses that every concrete material datum is subject to repeatability with respect to its component elements (cf. below, pp. 94 ff.). The well-known requirement that experimental effects be reproducible is connected with this structure.

---

[5]Alfred N. Whitehead, *Science and the Modern World,* Cambridge, 1946, p. 143.

A similar structure is connected with the above-mentioned controversy between the Greek thinkers Heraclitus and Parmenides whether material reality is mutable or immutable. For experimental research presupposes that matter is both mutable and immutable, i.e., that it possesses a structure which implies changeability as well as immutability. To realize the truth of this assertion, we must keep in mind that an experiment has value only within a whole of experiments. In an experiment we analyze the various factors by investigating the same object under variable conditions. Such an investigation is meaningful only if the object in question is in principle subject to change, it must be possible in principle for the object to react differently in different situations. If it could not react differently, then it would be impossible for us to derive any knowledge from the various experiments. (If an object is in principle capable of change, even its identical reaction in different circumstances supplies us with important information.) On the other hand, however, it is also true that, if the diversity of reactions under different conditions is to tell us anything, these reactions must be the expression of an immutable nature. The *difference* has to tell us something about *the same*. For instance, the different reactions of copper with water, hydrochloric acid, nitric acid, and sulphuric acid supply us with knowledge about the metal copper.

Both aspects, that of mutability as well as that of immutability, must be intrinsically proper to material reality, for otherwise experimentation would be devoid of any meaning. Accordingly, anyone who uses the experimental method of research presupposes that matter has a structure which includes mutability as well as immutability. It may be useful to note here again that what we are concerned with is the experimental method *as such,* regardless of the concrete methods in which it is embodied. The object of our interest here is that which makes a certain method an experimental method.

The view of matter which sees it as mutable and immutable at the same time is not one which imposes itself of its own accord. We owe it to the intellectual exertion of the old Greek philosophers to understand nature. Their vision has become a permanent cultural acquisition of Western thought, *inter alia* by being embodied in the method of physical science. It is thanks to this vision that we are now able to pursue physical science so readily and that this pursuit has become for us as a second nature. For this reason it is possible for us in our study of material reality to concentrate our attention upon the pursuit of physical science itself rather than upon the vision upon man and nature which is embodied in this science. This vision may now remain implicit. In physical science itself the vision even *has to* remain implicit, because the method and the range of concepts pertaining to physical science do not allow this science to analyze the methods upon which it is based. This is precisely what gives physical science its non-reflective character.

Reflection on the Presuppositions of the Scientific Method. Our assertion that since the discovery of the scientific method the original Greek vision may remain implicit should not be taken to mean that henceforth it would be useless to reflect upon the presuppositions of this method. For, if man wants to remain more than the mere user of a method, if he wants to remain the master of his science, he will have to be aware of what he is doing, of everything which he presupposes when he pursues his science, and of the intellectual attitude which he unconsciously assumes when he uses the method of the physical sciences. Thus it is not a pure coincidence and still less an aberration that the great physicists of our time are precisely the ones who are concerned about the philosophical implications of their science.

This concern expresses man's desire to reflect upon what he is doing, his desire also to make his pursuit of science subservient to the reflection upon man, the being which always asks questions about himself and about the meaning of his existence. Nevertheless, no matter how "natural" this reflection may be for man, it lies on another level than the pursuit of science itself. Physical science aims at the study of the material world as it reveals itself to man by means of the method proper to physical science. Reflection upon physical science, on the other hand, has a different goal. Its object is *man* who pursues science and man's vision of *nature* in which he encounters himself.

When in the subsequent chapters we will investigate several characterics of physical science somewhat more in detail, our considerations will bring us spontaneously into contact with the various presuppositions which are embodied in physical science and thus determine its character. In the present chapter our aim was primarily to show that a substantial amount of cultural possessions are embodied in physical science not only as material goods resulting from science but also in the method which science follows. For this method contains an important philosophical view of man and nature which, although it always remains implicit because of the non-reflective character of physical science, nevertheless does not cease to exercise great influence upon the whole of culture. The ambivalent position which many take with respect to physical science must be explained in part by this unconscious influence which simply *is* there because physical science exists.

Moreover, especially since the thinking of physical science has become practical thinking through its connection with technology, science is closely associated with man's spontaneous cognitive life, for this life is first of all practical thinking, a "thinking with man's hands." Thus physical science seems to be the fulfilment of what man's spontaneous cognitive life potentially intends to be, it seems to be its scientific refinement. Physical thinking is a kind of thinking which suits man, which justifies itself through its practical results, and thus easily leads to the atrophy of other forms of thought.

The Protest Against Physicalism. In this way physical thinking and technological doing exercise a fascinating attraction upon all other activities. Efforts have been made to pursue many of the non-physical sciences, including philosophy itself, in the same way as physics and technology. Typical of this effort is the tendency to make the philosophical reflection upon exact science an exact philosophy, i.e., a general philosophy which proceeds in the same fashion as exact science. True, voices are raised in protest, especially among contemporary philosophers, against the dominating and monopolizing tendencies of physical thinking. For instance, one of the reasons which led Husserl to originate phenomenology was the desire to give philosophy as well as psychology a method of their own.

Many of these protests, however, labor under the defect that they are based upon insufficient knowledge of the way in which physical science proceeds. The result is that not enough attention is paid to the relative correctness which is contained in the physical and technological approach, even when it is a question of studying man and things human. To what extent one may say that such an approach is correct is something which can become clear only through a thorough analysis of the physical method. For this analysis will show how physical science approaches its object, which will reveal at the same time to what extent other objects satisfy the conditions proper to this approach.

CHAPTER TWO

THE EMPIRICAL CHARACTER OF PHYSICAL SCIENCE

1. *External Experience*

The empirical character of physical science was mentioned in the preceding chapter when we pointed out that the decisive vote in this science is always cast by experience. No matter how esthetic a theory may be, no matter how much it may satisfy the intellect, if the facts, as we experience them, obstinately refuse to occur as the theory prescribes, then there is not the slightest doubt about what will happen: the theory will have to give way to the facts. In its general form this principle, of course, is not specifically proper to physical science, but a general characteristic of all human knowledge. Man's knowledge always has a certain element of passivity: it has always to be guided by the *datum,* by what is given and simply found as such by man. Later we shall have to revert to this point.

First Sense of External-Internal. At present, we have to probe somewhat more profoundly into the special way in which the experimental element plays a role in physical science, into the characteristic way in which this science makes use of experience. As should be evident, experience always takes place in physical science by means of the external senses. For its data this science relies upon what is seen by the eye, heard by the ear, touched by the hand, etc. Every time the scientific approach to an object takes place by means of the way in which this object gives itself externally to the senses.

This assertion is true also when physical science penetrates into the "interior" of a material object. It can do so only if this interior is in one way or another made exterior and accessible to the sense organs. Such an exteriorization occurs, for instance, when the knife of the anatomist almost literally makes the interior exterior. It occurs also, however, when we probe, e.g., the interior of crystals by means of X-rays. Because these rays penetrate into the interior, this interior is exteriorized and rendered externally perceptible. Precisely because physical science has to rely on external sense perception, an important part of its progress is determined by the development of means for making the "invisible" perceptible, i.e., for exteriorizing it and thus submitting it to the scrutiny of the senses. The development of these means has, of course, enormously increased our knowledge of matter; nevertheless, it remains true that this knowledge remains, in principle, dependent upon the means of exteriority.

Second Sense of External-Internal. If the characterization of physical science as a science which operates with the means of external experience is to be meaningful, the term "external" has to be opposed to internality in a different sense. For the content of any concept assumes a real meaning only if something else is opposed to the content as a negation (white—nonwhite), as a contrast (white —black), or as a limitation which makes the content in question delineate itself against the background of something transcending the limitation.

For instance, as human beings we have no other intellectual knowledge than human knowledge. Nevertheless, it is meaningful to speak of *human* knowledge, because we experience a limitation in human knowledge, i.e., we project this knowledge against the background of a possible knowledge which does not have the limitations of man's knowledge. The fact that man, despite his disposing only of human knowledge, knows that this knowledge is limited and therefore somehow knows about unlimited knowledge is one of the most mysterious aspects of human knowledge and constitutes the fundamental problem of all philosophical thinking. How is it possible for man, who is locked in by the limitation of human knowledge, to know of this limitation and thus to transcend it? All philosophical reflection takes place in the tension of this polarity, man's actual limitation and his awareness of this limitation.

Meanwhile we have not yet arrived at this polar tension. At present, we must ask ourselves what the opposite is of the knowledge proper to physical science. Evidently, *physical* knowledge is not the same as *all* human knowledge. It is a form of human knowledge— namely, the form which above was characterized as knowledge using the means of exteriority. Thus the answer to the question of what the opposite of this knowledge is does not prove too difficult.

Exteriority is opposed by interiority, but not in the sense in which this term was used above when we spoke about the interior of a crystal. True, in everyday language the inside of the crystal is the opposite of its outside. However, in principle both this inside and outside belong to the same order—the order of exteriority which can be made physically perceptible either directly or indirectly. The inside of a crystal can be exteriorized. If the term "external," in the sense which it assumes when we say that physical science operates through means of external contact, is to be meaningful, its opposite must be another kind of knowing which is not characterized by external cognitive contact. If there were nothing that could justifiably be called an "internal" cognitive contact, then "external" cognitive contact would be a meaningless term.

Such an internal kind of cognitive contact is well-known to man. All of us know from our own experience, for instance, what it is to think or to understand something. What thinking and understanding are we know because we are concerned with it from within, for we ourselves think. Strictly speaking, therefore, we can never perceive thinking. We do not mean to say that thinking does not exteriorize itself in any way, for we may sometimes say that we see someone thinking because his whole bodily being betrays his act of thinking. What we mean is that we will never be able to derive our concept "thinking" from this perception. This concept arises only in an act of reflection in which we return to our own act of knowing, to our internal contact with this act.

The Externality of Physical Science. In the reality of daily life we do not have any reason for making such a strict distinction between internal and external experience, because we know that our intellectual and affective lives express themselves in our body and therefore can to a certain extent be read from our bodily attitude. Physical science, however, limits itself rigorously and methodically to what can be perceived in a purely external way. The externality in question, therefore, never reveals interiority in the above-mentioned sense.

Of course, for any well-trained observer the readings of his instruments speak an eloquent language. So far as he is concerned, the pointer does not merely indicate, say, twelve, but its position means for him, e.g., a difference in potential and, through this difference, something else, such as the proper functioning of a dynamo. This "proper functioning of the dynamo" itself, however, is expressed in categories of externality. This is true even when the physicist measures, for instance, brain currents and concludes from his measurements that the brain is functioning properly. Speaking strictly in the way of physical science, it is merely a question of finding a connection between two external phenomena. As soon as any connection is sought with genuine "interiority," e.g., the connection between certain brain currents and thinking, one introduces an element that is not part of physical science.[1]

These ideas provisionally suffice as far as the character of exteriority proper to physical science is concerned. Of course, much could be added still, but it will be more convenient to do so after we have turned our attention to other aspects of physical knowledge.

2. *Physical Science and Objective Facts*

Objectivity. The fact that physical science operates in principle through the means of external observation impresses its mark upon the empirical character of this science. It gives to this science more than to any other the characteristic of dealing with objective facts. Anyone who wants can objectively establish its data, for the data of physical science are as they are. All of us may observe the same fact, and this fact will appear to all in the same way. Whether observer A looks at them or observer B, the facts are the same for all.

This rule does not apply to the facts of internal experience. It may be a fact that I am now feeling pain in my finger, but I alone can sense this fact. On the other hand, the fact that this finger is abnormally red and swollen is something which anyone can perceive who looks at it.

Thus it is apparent that the facts of physical science have a particular character by virtue of their belonging to the sphere of external perceptibility. This special character is appropriately expressed by the term "objective." The facts of physics are ob-jected, placed opposite us, and we cannot help observing them. For this reason they are also intersubjective, i.e., they are the same for all perceiving subjects.

Complications. A further study, however, of the "factual" character of physical science reveals a number of complications. Although they do not directly contradict the preceding assertions, they show them in a different light. First of all, it should be pointed out that, as experience shows, different individual observers often observe the facts differently. For instance, the phenomenon of color-blindness gives rise to deviating perceptions of color. Moreover, any text book of psychology contains a number of examples illustrating sense illusions to

---

[1]Cf. below, Ch. VII.

which *every* observer is exposed. Many of them are known from daily experience. For instance, lukewarm water is warm for a cold hand, but cold for a hand which was first dipped in hot water.

These things, however, do not have any fundamental importance. For such deviating or faulty perceptions can be eliminated through more refined forms of observational techniques. For example, a chemist who has trouble in perceiving certain colors may replace these perceptions by reading on certain instruments the position of a black line on a graded white scale or even have recourse to the use of another sense organ. The optical illusion which makes us see lines of the same size as different in length can be eliminated by means of a ruler. It is precisely these and similar means which make it possible for us to speak of an optical illusion. What is peculiar about these observational means, therefore, is that they manage to eliminate mistakes of perception by making an appeal to perception. For, when we have recourse to a ruler, we have to use our eyes.

It is interesting to note that, strictly speaking, the optical illusion is not established by our eyes but by our intellect. The intellect makes use of our eyes in a new way by inserting them into a new context in which our hands, manipulating the ruler, also play a role. Something similar is the case in any perception. Although the sense organ plays a decisive role, it never has an autonomous function, but is always subservient. For example, it is the eye which observes the correct temperature of water by means of the thermometer, but the eye did not construct the thermometer.

These reflections show us two points of great importance. First of all, no matter how much all kinds of instruments refine and relocate external observation in physical science, observation itself remains fundamental. There is always the fact which can be observed and registered only in a sensitive way. Secondly, however, this registration takes place only through an intellectual activity which creates the auxiliary means of perception. Both of these points need to be examined somewhat more in detail.

Reliability of the Senses. It is sometimes claimed that science has proved the fallability of the senses, thereby refuting the old philosophical saying that the senses do not deceive. What is quite remarkable here is that any proof for the fallability of the senses can be offered only by virtue of a fundamental trust in the reliability of the senses. If one shows that the sense of heat of our hand is not reliable because he judges the same water now as warm and then as cold, he will be able to verify his assertion only by reading a thermometer, i.e., by appealing to the fundamental reliability of the eye. For in one way or another the observation has to be made that the water which now feels warm and then cold is water having the same degree of heat, and this observation can be made only by means of a sense perception.

This point could be formulated also in a different way by using the terminology of the first chapter. We could say: physical science ultimately presupposes the reliability of the senses. No matter what theoretical and experimental ways we follow in order to establish something, ultimately we have to appeal to some kind of external sense observation. Perhaps facts which originally referred to the sense of taste are now perceived by means of the eye, but what remains is that they are registered by a sense organ.

The Role of the Intellect in Sense Perception. We must now consider somewhat more closely the function which intellectual cognition fulfills with respect to the role of sense perception in the physical sciences. The first thing to keep in mind here is that the above-mentioned instances of sense deception are merely border-line cases of a much larger realm in which the defects of the senses reveal themselves. We have only to think here, e.g., of something which remains invisible to the naked eye but is visible through the microscope to realize that here also we have to do with a kind of sense deception. If we relied on what the naked eye sees in a drop of water, we would conclude that this drop contains only water, while in reality the drop is full of hidden forms of life.

Despite its simplicity this example is fully worth our consideration. First of all, it shows again that we know about this hidden life only because we *see* it. The fact that this seeing takes place through a microscope does not take away that we do see it. Secondly, the example reveals that our conclusion regarding the presence of living beings in the drop of water depends also upon our reliance on the optical theory which underlies the construction of the microscope—namely, the theory that a microscope enlarges. In addition, our biological knowledge plays a role in making us evaluate the sighted things as living beings. Finally, there is a last important point. Once we have learned to use a microscope, we will be careful never again to present the fact that the naked eye sees only water as a proof that there is nothing else in the drop than water. In other words, the fact in question no longer speaks the same language to us now as it did prior to the invention of the microscope. Likewise, the concept "clean hands" now has a meaning which differs somewhat from the one it used to have before the discovery of microbes.

All this leads us to the conclusion that it is not the sense organ which misleads us, but the theoretical interpretation, the way in which we evaluate[2] the sense datum, the context in which we place it. This context plays an extremely important role. Its function is not limited to the cases in which the intellectual context is, as it were, objectified and given to us in the form of an instrument. For an instrument is an objectified part of a theory. The microscope, for instance, as an optical instrument embodies the theory of optics, the thermometer that of heat, a voltage meter or ampere meter that of electricity, etc. In all these cases the theoretical context in which the perception actually takes place is obviously present. The same, however, is true also of non-instrumental perception: it, too, takes place in a theoretical context. Let us illustrate this assertion by means of a single example which is not without historical significance in the story of physical science.

Experience shows that if a ball is rolled over a smooth surface, it will "of itself" cease to roll after some time. At least that is the way in which we would naively describe our experience—just as it was done in the Middle Ages and in ancient times. Anyone who is trained in physics, however, will describe the fact quite differently. He will say that the ball is brought to a stop by friction against the floor and the air. For he has come to the realization that the naive formulation used in everyday life is very deceptive, even though it may not be incorrect. It is not incorrect insofar as it expresses that the ball will stop even if it does not meet any visible obstacle. But insofar as it suggests—by saying "of itself"—that there are no other obstacles than visible ones, the formula is deceptive. On the other hand, it should be clear that the corrected formulation could not be given before man had acquired a more profound theoretical understanding of mechanics.

An Atheoretical Expression of a Fact is Not Possible. Deceptive formulations can, as we have seen, very easily enter into the descrip-

---

[2]This evaluation does not necessarily have to be of a theoretical nature. There exists also a kind of more or less spontaneous and purely practical evaluation. However, this point does not concern us here.

tion of facts. For this reason there is an obvious temptation to demand methodically that facts be expressed in such a way that their expression does not in any way anticipate upon a theoretical context. For thus the facts would be allowed to speak for themselves rather than being represented by an interpretation which, as experience shows, can easily give rise to all kinds of misconceptions. Such a methodical requirement, however, cannot be met; a perfectly atheoretical expression of fact is in principle impossible.

Let us examine why this atheoretical expression is impossible by means of a deceptively simple example, such as the proposition "this paper is white." At first sight, this proposition seems to be a simple statement of a fact without any theoretical context. On closer inspection, however, the situation appears to be somewhat different. The concrete "givenness" which is actually before me here and makes me formulate the judgment "this paper is white" is much more complex than appears from the judgment. For I see something having a certain shape (surface, thickness), a certain structure, in the midst of all kinds of other things, which under a certain illumination is "white." Strictly speaking, therefore, I ought to say: "This thing, here and now, under this light, makes upon me a certain impression which in English is indicated by the term 'white.'" That I first mentioned *paper* in this connection contained an important item of theoretical evaluation. Perhaps it is not at all paper. However, even if we leave the identification of the object as paper out of consideration, several remarks remain to be made about the statement of the fact.

The Element of Language. The very existence of the English term "white," as corresponding to the French "blanc," the German "weiss," the Italian "bianco," etc., expresses that the content of my perception is not considered in itself, but is placed within the general context embodied in the structures of these languages. Anyone who learns to speak a language acquires together with the language a certain view of reality. It is not without reason that our time has seen the rise of several philosophical currents which consider the analysis of language as their principal task. A language thinks for us, because it embodies the wisdom of generations, their view of reality, their experiences and their world-view, as well as their primitive ideas and mistakes.[3]

---

[3]Cf. Remy C. Kwant, *Encounter*, Pittsburgh, 1960, Ch. 4.

A well-known thesis of logical empiricism claims that many philosophical problems arise from the fact that ordinary language is ambiguous in its meanings and in the constructions which it permits. If language is used in a responsible way, these problems would be automatically unmasked as pseudo-problems. For this reason logical empiricists endeavor to follow the example of exact science and to construct a rigorously formalized language from which all ambiguity is removed. Whether the ideal in question is correct and capable of realization not only in the realm of exact technical language but also in general is a question which cannot be examined here. It would, moreover, be irrelevant to the question which occupies us at present. For it is certain that every language, whether natural or artificial, thinks for us when we think in it. The physicist who expresses his findings in mathematical language *ipso facto* accepts the road taken by physical science in the past when it began to express itself mathematically. He lives his professional life in a certain climate of thought which codetermines his future thinking.

The same is true for ordinary language. By saying "this is white," I find myself in a language which makes a distinction between things and their properties, a language which knows that such a property as "white" is not unique but occurs in many things, a language also which knows that things are capable of having other qualities besides whiteness. Things, therefore, can agree in whiteness although they are widely different. Accordingly, "this is white" is an extremely abstract way of expressing a concrete situation. I could also have said: "this is rectangular," "this is of light weight," "this can be used for writing," or "this is somewhat transparent." Each of these formulations is correct, each refers to a fact, but each of them also is a one-sided expression of a complex datum. Language forces me to use such a selective and abstract mode of speech.[4]

No Complete Description is Possible. The only remedy against this one-sided expression of facts seems to lie in making the description complete. Unfortunately, a really *complete* description is utterly impossible. It would never come to an end, and the reason for this does not lie only in the deficiency of language. For, while I am looking at the paper and call it white, I find myself in a very concrete situation. The sun is shining, the weather is rather warm, my desk

---

[4]Whether it does so correctly is a point that provisionally may be left out of consideration.

is covered with books, I am writing with a green pen which I bought six months ago, outside a blackbird sings and a finch warbles—do I have to mention all these things when I want to say under what circumstances the paper here in front of me is white? I would not even be capable of doing it, for in concrete reality things are interconnected in all kinds of ways.

Of course, everyone will say, all these things do not have to be mentioned, for many of them are wholly irrelevant. The paper is white, regardless of the singing blackbird and all the other circumstances. But, are all these circumstances really irrelevant? The singing blackbird (is it really a blackbird?) perhaps yes, but perhaps not the sunshine, for when the sun sets and I do not put on the light, the whiteness of the paper disappears. And what about the temperature? If the paper gets very warm, it loses its color.

Accordingly, when I say "this paper is white," I undoubtedly express a fact, but I do so in a very selective way. My expression places the fact in a very definite context. I think that I am justified in doing so on the basis of all kinds of experiences and convictions which are, *inter alia,* embodied in the actual structure of the language that I use. Only by means of this selective expression of a fact is the fact in question useful for daily life, only in this way can it be incorporated in the whole of human experiences.

In principle, exactly the same occurs in the scientific formulations of facts, but the theoretical context as well as the terminology are, of course, more refined. We will return to this point later. First we must consider certain other aspects of physical science against the background of human knowledge in general, for it is only against this background that physical knowledge can be properly understood.

The necessity of bringing human knowledge in general to bear upon man's understanding attained through physical science has demonstrated itself clearly with respect to the two characteristics of physical knowledge considered in this chapter—namely, knowledge through the means of exteriority and the "factual" character of physical science. Neither one nor the other is specifically proper to physical science, for in daily life also we often use judgments possessing both characters. An example is the above-mentioned statement "this paper is white." It is concerned with a fact, and this fact can be observed only through the means of external sensitivity. The statement, therefore, is a genuine empirical judgment. In principle, it has the same character as the judgments of physical science. It likewise exhibits the typical character of dealing with a fact which is characteristic of the judgments of physical science. Moreover, just as in physical judgments, the fact expressed in the judgment in question is placed in a theoretical context, although this context is much less refined.

Summary. Summarizing the result of the investigation we have made about the concept "fact," we must say that being concerned with facts does not at all mean that the judgment about a fact is solely a faithful mirroring of an actual condition or state existing entirely outside the knowing subject. Such a mirroring is simply impossible. What is expressed in a judgment is something which undoubtedly has a certain aspect of being a fact but always also transcends this factual aspect. In a certain situation and within a certain framework the paper is white, no matter what I want. I may close my eyes, and then the factual whiteness disappears for me. I may look at the paper and devote my attention to something entirely different, e.g., the thickness of the paper, but in that case the thickness is something that is factual. Thus we always encounter an aspect of being-a-fact, but it is never the only aspect.

We must now consider these other aspects, and especially that of abstraction which appeared to play such an important role in the expression of the facts, for without abstraction it is not possible to express or describe the facts.

CHAPTER THREE

THE ABSTRACT CHARACTER OF PHYSICAL SCIENCE

1. *The Abstract Nature of Human Knowledge*

In the first chapter we pointed out that physical science is non-reflective. It does not pay attention to itself but is oriented toward the material world. Thus the body of concepts pertaining to this science has no room for reflection upon the human activity which is the pursuit of physical science. Although physical science forms all kinds of concepts in order to arrive at a cognitive grasp which seizes the material phenomena in their interconnection, these concepts are not suitable for an understanding of the human activity which is physical science. This science methodically refrains from considering physical science as an intellectual activity of man. In other words, it abstracts from this consideration, for abstraction means methodic limitation.

The Limitation of Perception. As has been mentioned in the preceding chapter, this methodic limitation is something which characterizes the whole of man's knowledge. It is intimately connected with the sensitive-intellectual character of human knowledge. Let us illustrate this point again by means of a simple example, chosen from the realm of external observation, such as the perception of a motorcar. Without wanting or being able to develop here a complete theory of perception, we may briefly make a few remarks which, despite their apparent simplicity, have far-reaching consequences.

First of all, the perception of any object, such as the motorcar, will always be an approach that is limited very distinctly in a three-fold way:

1. The perception takes place from a determined standpoint, in the literal sense of the term. The observer occupies a determined position with respect to the car.

2. Thus he attains only a determined side of the car—namely, the side which is turned toward him, so that he perceives the car against a determined background.

3. He makes use of a determined means of perception. When he looks at the car, he reaches other aspects than when he touches it or knocks against it.

Of course, we could walk around the car and see it from all sides, we could look at it, listen to it, touch it, and in this way build up an impression of the whole. However, this impression is never fully knowledge of the whole in its entirety, the total impression remains fragmentary, because it is built up in a piecemeal fashion.

Accordingly, the nature of sensitive knowing, bound as it is to an organ with a determined spatial situation and a determined natural mode of operating, always implies that the object is approached in a determined concrete way. Sensitive knowing is always piecemeal knowledge. The same is true for man's intellectual knowledge which has to be based upon sense knowledge. For instance, one who knows a car only from having seen it from a distance will have an idea which differs widely from that of a racer who feels his "rod" as one with his body, and the idea of the racer differs in its turn from that of the mechanic who knows the car, as they say, inside and out. Of course, these partial concepts of the car are not derived solely from different sense experiences, nevertheless these experiences constitute their basis. For it is impossible to acquire at the same time all the experiences which are conditional for the various partial concepts. True, exceptionally it may have been possible for an individual to experience motorcars from so many angles that we may speak about something like a total concept. However, even such a total concept is built up from partial concepts and, in addition, it is never fully complete.

Insertion of the Object Perceived into the Existing Whole of Concepts. Apart from the fragmentary approach to the object by the senses, there is another reason why only exceptionally is anyone capable of even approximating a total concept. To use again the same example, anyone who wants to be a good mechanic and know motorcars from this viewpoint must have a solid practical knowledge of mechanics. This means that he must first become trained in looking at and studying cars from the mechanical point of view. The resulting familiarity with mechanics gives rise to a whole of concepts which makes the technician automatically look at the car as a mechanical contraption. When a mechanic looks at a car, he does not see its color or its external shape, but the details of its construction.

Thus different people look in decidedly different ways at one and the same car because of their past experiences, their ambitions, their character, their age, etc. The concepts they form of the car are different. For one it is an interesting mechanical contraption, for another a thing to impress his neighbors or his girl friend, for a third the means to move around and earn his living or make a quick getaway, for the fourth an ideal noise-maker to disturb peaceful neighborhoods, for the fifth the object of a psychological study, for the sixth a delight for the eye, for the seventh a typical product of modern lack of taste, and for the philosopher an object to demonstrate, as we have just done, the abstract character of human knowledge.

The Abstract Character of Man's Knowledge. What has been explained above by means of the concrete example of a motorcar has a universal validity. Every concrete material thing can be taken up into widely different conceptual contexts. This is true not only with respect to the reality of daily life but in a very special way also for the various sciences. Every science is a whole of interconnections in which things are approached and known from a definite formal aspect. In other words, every science is abstract. Only certain concepts belong to it, while others are excluded. And even if different sciences use the same concepts, they incorporate them into a different conceptual whole.

2. Abstraction in Physical Science

Like every science, physical science has an abstract character of a very definite nature. What is the nature of the abstraction proper to physical science? Or, to express it differently, what kind of concepts are used in physical science? The preceding chapters have supplied us with a few indications regarding the reply to this question. For instance, the concepts of physical science are not derived from man's self-reflection, they do not belong to the sphere of internal cognitive contact but to that of external contact. They develop the data supplied by the external senses. This means at the same time that physical science is nothing else than a definite refinement of that which is already found on the pre-scientific level. Let us illustrate this point by means of a few examples, which will show also how physical science systematically develops the whole of its concepts.

Physical Science Refines Prescientific Concepts. In daily life we are familiar with the concepts of velocity, force, and resistance. These concepts play a fundamental role also in mechanics. However, the concept "velocity," as it is defined in mechanics, exhibits a peculiar deviation from the customary content it has in daily life. Both in mechanics and in everyday life velocity means distance divided by time. But while in everyday life it makes no difference whether the path along which the distance is travelled is straight or bent, mechanics distinguishes these two cases. To ride around in a circle with a constant velocity is a meaningful expression in the language of daily life, but not so in mechanics. For, according to mechanics, every change in direction is at the same time a change in velocity, because velocity is not a scalar but a vectorial magnitude, i.e., it has a determined value in a determined direction.

Why has this refined notion of velocity been introduced in mechanics? The sole reason is that in this way it became possible to describe motions in a coherent way. For an additional force is necessary to make the object leave its straight path; force effects a change of velocity; therefore, if a velocity changes direction, the velocity itself must be considered to change also. In this way the law which makes the force proportionate to the change of velocity assumes a general character.

Reversely, everything also which effects a change of velocity is held to be a force, regardless of whether or not this force exhibits any external similarity to the original experience of muscular force. In this way the concept of force also is given a general meaning and detached from the original experience of force. Force is anything which makes an object change its velocity, so that the concept "force" becomes exclusively connected with externally observable phenomena. It is completely detached from the internal experience of force. In this way the magnitude of a force is also made measurable by an external given measure. In other words, it has become a purely scientific concept which is connected with a determined mode of measuring.

The advantages of this generalization of the concept "force" should be evident. For it makes it possible to measure forces which would otherwise be wholly beyond our possibilities of perception because they are literally beyond our own strength. Small forces, such as that of a coiled spring, can be measured through our own muscular power. As soon, however, as the force to be measured greatly exceeds our muscular power, there can no longer be question of a direct measurement.

Likewise, we are capable of comparing small weights by taking them in our hand. Although the comparison may not be very accurate, in principle it can be made. But as soon as a determined limit of weight is reached, we are powerless. Nevertheless, objects also which transcend the limits of our muscular powers still have something that may be called "weight," though we can no longer take them into our hands to weigh them. By means of a lever we are even able to compare their weights. Thus the tendency to universalize, which is present in man's mind, forces us to define weight in such a way that it can be applied as widely as possible, just as it was done for the concepts "force" and "velocity."

Modification of the Abstracted Content of Physical Concepts. In a a similar way it is possible to explain how all kinds of other physical concepts have developed from concepts which are immediately connected with ordinary experience. It is always a question of an urge to generalize, to make universally applicable what is directly accessible only in particular cases. This tendency to generalize is connected with another procedure which is also frequently used in the formation of physical concepts—namely, a shift in the abstract content of the concepts. We do not mean here a modification which would make the new content lie beyond the general level of abstraction proper to physical science, i.e., the level which is characterized by its connection with external experience. The modification in question occurs within the confines of this level and implies that new contents are assigned to old terms.

We should keep in mind here that every perception, whether instrumental or non-instrumental, has an abstract character of its own within the general abstraction level of physical science. For instance, the eye perceives colors but not sounds. A thermometer is an instrument for measuring temperatures but not for determining colors. If we have to determine colors, we use a spectrometer. Accordingly, just as we perceive different aspects of reality through distinct sense organs, so also we perceive distinct aspects through different instruments. Thus the results of the various perceptions will fall under different abstract conceptual contents; for instance, the concept "color" has a different content from that of "temperature." Frequently, however, these distinct conceptual contents may easily be connected. Ordinary experience, for example, shows that color is not independent of temperature, for under suitable conditions we are capable of observing temperature changes by means of changes of color. We can *see* whether or not an electric heater is on by looking at the glow of the wires, we can see whether an old-fashioned poker is hot. Here also our sense of heat lets us down if temperature has to be registered above a certain degree of intensity, for by touching the hot object we burn our fingers.

Nevertheless, our sense of heat does not let us down completely. It warns us when we are still at a certain distance from the hot object that the thing is hot, and the experience of heat becomes more intense according as we come closer to the object. Thus we observe a certain relationship between the heat of the object, its distance, and our perception of heat. In principle, we have here again a more universal method for measuring heat than when we make use only of the sense of heat, for now we have to estimate also the distance. In this way the conceptual content of "heat" acquires a new element, for the concept of distance begins to play a role in it.

Usually we measure temperature by means of a quicksilver thermometer. In this method we make use of another phenomenon—namely, the fact that becoming hotter is accompanied by expansion. This method is very appropriate for exact measurements and has, in addition, the advantage of covering a much wider range of temperatures than that of our sense of heat. Many other methods could be devised to measure temperature, and several of them are actually used.

All these methods are connected in the common scientific concept of temperature which has lost its original close relationship with the sense of heat. The scientific concept is connected, on the one hand, with a certain method of measurement—that of the gas thermometer —and, on the other, it is empirically and theoretically embedded in a network of relationships with other physical concepts, through which the various methods of measurements are once more interrelated.[1] In this way the physical concept of temperature has become also much more abstract and general than the natural concept of heat. It is no longer bound to the sense of heat and not even to a single instrumental method. The temperature is determined by means of widely divergent instruments and read with the eye, although in principle the same could be perceived also by means of an other sense organ. Never-

---

[1]Because of these interrelationships it is possible to measure temperatures even when the gas thermometer cannot be used. This happens, for instance, in the realm of very high temperatures, where recourse is had to the color analysis of radiation.

theless, although the concept of temperature has become more general and more abstract and is no longer bound to a single sense, it is still bound to some act of sensing.

Physical Abstraction is Not Artificial but Natural. This brief sketch shows how the physical concept of temperature has originated. Although it may seem to be very far removed from our natural concept of heat, it should be clear that the way in which physical science has arrived at its abstract and general concept is fundamentally quite natural. Even in pre-scientific experience we have recourse to the eye to discover something about the degree of heat when we look at the color of the poker, even in pre-scientific experience we make use of simple laws which have been observed, such as that the radiation of heat diminishes when the distance increases, and we connect heat with distance. Physical science has not made any fundamental change in this natural method, but merely generalized and refined it. The abstract character of physical science fits in with the abstract nature of sensitivity and with the intellect's desire of universality. Thus the fact that physical science seeks methods and means to utilize the concept of temperature also when our sense of heat lets us down is not at all foreign to what man does in the ordinary course of life.

We have insisted somewhat more extensively on this point, because nowadays the abstract character of physical science makes it almost fashionable to accuse this science of being unnatural. This reproach, however, is without justification, at least insofar as the above-mentioned aspects of its abstract nature are concerned.

3. The Inductive-Analytic Character of Physical Science

If we want to penetrate deeper into the special features which the abstract nature of human cognition assumes in physical science, we have to consider also the inductive character of this science. What applies to abstraction in general is true also of induction— namely, that it is not a process which pertains specifically only to physical science. In daily life also we make use of induction. The difference between scientific induction and the type that is used in daily life lies again in the consummate skill and refinement with which physical science utilizes the inductive method.

Conceptual Induction. In a very general way induction may be described as the process of thought from the individual to the general. By describing it as a process of thought we eliminate immediately so-called "conceptual induction." One may speak of induction with respect to concepts, for in the formation of concepts there is a transition from the individual to the general, because of the fact that a concept is abstract and therefore detached from what is concretely given. The concept "red," as a concept, does not refer only to the concretely red which I am seeing now, but applies to everything that is red. This formation of concepts, however, runs its course spontaneously because our thinking is abstractive; hence conceptual induction does not cause any *methodic* problem. There is, of course, a *philosophical* problem, insofar as it raises the question about the nature of human knowledge and especially the relation between knowing and reality.

Induction of Judgments in Mathematical Relationships. A methodic problem, however, exists, although not always, in the inductive formation of judgments. We say "not always," because sometimes we are able to see the general relation immediately in the concrete case under consideration. A concretely executed arithmetical operation, such as calculating with pencil and paper what 53 x 23 is, terminates in a universally valid result which we can immediately express in a judgment: 53 x 23 = 1219. For in this case we see immediately that calculating the sum on paper by means of a certain type of pencil cannot have any influence whatsoever upon the final result. Whether we use ink, chalk, or a pencil, a piece of paper or a blackboard, is wholly irrelevant. It would be utterly meaningless to repeat in ink the calculation made with a pencil. The implication of this situation is that the concrete arithmetical operation was accompanied by formal abstraction: we knew that only the value of the numbers was relevant and not the way in which the symbols expressing these values were materially realized. For this reason the universal is seen immediately in the concrete, the result of the concrete calculation has universal value.

Accordingly, induction, considered as the transition from the concrete to the universal, does not constitute a methodic problem here. We say in such a case that we have an insight into the necessity of the relationship. This expression really means: we understand that the result of the calculation depends solely upon the formal units under consideration and not upon the way in which they are materially realized. To know what the result will be, we have to perform an actual calculation. We do not know the result beforehand. However, we do know that the material element is irrelevant and, therefore, a single calculation is in principle sufficient.

We abstract here from the philosophical foundation upon which this insight is based. Plato, Aristotle, Hume, Kant, modern intuitionists, and contemporary logical positivists, each, have their own view in this matter. The situation here is similar to the one mentioned in the first chapter with respect to the distinction between the method of physical science and the philosophical reflection upon this method. There is no disagreement regarding the actual calculation, but only regarding what exactly it means to calculate.

The easy transition from the concrete to the general which we find in arithmetical operations exists also in geometry. Here also the form of the figure is important, but not its material realization. Geometry is interested only in the formal aspect and formulates relationships concerning this aspect. All other aspects are irrelevant. For this reason a demonstration made by means of a single triangle having certain formal properties is valid for all triangles with the same properties.

Inductive Formation of Judgments in Empirical Relationships. As soon, however, as material-qualitative relationships enter into the picture, the situation becomes entirely different. Let us consider a concrete triangle made of iron. The fact that the angles of this triangle total 180° is attributable to its triangular figure, and the fact that it sinks in water follows from its iron construction. At first sight both statements may seem to be similar in nature. The first connects a certain property (180° as the sum of the angles) with another property (the triangular shape), the second likewise expresses a connection between two properties—namely, sinking and being made of iron. The big difference, however, is that there is no insight into the last-named connection. It is merely established in an empirical way. Strictly speaking, there is even less, for we observe only that this particular iron triangle in these concrete circumstances sinks in water. While it is universally true that the sum of the angles of a triangle is 180°, it is not universally valid that iron objects sink. The triangular form is certainly relevant in the concrete case mentioned above, for iron objects may be shaped in such a way that they do not sink. Moreover, if a magnet had been placed in a suitable position near the iron triangle of our concrete experiment, the triangle would not have sunk.

All this shows that we are confronted again with the enormous complexity enveloping every factual datum. It is so complex because we do not know *a priori* which factors are relevant and which ones are irrelevant. This is the reason also why we are unable to describe a datum atheoretically. Nevertheless, we do not hesitate to say that iron objects sink in water and that our triangle sinks because it is made of iron. The reason why we say this is not that we have a formal insight into the relationship between being-made-of-iron and sinking, but because varied experience has taught us that iron objects sink unless special circumstances prevent it.

Thus the problem of induction may be approached from two angles. On the one hand, the question may be asked as to what justifies us to conclude to a judgment stating something about *all* iron from an experience of sinking iron objects which is necessarily incomplete? This is the problem which is concerned with the transition from the individual to the universal judgment. It is especially acute here, because we lack an insight into the formal connection and have to rely on individual experiences. On the other hand, there is a second problem, which may be expressed in this way: once it is known that every concrete event can always be described in terms expressing general aspects, which are these general aspects in a concrete case?

Scientific Induction. The first problem is the general philosophical problem of induction. Strictly speaking, it is the same as the above-mentioned problem of conceptual induction, which will be examined more in detail later. It is the problem as to what justifies us at all to formulate universal empirical judgments.

The second problem, on the other hand, is the one with which concretely we have to deal most frequently in physical science. Why did we in the above-mentioned example attribute the sinking of concrete objects to the fact that they were made of iron? In this question we face the problem of scientific induction. Scientific induction assumes that every concrete event can be placed in certain general relationships. As we indicated in the preceding chapter, this assumption really is a condition for the description of any concrete event, for otherwise language could not even make use of general terms. It will appear also to be a condition of the application of the experimental method and therefore a presupposition of all physical sciences.

Accordingly, in scientific induction, as a *scientific* problem, there is never question of the general problem of induction, but only of its concrete application to concrete phenomena. This application consists in the search for general relationships or connections. Given, therefore, that this concrete, white, iron triangle sinks in water, the question is asked as to which aspect of the concrete triangle is directly connected with the sinking. In principle, two ways can be distinguished, at least in the beginning, by which this and other similar problems can be tackled methodically.

First Method. First of all, we can compare a large number of experiences regarding sinking and non-sinking objects. They show that iron things always sink (abstracting here from some very special forms), while wooden objects do not sink. Through this comparison ordinary experience leads us to the rule: iron objects sink in water.

Second Method. The second method does not start from the cataloguing of many experiences but from the careful analysis of a determined concrete case. In this analysis full attention is paid to all possible relevant aspects. To determine whether or not aspects are really relevant, they are "artificially" separated from the object in the experiment. Of course, frequently a real separation is not possible. If, for instance, we want to know whether or not a certain shape influences a particular phenomenon, we are never able to experiment with an object that has no form. All we can do is to vary the form, while we leave the matter of the object unchanged. Accordingly, we investigate the various possible relevant aspects by constantly varying one, leaving the others as much as possible the same, and watching to see what will happen.

Because of the endless plurality of aspects possessed by a concrete object, this procedure would be impossible unless we had already at our disposal a large number of general laws which apply to the situation in question, so that we can immediately exclude many aspects from our experiment. Physical science could not even have begun to conduct systematic experimental research if many regularities had not already been known from daily life and from the technical manipulation of objects. Even so, the start was difficult enough. This explains also why the sciences in which the Greeks were able to make the greatest progress all lay in realms in which the separation of the relevant and the irrelevant was in principle independent of analyzing experience. As we will see, this is the case with mathematics, philosophy, logic, and to a certain extent also astronomy.

In these sciences the Greek mind acquired an intellectual grip on things, and in them the Greeks developed an authentically scientific attitude. Because of the onesided character of the sciences in which the Greeks were successful, their scientific attitude as well as their philosophy of science showed the marks of onesidedness also. This onesidedness, however, is much less important than the fact that they did acquire a scientific attitude of mind. In due time the same scientific attitude could be extended also to the physical sciences.

In antiquity itself, however, the time was not yet ripe for such a development. The reason was that the conditions which allow physical science to arise have somewhat the character of a vicious circle. Physical science has an experimental nature. Success in experiments presupposes that many theoretical data are already available to limit the total number of aspects that have to be investigated. On the other hand, any physical theory has to be based upon experiment. Thus it is not surprising that it took such a long time before physical science could get started. The fact that a real start could be made around 1600 was due to two factors. The first was the scientific attitude of the Greek and medieval thinkers, which gave them the profound conviction that rational interrelationships could be established between various phenomena. The second factor was the gradual increase in differentiated knowledge of concrete phenomena through the growth of practical experience. In this way it became possible to formulate gropingly some general connections, which then could be used as the starting point of further research.

The proper element of this research, therefore, consists in this that through systematic observation and experimentation it resolves the phenomena into their various aspects and through this analysis investigates which general relationships can be formulated. For instance, the fact that a stick which is partially submerged in water seems to be broken has no connection with water as such, but only with the fact that water has a greater optical density than air. Thus the physical description of this phenomenon retains only one datum of water—namely, that it is a medium having a certain optical density. Likewise, the sinking of iron in water is no longer concerned with water and iron but only with a difference in specific gravity. For the nutritionist an orange is no longer the well-known fruit indicated by that name, but something containing a copious supply of vitamine C and many other components. In the nutritionist's tables the orange gives way for the listing of the component parts which have nutritional value. All this gives physical science its specific abstract character. Science does not see totalities but only a composite of factors and aspects which varies according to the scientific relationship in which the man of research is interested. The character which an orange assumes for the biologist differs from that which it has for the nutritionist.

The Systematically Abstract Character of Physical Science. Abstract considerations certainly are not found exclusively in physical science. As we pointed out before, even in everyday experience widely diverse things are put together under a single limited heading which is often chosen in a very arbitrary way. For instance, all kinds of utensils, such as an ashtray, an inkwell, or a letter opener, provided that they be heavy, can all be used to prevent papers from being blown around. The diversity of their specific functions is relegated to the background in favor of one function which requires only heaviness and stability. We could use also a book or anything else, as long as the object has the qualities in question. The concrete situation in which the papers are in danger of being scattered by the wind makes us seize one or the other object, only two of whose many properties draw our interest—namely, sufficient weight and stability.

In this way every concrete object can be placed in widely diverse interconnections and used for all kinds of arbitrarily chosen purposes. A minute later or so, for instance, we will use the same book as a prop or to show the painter what color we want. We could have used also the letter opener for the last-named purpose, if it happens to be of the same color as the book. Accordingly, by analyzing concrete objects in their manifold aspects, physical science does something which is not at all foreign to ordinary life and thought. The difference is only that physical science proceeds in a much more systematic way, because of its desire to understand the events of nature.

Nevertheless, this systematic procedure contains, alongside great scientific advantages, also a certain danger. Although in daily life there is a constant but changing consideration of aspects, things largely retain their concreteness because they are inserted in the concrete fullness of life. Physical science, on the other hand, dwells much more on the abstracted aspect. In daily life the letter opener remains primarily a letter opener, even if it is from time to time placed in a different context. For physical science, however, the letter opener is nothing else than an object having a certain mass, a certain shape, a determined volume, a determined color, a certain chemical composition, etc. The concrete thing evaporates into being a mere example of these various properties.

Thus the center of attention in the physical sciences is placed in the relationships existing between abstract properties. Eddington offers an eloquent illustration of this point.[2] Let us assume, he says, that a question of an examination in mechanics begins with the statement that an elephant slides down a grass-covered hill. Not a single student will pay the slightest attention to this sentence, because all know that the statement is irrelevant. But their attention will be drawn by statements saying that the weight of the elephant is two tons and that the angle of the slope is sixty degrees. With these data the elephant and the hill disappear and become mere instances of a certain weight and of a certain inclined plane, i.e., things which are related to each other within the context of the mechanical laws of motion. The grass, likewise, has disappeared and is replaced by the co-efficient of friction.

This example reveals something else in addition to the disappearance of concrete reality behind abstract mechanical magnitudes. Reality is not merely considered from abstract viewpoints, but it is also schematized. This schematization is not quite the same as abstraction. Let us devote a few moments to this difference.

4. The Difference Between Abstraction and Schematization

When a concrete situation is abstractly expressed, everything is left out which is irrelevant to the problem under consideration. In Eddington's example, for instance, it is irrelevant whether the two ton weight is the weight of an elephant or of a hippopotamus. The important point is that the object is an example of the weight in question. The nature of this object, as such, does not play any role in the mechanical problem. Thus, likewise, with respect to the lifting power of an airplane, it is irrelevant whether the load to be transported consists of elephants, hippopotamuses, or bags of sands. However, let us return to Eddington's problem of the sliding elephant.

For this problem the shape of the sliding object is, of course, not irrelevant. In the mechanical problem illustrated by the elephant, the

---

[2] *The Nature of the Physical World,* Cambridge, 1928, Ch. 12.

sliding object will be given the shape of a block. This, however, is a schematic representation. We say "schematic," because the representation leaves out of consideration certain aspects of the elephant which are in principle relevant to the problem. They are omitted because they are not too important or because otherwise the problem would become too involved. Physical science abounds in this kind of schematizations. For instance, the earth is represented as a point in celestial mechanics, but as a perfect sphere or as a sphere flattened at the poles in other branches of mechanics.[3] With respect to celestial mechanics the radius of the earth is so small that it may indeed be neglected in relationship to the distance from the moon or from the sun. Nevertheless, this neglect is a real neglect. If the earth were closer to the sun, the radius would certainly have to be considered. Another example may be taken from the kinetic gas theory. In this theory a certain law governing very rarified gases is deduced from the assumption that gas molecules are small spheres whose radius may be neglected. If, however, gases are less rarified, there are deviations from the laws which have been deduced in this way. These deviations can be accounted for by taking the radius into consideration, as is done in the well-known formula deduced by van der Waals.

Accordingly, the models used by physical science have a character that is not only abstract but also schematic. It is abstract, because they make use only of the aspects which are relevant to the problem under consideration, and schematic, because these abstracts have been idealized in such a way that they can be handled easily.

In a later chapter we will have to return to this abstract and schematic character of physical science, especially in connection with the question whether and to what extent models possess value for reality. Meanwhile one point should be certain—namely, that the abstract character of physical science naturally fits in with the character of human knowledge. Several parts of this chapter have illustrated this point. The same conclusion will be reached again when we investigate other aspects of the knowledge man obtains in physical science.

---

[3]Cf. A. M. G. Kuypers, *Model en Inzicht,* Assen, 1959, pp. 107 ff.

CHAPTER FOUR

THE EXACT CHARACTER OF PHYSICAL SCIENCE

1. *The Concept "Exact"*

Mathematics and physical science are considered to be exact sciences. In this chapter we want to investigate somewhat more closely what is meant by the predicate "exact." Why are some sciences called exact in contrast to others? In what does their exactness consist?

At first the answer does not seem to be very difficult. For exactness is a typical property of mathematics to such an extent that it is a redundancy of language to speak of "exact mathematics." Non-exact mathematics would be a kind of contradiction in terms, because mathematics is by its very nature exact. Accordingly, we usually call those sciences exact which either themselves belong to mathematics or make use of mathematical methods. Nevertheless, for two reasons this reply is not entirely satisfactory. First of all, strictly speaking, the exactness of mathematics disappears as soon as we apply mathematics to physical science, because no measurement is fully exact. Secondly, there are several forms of physical science in which there is only a minimum of applied mathematics and which nevertheless have to be included among the exact sciences. We may mention, for example, qualitative chemical analysis and classical organic chemistry.

The Difference Between Mathematics and Physical Science. Thus it cannot solely be the application of mathematical methods which determines the more or less exact character of a science. Something else than a mathematical aspect appears to play a role when the predicate "exact" is attributed to physical science. This should not be surprising if attention is paid to the striking difference between physical science and mathematics from the viewpoint of the theory of the sciences. This difference, which was known even to the ancients, has not diminished with the passage of time but rather become more emphatic. Aristotle, followed by the medieval schoolmen, expressed the difference in question by saying that physical science and mathematics move on a different level of abstraction: mathematics is concerned only with the quantitative aspects of reality, while physical science takes also qualities into consideration. For instance, mathematics considers only the circular shape of a shield, but physical science pays attention also to the shield's color, hardness, material composition, etc.

True, the remark could be made that in its development physical science increasingly considered the so-called qualitative properties in a quantitative fashion and that this phenomenon was accompanied by an increasing exactness of physical science. Nevertheless, this does not mean that the difference between physical science and mathematics was gradually eliminated. For, just as physical science, mathematics also grew and developed, and its development was in harmony with the initial difference between the two sciences. It remains typical of mathematics that, insofar as its considerations are concerned, it is irrelevant whether or not a figure is exactly realized. Whether the shield is really circular or not does not interest mathematics. Mathematics, as mathematics, abstracts from this realization and considers the ideal circle, the ideal triangle, the ideal line. Thus Euclidean geometry gave rise to the development of a non-Euclidean geometry, i.e., a geometry which does not formulate its axioms and definitions as idealizations of what approximately agrees with sense perception, but in a free fashion. This freedom of mathematics is sometimes expressed in the statement that mathematics is not a "science of the real" (*Realwissenschaft*), not a science which is concerned with reality as it is experienced, but with freely created entities.

Physical science, on the other hand, as an empirical science, remains concerned with reality. Even though physical science has gradually reduced its qualitative aspects more and more to quantitative data, the essential difference between physical science and mathematics remains. For the quantitative data are always obtained through measurements, and measurements always presuppose something qualitative. The object to be measured has to be distinguished from its surroundings, either through a difference in qualities, e.g., redness against greenness, or through a difference in the intensity of the same quality. Without such a difference there would be no possibility to perform the measurement which is to supply the quantitative data of physical science. Accordingly, in this science the qualitative aspect is closely connected with the quantitative aspect. There is no question of reducing quality to quantity, but at most of making increasingly greater use of the quantitative aspects possessed by qualities.

The situation is wholly different in mathematics. True, mathematics has to make use of qualitative elements in representing its magnitudes in mathematical figures, such as drawings of triangles or lines, or in symbols, such as 5, *a,* and +. However, these representations are merely aids to mathematical thinking, they do not constitute the object of mathematics. The concept "line" and not the white chalk line on the blackboard is the object which interests the mathematician. He is not interested in the chalk line which of necessity always has some thickness, but in the one-dimensional line without thickness. For this reason the drawn triangular figure from which the mathematician deduces his theses about the triangle may be inexact, and the figures 1, 2, 3, etc., used by the arithmetician, need not have physically exact equality. It suffices that what they represent be equal. For the measurements of the physicist, on the other hand, it is of the greatest importance that his measuring tools be exactly equal. Otherwise his measurements are valueless. It remains true of course, that completely exact equality cannot be realized. Nevertheless, the physicist tends to make it as exact as possible, because every inexactness adversely affects the results of his measurements.

Mathematical and Physical Exactness. Above we have used the term "exact" in connection with physical measurements. Its meaning there was "accurate." Thus it seems that physical exactness comes close to mathematical exactness, in the sense that a given measure always has exactly the same value. For instance, a ruler of one meter is *always* equal to 100 cm, and not now 100.2 cm and then 99.8 cm. In other words, it seems as if numerical values are decisive for physical exactness. Although in a sense this is true, nevertheless the problem of physical exactness is not a mathematical problem. For, from the mathematical viewpoint a meter is always by definition 100 cm, because one centimeter is $\frac{1}{100\text{th}}$ of a meter and $100 \times \frac{1}{100}$ is always 1. The problem is, therefore, always strictly a physical problem—namely, how to make certain that a measure remains equal to itself and always retains a constant relationship to the accepted standard. Thus to say that a particular measuring rod of one meter is *de facto* only 99.9 cm means that the rod in question is 99.9 times as long as $\frac{1}{100}$ of the standard meter, which is a concrete physical object. Although mathematics may be able to render services in establishing a measure, mathematics itself is not capable of solving the problem in question.

Of course, we are not particularly interested here in the problem of standards of measurements, but are concerned with clarifying the difference between mathematical and physical exactness. The former refers to ideal statements, i.e., definitions and axioms and the logical consequences deduced from them, the latter is primarily concerned with more or less accurate observations and the comparison of real physical things. For this reason there is an essential difference between the statements "one meter is one hundred centimeters" and "this measuring rod is one hundred centimeters." In the first statement one hundred means exactly one hundred, and it would make no difference whether we write 100 or 100.0, except that the last zero is superfluous. In the physical statement, however, 100 cm does not have the same meaning as 100.0 cm, for 100.0 indicates a greater accuracy of measurement.

Despite everything that has been said here about the essential difference between mathematics and physical science and their exactness, it should be clear that both sciences are closely related in their exactness. Physical science appears to tend to mathematical exactness. It may be called more exact according as it is more successful in this tendency. Thus it would appear that the customary descriptions of the exact sciences are right when they seek to connect exactness with mathematics.[1] As a matter of fact, there is a close relationship. The emphasis which we placed upon the difference between physical science and mathematics did not intend to deny this relationship. It merely wanted to show that the relationship is not at all as obvious as is usually thought and even more or less suggested by European university systems which put mathematics and physical science together in a single Faculty.[2] Their classification in a single

[1] The *Shorter Oxford English Dictionary* describes exact sciences as "those which admit of absolute precision in their results, especially the mathematical sciences."

[2] Historically speaking, the Faculty of Mathematics and Physical Science descends from a sector of the medieval Faculty of Liberal Arts—namely, the sector which alongside mathematics contained also astronomy. (Although for us astronomy is a physical science, for the ancients it was more mathematics than physical science.) The Faculty of the Liberal Arts, which constituted a kind of propaedeutics for the three major Faculties of Theology, Medicine, and Law, was composed of the trivium and the quadrivium. The trivium contained logic, grammar, and rhetoric, the quadrivium arithmetic, geometry, astronomy, and music (considered mathematically). In some parts of Europe

Faculty is, of course, not purely a coincidence, and, likewise, it is not to be explained on purely historical grounds. For in physical science extensive use is made of the mathematical method.

The Data of Physical Science Possess a Special Convincing Power. The use of mathematics in physical science leads to the question why, despite the essential difference, physical science is so accessible to the use of mathematical methods. A second question is immediately connected with the first—namely, is this openness for the use of mathematical methods specifically proper to physical science or is every science, provided it be sufficiently developed, open for mathematics? If the openness in question is not specific, then the lack of exactness in the sciences of man and in philosophy will be connected with a relative backwardness of these sciences in comparison with physical science, and not with the proper character of these sciences.

The raising of this question gives rise to another problem, which was previously mentioned in an incidental way and which is of no little importance with respect to the question of exactness. We mean the typical unanimity which reveals itself in the pursuit of physical science. This unanimity characterizes all exact sciences. It strikes any observer that mathematicians as well as physicists and chemists are in mutual agreement as to what their particular science posits as certain.

Let us repeat it, this unanimity, of course, does not mean that they never disagree whether or not a certain statement belonging to their science is correct. It does mean, however, that when there is such a difference of opinion, there is as a rule agreement that no crucial proof has yet been presented. Accordingly, in principle, physical science knows decisive arguments which every specialist will recognize. The most remarkable point in this matter is that these decisive arguments possess only a relative value, at least in physical science. (In mathematics the situation is different.) For every physicist or chemist recognizes in principle that a future development of physical science may force him to abandon a position hitherto taken. Accordingly, on the one hand, the decisive arguments of physical science which lead to unanimity lack an absolute character, but,

the Faculty of Liberal Arts was split after the French Revolution into the Faculty of Letters and Philosophy and that of Mathematics and Physical Science. It is interesting to note that in the United States the College of Liberal Arts, as a preparation for high level studies, recalls in name and to some extent even in purpose the structure of the medieval university.

on the other hand, this lack of absoluteness does not prevent all scientists from being at a given moment unanimous about what the situation is in their science.

Perhaps it is because of this remarkable convincing power of physical data that we ascribe the character of exactness even to parts of physical science, e.g., qualitative chemistry, which are hardly exact in the mathematical sense of the term and which also hardly make use of mathematical methods. A closer consideration of the method used by the last-named science may be able to lead us to the proper character of exactness in physical science as distinguished from that of mathematics. How does a chemist determine whether or not a coin contains silver? By dissolving it in nitric acid and then adding a solution containing chloride. If the addition results in a white precipitate, the coin contained silver; otherwise not. Accordingly, the process in question determines unambiguously whether or not silver was present. But it is not suitable for determining the amount of silver that was present. Of course, an experienced chemist will see by the thickness of the precipitate whether there was little or much silver, but his estimate is never exact in the quantitative sense. If he wants to know the percentage exactly, he has to weigh the precipitate. On the other hand, without weighing he is able to determine whether or not there is silver. Thus *exact* here has the sense of *unambiguous.*

The Basis of Exactness in Physical Science. What **gives the** statement that silver is present its convincing power, its non-ambiguity, its inescapability? No other reason than that a determined unambiguous procedure—"take *this* and add *that* to it"—has led to a very definite result, namely, a white precipitate. Within the framework of chemical analysis a constant appeal is made to what is immediately given in sense perception. For anyone who is familiar with the process the appearance of the white precipitate in that particular phase of the investigation establishes the presence of silver. Only one interpretation of the appearance is possible, and for every observer the appearance has one and the same primary meaning.

Accordingly, analytic chemistry is set up in such a way that, in order to determine the presence of a particular substance, it is sufficient to refer to a particular sense-perceptible effect which within the totality of the manipulations performed by the chemist here and now can have no other meaning than the presence of the substance in question. It is this method of procedure which constitutes the basis of the exactness of the *physical sciences*. It is the foundation also of the so-called quantitative determinations and consequently also of the possibility of applying mathematics in physical science. To use again the same example, when we proceed to weigh the precipitated quantity of silver chloride, the weight is established by means of a balance, i.e., the counting of a certain number of weights or the reading of a certain position of the pointer on a dial suffices to determine the weight.

Here, again, the task of the senses is reduced to an unambiguous registration, e.g., this pointer stands on 2. The exactness of mathematics would lose all its value if the perceptional aspect itself which is of necessity an essential element of any empirical science, including physical science, did not offer a basis for this exactness. Of course, both the observation of the occurrence of a white precipitate and the reading of the position of the pointer as 2 allow all kinds of inaccuracies. For instance, the precipitate may be grey rather than white. However, there exist clearly defined chemical procedures to solve such doubts. Moreover, the general tendency of physical science is toward perceptions of such a nature that ambiguities are excluded. This tendency manifests itself, e.g., in its preference for pointer readings. True, even pointer readings are inaccurate, but their inaccuracy is known and can be indicated in the expression of the results.

Accordingly, what is typical of physical science and constitutes the basis of its exactness is the following. First of all, the inevitable sense perception is reduced to the registration of an unambiguous datum, such as, this precipitate is white, this pointer stands on 2 or between 2 and 3. Secondly, the procedure which leads to the appearance of the datum likewise is unambiguous. Both the acts of perception and the operational steps are univocal: they can be performed and controlled by anyone in the same way. The third element also which is present in physics as a science—namely, its rationality—is permeated by this univocity. In subsequent chapters we will investigate in the operational element as well as the rationality of physical science. In the context of the present chapter, which is concerned with exactness, we must limit ourselves to a consideration of the exact character of mathematical reasoning.

2. *The Exactness of Mathematics*

Univocal Character of Mathematics. As we have seen above, the basis of the exactness that characterizes physical science lies in the univocity of its acts of perception and of its operational steps. The use of mathematics as the rational element of physical science harmonizes fully with this univocity. For mathematics makes use of concepts which are wholly univocal. This assertion applies both to the first phase of mathematics, in which there is still a very intimate connection with sense data, and its subsequent, more abstract phase.

Euclidean geometry arrives at its concepts by means of a simple abstraction combined with an idealization of the sense datum. What is meant by a line, a point, or a circle, therefore, can be conceptually determined in an unambiguous way by means of a reference to a drawn figure or also defined in an operational fashion, e.g., by indicating how a circle is made by means of a compass. Although the drawn line is not a pure representation of the concept "line," nevertheless the content of this concept can be clarified by means of the drawing. This content becomes a part of the mathematical system and continues to retain there always exactly the same meaning. The same applies to elementary arithmetic. What is meant by the number 5 may be unambiguously determined by means of a counting operation of concrete things.

In abstract mathematics the situation is even easier with respect to univocity. For the meaning of the concepts used is established within the system itself and fixed by means of combinations of symbols. Wherever the same symbol or the same combination of symbols is used we have to do with the same meaning, so that the univocity of meanings is safeguarded.[3]

Univocal Description of Physical Data in Mathematical Language. Because mathematical language is characterized by univocity, it lends itself excellently for *describing* the univocal data of physical science, so that these data can be fixed unambiguously for all. Not only can the individual data be fixed in this way, but mathematics offers also an ideal possibility of describing the interrelationships between these data. The reason is that in every mathematical system the interrelationships between the magnitudes occurring in the system are unambiguously determined because of the axioms and the rules on which the system is based. It is this which gives mathematical reasoning its typical exactness. This exactness is communicated to the reasoning of the physical sciences through their use of mathematics.

---

[3]In Chapter VI we will speak in a different context about the development of mathematics into abstract mathematics.

Nevertheless, this mathematical exactness would be of no value whatsoever to physical science if the specific data of this science were not put into a form which make them accessible for mathematical treatment. Above we have seen what this form is—it consists in the univocal character of sense registration and of experimental operations.

3. *The Absence of Exactness in Other Sciences*

Meta-Exact Knowledge. The preceding considerations of the exactness proper to physical science and mathematics themselves were inevitably non-exact. We want to state this here, not to deprive these considerations of their convincing power, but to make clear that the ultimate evaluation of physical and mathematical exactness itself is not a treatise pertaining to physical science or mathematics. Moreover, the statement may serve to introduce the conclusion to be reached in this section—namely, that exactness is not a characteristic of *all* science.

It would be better perhaps to use the term "meta-exact" rather than "non-exact" when there is question of sciences other than physics and mathematics. For "non-exact" should be reserved to describe a study which ought to be exact but is not, e.g., a non-decisive mathematical proof, a non-exact physical perception, or an insufficiently described precept of chemical analysis. "Meta-exact" expresses more clearly that we are in a realm which lies beyond physical or mathematical exactness, as is the case, for example, in a philosophical treatise *concerned with* physical exactness. For such a treatise itself is based not on sense registration, but on reflection upon the nature and meaning which sense registration possesses for the exact character of physical science.

Accordingly, the exactness which is specifically proper to physical science is absent from philosophy. Not only, however, from philosophy but also from the empirical sciences of man. Of course, this absence of the exactness which is specifically proper to physical science does not mean that all exactness is absent from these sciences. In the sciences of man as well as in philosophy it is equally necessary to give the most accurate descriptions possible and to fix the meaning of the terms that are used in the clearest possible way and without danger of being misunderstood. However, it will never be possible to do so by means of the typical registering method of physical science or the formal method of mathematics.

Physical and Non-Physical Empirical Sciences. The fact that we speak of *empirical non-physical* sciences indicates that, like physical science, the sciences in question are based upon sense experience. The way, however, in which they make use of experience differs. This difference is connected with the difference in object but, as we will see, there is more than just a difference in object. First, however, let us devote a few words to this difference in object.

By non-physical sciences, such as history, sociology and psychology, we mean those sciences which have as their object man himself in his spiritual or mental aspects. Human physiology, therefore, is not a non-physical science, although man is its object. For it does not study man as a spiritual being, but as a special kind of animal, the *homo sapiens.* In principle, the method of human physiology is the same as that of animal physiology. Thus the material objects of human physiology and of animal physiology are different, but differences in the material object are not important when it is a question of indicating the fundamental distinctions between different sciences. Fundamental distinctions are based upon differences in the formal object.[4] This rule applies also to the distinction between physical and non-physical sciences. Sciences which study man solely insofar as he is of a material nature belong to the group of physical sciences. On the other hand, sciences which study material things insofar as they are cultural products of man, as, e.g., the history of art, do not belong to the group of physical sciences.

Non-Physical Sciences Probe Beyond the Realm of Physical Science. As we pointed out above, both physical and non-physical sciences make use of the empirical method, but they do it in different ways. Non-physical sciences probe into different and more profound realms of reality than does physical science. A few examples may serve to clarify this point.

---

[4]By the material object of a science is meant that which is studied; by the formal object the aspect under which the material object is studied. We may say, for instance, that astronomy and law have different material objects, for the former deals with stars and the latter with legal situations among human beings, which are two entirely different matters. The sciences of law and of language on the other hand, both deal with man. They agree therefore in this material object, but differ in their formal aspects. Meanwhile, these very examples show that, strictly speaking, it is always the difference in formal object which determines the distinction of the sciences. For even the stars can become the object of law—as soon as they begin to fall within the sphere of human property relationships. Moreover, the stars belong to the science of language insofar as man speaks about stars and sometimes even to them. They belong also to cultural history insofar as man has considered them in a plurality of ways throughout the course of history.

When a plane crash occurs, this crash is a sense perceptible fact. This one and the same fact may be considered in the sphere of physical science as well as in that of the science of law. As a fact considered by physical science, it gives rise to the question as to which material datum caused the crash. This question may be solved, if it is solved at all, by a series of laboratory experiments and performance tests. These experiments, however, do not solve the juridical problem of who is to be held responsible for the crash. This problem does not even enter the picture in these tests.

The investigation on the level of physical science merely shows that the plane crashed because, let us say, the way in which the wing was attached to the body was faulty and could not resist the forces acting upon it at great speeds. As a result, the wing broke off and the plane crashed to earth. The search for this fact remains wholly within the sphere of sense perception—in this case in the form of an instrumental registration which, of course, contains also a theoretical aspect. But this theoretical aspect is solely concerned with connections between data that can be registered in an instrumental way. Experiments in strains and stresses have led to the determination of certain values, and from these values conclusions are drawn with respect to the crash. From the totality of the event, the construction of the plane and its crash, the investigation of physical science selects only those data which lend themselves to sense registration by means of instruments. All other aspects are left out of consideration.

For instance, the juridical problem of responsibility for the crash remains entirely outside the realm viewed by physical science. When the question arises why the wing structure was faulty, the physicist or the technologist can offer a reply by pointing out that the material used did not possess sufficient strength or sufficient elasticity. He may be able to indicate what strength the material used did have and what it should have had to make the structure safe. But he is unable to establish legal responsibility by means of this kind of registered or calculated data.

Was the use of the faulty material a question of carelessness, sabotage, an accident, or the result of insufficient scientific and technological mastery over matter? Although, of course, the question cannot be answered without physical research and expert technological knowledge, it should be evident that the reply will have to make use of concepts which lie beyond the domain of the physical sciences.

The concepts in question cannot be found on the level of things that can be registered by the senses.

Man himself, *as* pursuing technique, enters into the picture here. The data of physical science and technology are integrated into a more comprehensive whole. To determine whether or not a certain action was sabotage or not, the exact registration of what has happened is indispensable, but it does not settle the juridical question. The addition of a particular substance to the structural material may be registered by the senses but, physically considered, this addition remains exactly the same, whether it be done for reasons of sabotage or not. Likewise, physically speaking, a thief who transports his booty has to use exactly the same amount of energy as the legitimate owner of the stuff. Nevertheless, for the judge who has to pronounce a verdict there is a great difference. In other words, within the sphere of legal science a role is played by categories which escape instrumental registration and physical interpretation. The *physical* event has to be evaluated within the totality of *human deeds*. The meaning of the deed has to be established. The physical and technological investigation is unable to do so, even though the judge who has to decide the issue will have to possess some knowledge of physics in order to be able to evaluate the result of the scientific investigation. No matter, however, how much physics he knows, this knowledge will not enable him to judge the crash from the legal point of view.

To use another example, through the means of his science a chemist is capable of determining that a certain statue is eighty percent gold and twenty percent silver and traces of other elements. The result of this analysis is connected with a network of data, such as hardness, melting point, and the influence exercised by atmospheric conditions. The historical or artistic value, however, of the statue in question is not at all established in this way. True, it may happen that chemical analysis becomes an important means in determining the age of the statue. But even then this analysis is only indirectly valuable for the historian. When questions are raised of whom the statue represents or what function it fulfilled in an ancient civilization, chemistry can give no reply whatsoever, because there is question here of a human meaning which is beyond the knowledge of chemistry.

Non-Physical Sciences Go Beyond the Exactness of Physical Science. For a proper understanding of the character of physical science in contradistinction to non-physical science it is not sufficient to realize that physical science explores only a limited sector of the empirical data, i.e., that physical science views these data from a certain viewpoint, so that other sectors or other viewpoints do not receive any attention. What is even more necessary is to realize that the way in which physical science views the data is very intimately connected with its exactness. As has been pointed out above, this exactness is a result of the registering sense character of physical science, which confers something unambiguous upon these data in their immediacy. In the non-physical sciences, on the other hand, the attention is no longer concentrated upon these data in their immediacy but upon what they reveal about man and his culture; hence the character of exactness is lost.

Of course, we do not mean to say that the data become non-exact, but that non-physical science cannot rest in the exact aspect of these data. When there is question of whether or not a particular science is exact, one has to put aside a number of sentiments that are evoked by the term "exact." Exact knowledge, for instance, may not at all be equated with perfect knowledge. If one wants to know a friend better and restricts his efforts to the exact data that can be obtained by means of the registering research of physical science, he will hardly acquire any pertinent knowledge at all. The knowledge reached in this way may be exact, but it is not perfect or even sufficient. He simply does not even reach his friend as a human being. Scientific data obtained by means of the most refined physical methods, as knowledge of this human being, remain far behind what the other in a single encounter could reveal about himself.

Accordingly, the non-exact character of the non-physical sciences does not indicate a kind of inferiority, but points out that the sciences in question do not possess the typical exactness of physical science, because the empirical data are viewed in a different context. Meanwhile it remains true that apparently it is easier for man's knowledge to move in the realm of the physical sciences than in that of the non-physical sciences—at least, if our criterion is the degree of unanimity with which these sciences can be pursued. However, this statement should not be construed in any way as a disparagement of the non-physical sciences. Yet, we are faced here with a paradox— namely, that man's mind which, in the words of Henri Bergson, "should feel at home" in the sciences of man,[5] is less capable in this

---

[5] *L'évolution créatrice,* Paris, 62nd ed., 1946, p. 214.

realm than in a science of matter. We must consider the reason for this paradox in the following section.

4. *Univocal and Analogous Concepts*

As has been mentioned repeatedly, the exactness of physical science refers to the non-ambiguity of its data, and the mathematical deduction which it uses owes its stringency to the univocity of mathematical concepts. It will be necessary to delve somewhat deeper into this matter and to view the exactness of physical science and of mathematics in the light of man's cognitive situation. At the same time a measure of light will be thrown upon the above-mentioned paradox of human knowledge.

Univocal Concepts. We will begin by examining the proper character of the concepts which we have called "univocal." What is meant by this term, and which concepts are contradistinguished from univocal concepts? A univocal idea is a concept whose content is always presented in exactly the same way when we make use of the concept. For instance, in physical science the concept of velocity is univocal; likewise, the concepts of copper, water, and electron. Whenever we say of something that it is copper, the term indicates exactly the same, whether or not we are dealing with things which are as different as a penny, a door knob, and a water pipe. The concept of copper abstracts from the different forms and functions of these objects and, therefore, is univocal. Of course, it may happen that in American English the *term* "copper" has also another meaning (policeman), so that it is ambiguous or equivocal. Nevertheless, the two concepts corresponding to this single term themselves are univocal and not really related, as is confirmed by the fact that in other languages the same equivocal meaning will usually not be found.

Analogy. There are, however, other cases in which the situation is different. Let us take, for example, the term "to see." This word may mean to perceive something with the eye, but also to understand something. There is no question here of pure equivocity, for we use the same term in both meanings precisely because of a certain relationship, a certain analogy between the function of the eye and that of the mind. Language—we mean not only English, but every language—is full of terms that are used in such an analogous way. Apparently, therefore, this phenomenon has something to do with human knowledge and human expressions of knowledge as such, and is not merely a peculiarity of a particular language.

That we do not have to do here merely with a question of language appears also from the fact that even when linguistically there is a clear difference, the corresponding concepts continue to retain their relationship. For instance, the German word *begreifen* is used to indicate an intellectual activity and is distinct from the term *greifen* whose meaning primarily refers to the physical grasping of an object with the hand or with some other grasping organ. Nevertheless, *begreifen* clearly refers to *greifen*. Man appears to see his intellectual activity through analogy with the activity of his hands: both, in their own way, have a "grip" on something, both seize something. With respect to the terms *greifen* and *begreifen* the important point is not so much that the two words show their conceptual relationship by means of the same verbal root, used with or without a prefix. For there are innumerable cases in which there is no verbal relationship or at least no obvious relationship, nevertheless, the corresponding concepts continue to show their interconnection. Take, for example, the term "to know." The word "to know" does not at all refer to grasping, nevertheless any effort to understand what is meant by knowing will make us seize(!) the example of grasping something with the hand. Thus our concept of knowing is based upon a certain analogy between grasping with the hand and grasping with the mind. It is not without reason that we speak of an intellectual "grip."

Similarity and Dissimilarity. Thus what is characteristic of the analogous use of terms such as "to see" and "to grasp" is that one and the same term refers to two or more diverse things one of which, however, cannot be conceived independently of the other. On the one hand, there is a clear difference: to grasp something with the hand is absolutely different from grasping something with the intellect. On the other hand, there is also a clear similarity. If we attempt to investigate where exactly this similarity and difference lie, we find a particularly striking phenomenon: it becomes apparent that we are unable to make a clear conceptual distinction between the dissimilarity and the resemblance. Both what is done by the hand and what is done by the intellect involve the exercise of an act of grasping. We could say that in one case the hand really goes out to the thing that is grasped, while nothing goes out from the intellect to the thing that is known. However, this statement does not contribute very much, for we could also maintain that the intellect really goes out to the things, albeit in a wholly different fashion.

To express the matter somewhat paradoxically, we could say that in analogous concepts the difference lies precisely in the similarity and the dissimilarity lies in the resemblance. For the "going out to," which expresses the similarity contains also the dissimilarity: in one case there is a visible process, a grasping that can be observed with the eye, and in the other case there is no such visible process. However, this difference contains also a similarity, for it is precisely the aspect of "going out to" in the visible and in the invisible process which makes us speak of "grasping" in both cases.

Man's Complex Nature as the Basis of Analogy. We have dwelled somewhat extensively upon this example to emphasize the complexity of the situation. The example does not interest us for its own sake, but only insofar as it reveals something about the characteristics of all human knowledge. As sensitive-intellectual knowledge, human knowing is primarily tuned to the sense perceptible, and it is in the light of the sense perceptible that our concepts are formed. When, however, our intellect turns to that which is not perceptible by the senses, it has to make use of concepts borrowed from the realm of the senses. Of course, in such a case the content of the concepts undergoes a modification, but this modification is not so great that the connection with the senses is wholly lost. It is by means of our concept of physical grasping that the idea of intellectual grasping is clarified. Perhaps it would be better to say that this clarification is at the same time an obscuration. We know intuitively what it is to understand through actually understanding something. However, this knowledge is, on the one hand, clarified through our intellectual analysis of understanding when we make use of such terms as "to see" and "to grasp" but, on the other hand, it is also rendered obscure because these terms refer primarily to different kinds of activities.

It is from this innner tension that the use of analogous concepts arises. We mean the tension between relying on intuitive knowledge from immediate experience and on the use of concepts acquired in the realm of the sense perceptible which the intellect can handle more easily. It is here therefore that the mystery of man's being reveals itself most clearly. There is in man a spiritual self-presence, a being with-himself, a being aware of himself. But this knowledge remains intuitive and implicit. If man wants to explicitate this self-knowledge and embody it in words, he has to make an appeal to what he knows by means of the external senses. It is for this reason that concepts whose content really stems entirely from man's self-awareness are formed as if they were concepts derived from external perception. For instance, we know what knowledge is only from self-experience, but the concept "knowledge" is explicitated by means of the visible activity of grasping.

This state of affairs appears to be a consequence of the fact that man is a "spirit-in-matter." Although, as spirit, man knows about himself, it is through matter that he has to rise to a more complete knowledge of himself. For it is by means of analogous concepts, borrowed from material reality, that reflection takes place and that man refines his own self-knowledge. This cognitive situation has repercussions also in other activities of man. We will meet it again when we will consider the meaning of technology.

Accordingly, the analogous use of concepts is the only way in which we can form concepts of things which are not directly given in sense experience. Our entire reflection on man's cognitive activity is permeated with analogous concepts. A simple look at the preceding pages suffices to make this clear. In our *considerations* we made use of *concepts* such as *connection, clarification, obscuration, analysis, tension, permeated, forming ideas,* and *explicitation,* all of which are *examples illustrating* the *idea* which we *intended* to *explain.*

The Necessity of Analogous Concepts in Non-Physical Sciences. It should be evident that there is no need to use analogous concepts in the study of the material world, as it presents itself to our external senses. For this reason physical science may use univocal concepts, i.e., concepts which whenever they are used have exactly the same meaning, and this meaning is immediately connected either with a sense datum or with a strictly univocal mode of definition. In this way it becomes evident why physical science is exact.

At the same time it shows why non-physical sciences, by virtue of their very nature, have necessarily to be non-exact sciences. Their concepts cannot be restricted to sense data or to mathematical entities, but have to refer to man's spiritual activity, as known to man from his internal experience. For convenience' sake we speak here of spiritual or mental activity, although it should be clear that even this spiritual activity is a total activity of man. By calling it a spiritual activity, we express that in non-physical science man's aspect of interiority as such plays a role. For this reason such a science will never be able to attain to the exactness of physical science, the exactness which is specific of the sciences that do not transcend matter and make use of the means of external observation. As we mentioned before, however, the denial of this exactness to non-physical sciences does not imply any disparagement whatsoever of these sciences, but merely indicates certain difficulties that are encountered in the attempt to form concepts in these sciences.

Science is a means through which man knows and as such shares in all the limitations of man's act of knowing, it is an instrument of a "spirit-in-matter" and as such most adapted to matter. In a sense it may even be said that it is precisely the eminence of the object considered in the non-physical sciences which makes them lose exactness. Man's being a "spirit-in-matter" makes intelligible also the paradox that his mind in certain respects has less cognitive means at its disposal in the non-physical sciences than in physical science and that his mind can achieve less where it should "be more at home." The reason for this state of affairs lies in the fact that the human mind has to make use of means which are bound to matter. Thus physical science has a certain advantage over non-physical science but at the same time also it is subject to an essential limitation.

There Is No Sharp Dichotomy of Physical and Non-Physical Science. Meanwhile it is necessary to add something to what has been stated above, lest a misunderstanding occur. Hitherto we have simply spoken of physical science and non-physical science, thus suggesting a sharp dichotomy which, however, does not really exist. As in man himself, so also there is no such dichotomy in science. In man himself there is no dualism of spirit and matter as if these two were two entities existing one alongside the other. Man is an embodied spirit or a spiritualized body. For this reason it is not correct to speak of non-physical sciences in opposition to physical sciences. It would be preferable to speak of a spectrum of the sciences, in which the sciences on one end of the spectrum have strikingly the character of physical science with its consequent exactness and those on the other end that of non-physical science, while in between these two extremes there are all kinds of transitional forms.

However, even this way of representing the state of affairs is too onesided or rather too one-dimensional. Every non-physical science has parts which have a strongly exact character alongside others which lack this exactness. For, if man is a "spirit-in-matter," the study of any spiritual activity of man will have to pay attention to the material way in which this activity expresses and exteriorizes itself. For instance, psychology has sections which are very close to the physiology of the sense organs, and others which are rather philosophical. Psychology uses certain methods which are closely connected with those of physical science, but also others which definitely are not related to physical methods.[6]

Similar situations occur also in physical science. For instance, biology knows not only physico-chemical methods, but also others which are less exact, such as those that are used to study animal behavior. Moreover, from the viewpoint of historical perspective, modifications occur sometimes in the character of a particular science. Especially as far as physics and chemistry are concerned, it is true that they have become increasingly more exact. This increase is connected with the progressively more quantitative character of these sciences and the methods of perception that are connected with this character. For these sciences have increasingly eliminated from their experimental perception the fullness of what is qualitatively given in order to concentrate on sharply defined and sharply registrable quantitative magnitudes (even though these magnitudes must necessarily have a qualitative aspect to be measurable). This elimination is a tendency to strictly univocal concepts having a sharply defined content. The vague concepts of "warm" and "cold" and the vague relationships "warmer" and "colder" are replaced by accurately registrable and univocally determined positions of the thermometer. The vague concept of "red," which permits all kinds of differentiations that cannot be sharply distinguished either in perception or in concepts, gives way for the magnitudes of the wave function, which in theory are clearly distinguishable and can also be exactly registered by appropriate instruments.

Refinement of Univocal and of Analogous Concepts. For this reason it may be said that the method of contemporary physical science manages to use to its full advantage the univocity of its concepts and has succeeded also in clarifying these concepts by bringing into play all its theoretical and perceptional possibilities. For, although such

---

[6]In practice, moreover, there are not only different methods in psychology, but there are also different views among the psychologists regarding the question which methods should be considered to belong or not to belong to their science.

concepts as "warm" and "red" are univocal insofar as they are always applied in the same sense to material reality, their content is vague, because it is bound up with inaccurate perception. Through the refinement of perception, however, which has been made possible through the development of theories and of instruments, this content also is fixed in an exact fashion. From being non-exact univocal concepts the physical concepts have become exact univocal concepts. But concepts that are not univocal but analogous can never become exact, because the necessary foundation of exactness is missing since their content can never be attached to what is sensitively given in its immediacy.

This lack of exactness does not mean that in the realm of the analogous there is no possibility of refining the concepts. It can be done by means of extensive empirical research, accurate phenomenological description of what is given, penetrating analysis of the various aspects of human existence, etc. Nevertheless, the result attained in this way will always be different in nature from the exactness of physical science. Making use of what has been said above about the analogy of concepts, we could say perhaps that the exactness to be pursued in non-physical science is, as it were, the analogous counterpart of the exactness proper to physical science. This formula expresses at the same time the difference and the similarity of the two types of science and their exactness. The *similarity*, because in both cases man aims at science, uses the same cognitive means, and has the same desire to arrive at concepts; the *difference*, because the object of the two is not the same and, consequently, the way in which the object is reached is also different.

Because of the analogous relationship of the exactness to be pursued in the non-physical sciences with that of the physical sciences, any effort to make non-physical science exact in the same fashion as physical science is an extremely hazardous venture, which in practice leads to gross inexactness. For instance, if one thinks that a man's behavior has been exactly described when all perceptible aspects of it have been analytically registered, he fails to see precisely that which is most important—namely, the self-revealing totality of man. For it is precisely in this totality that man shows himself as man.

Philosophical Language. In this connection it will not be amiss to add a few words regarding the technical language of philosophy.

This language has of necessity to make use of terms expressing analogous concepts. Philosophical language is an important aid in philosophizing, because in this technical language the analogous meaning of the concepts is fixed as accurately as possible. Nevertheless, this language can never be used in a quasi-automatic fashion, as can be done with mathematical and physical formulae. For instance, there is no need for anyone to recall the derivation of the formula $h\pi r^2$ which indicates the volume of a cylinder. To apply this formula, one has to know only what the symbols composing it mean. But a person who uses a philosophical thesis, e.g., "human knowledge is abstract," without concretely reflecting on knowledge and thus having, as it were, also the "derivation" of this thesis in mind, does not state anything and does not think anything. For it is only in the concrete personal thinking and experiencing of the thesis that this proposition has meaning and value.

The above-mentioned difference between the meaningful use of philosophical and physical language is connected also with the non-reflective character of physical science as well as with the exact character of this science. For it is the constant connection with the sense datum, as it is open to immediate registration, which makes physical science both non-reflective and exact, so that its concepts can remain univocal. Although this exactness may be considered a scientific advantage, on the other hand, the non-reflective character which prevents physical science from knowing itself is a definite disadvantage.

CHAPTER FIVE

THE COGNITIVE-OPERATIONAL CHARACTER OF PHYSICAL SCIENCE

To Explain is "to Take Apart." The abstract nature of human knowledge, which was considered in Chapter III, forces us to consider separately the various aspects of physical science. We have to "take them apart," because we cannot see them all at the same time. We have to direct our attention to one aspect after another. Thus the expression "to take them apart" is not at all an empty metaphor, but is a genuine analogy in reference to the physical taking-apart of a material whole, in which the various component parts are really separated so as to make it possible to know the whole better and to obtain a comprehensive view of it. The fact that there is a real analogy between the activity of the mind and the physical handling of things is based upon the intimate union of human knowledge with matter. For, as we have seen, the abstract character of our knowledge is closely connected with sensitivity. We are not able to know the whole of physical science as a human activity in a single intellectual glance, because this mental glance depends upon the limited "glances" of our senses.

Accordingly, as in any true analogy, there is here a real internal similarity as well as a real internal dissimilarity. In an explanation, in "taking apart," it is not possible really to separate the different aspects as we do in separating the parts when we take an object apart physically. For this reason any explanation contains objectionable features, precisely because it is a "taking apart." Strictly speaking, the various aspects of physical science considered successively in these chapters cannot be taken separately from one another. For instance, a study of the empirical and factual character of physical science demands of necessity that this character be viewed in connection with the rational character proper to the same science. For facts make their appearance only in the light of a certain theory, because sense perception, which makes us know facts, is in the service of man's rational element. Thus everything is connected with everything else.

74

Knowing and Doing. Because of this interconnection, the rational and operational character of physical science with which we are concerned here has been mentioned repeatedly in the preceding chapters, and for the same reason this chapter will have to make frequent references to considerations of former chapters. This situation is not very satisfactory, but nothing can be done about it, for the different aspects condition one another. For the same reason we will also speak here in this chapter about both the rational and the operational aspects of physical science, although many reasons could be put forward to treat them separately, not the least of which is that thinking and doing are strikingly diverse actions.

However, as we will see, precisely in physical science thinking and doing are intimately connected: together with sense perception, they constitute a trinity which is the essence of the experimental method. Since many aspects of the rational element of physical science have already been treated in the preceding chapters, we will be able to devote our attention here mainly to the theoretical function of the rational element. We will see how it is precisely this theoretical function which in physical science demands that man actively operate in nature. The analogy between physical and intellectual grasping, mentioned in the preceding chapter, becomes even more pronounced in physical science, in the sense that here the intellectual grasp is directly dependent upon the physical grasp. Without a technical grip on nature, there is here no intellectual grasp, and reversely, without the intellectual grasp, there is no technical grip.

It may be useful to summarize here the aspects of rationality which have been considered, before we pay attention to the interconnection between knowing and grasping in physical science. Although Chapters III and IV did not specifically name the rationality of physical science, they were concerned with it also. The third chapter, which was devoted to the abstract character of physical science, in speaking about the empirical aspect of this science, showed how the abstractness which characterizes all the intellectual knowledge of man, including all science, assumes a special form in physical science because of the presence of the empirical aspect. The fourth chapter supplied us with additional information by considering the exactness of physical science. Thus the form of rationality proper to physical science has already been viewed from different angles. We will make a grateful use of these considerations in the following pages.

1. *Physical Science as Theory*

Fact and Theory. What the senses make known to us always contains an aspect of being-found there, of being-so-as-a-matter-of-fact. This object, for instance, is now black and then red. Whether we understand it or not, it shows itself to be so. Sense data impose themselves on us, we have to take them as they are. They are brute, stubborn facts which we cannot change. However, our intellect never simply accepts facts as they are. It endeavors to make them intelligible and thus to make them lose something of their brute givenness and opaqueness. In other words, we attempt to explain them and make them transparent to the consideration of the intellect. This explanation diminishes also somewhat the aspect of things which above we called their being-so-as-a-matter-of-fact. We are made able to predict what is going to happen, which means that we see connections and interrelationships between the various data.

Meanwhile, no matter how much we explain, the aspect of being-so-as-a-matter-of-fact never disappears entirely. It is merely shifted to a different position. A clear example is provided by chemical explanations. In pre-scientific experience we encounter different substances in nature, each of which has its own characteristic properties. Even on this level, there is an element of intelligibility. For the simple fact that we speak of wood, copper, water, air, and the qualities which characterize these substances means that we are aware of it that material things occur in kinds. Thus our experiences are theoretically organized even on the pre-scientific level. This should not really surprise us. Human knowledge is a sensitive-intellectual knowledge; hence there is never a purely sensitive givenness, purely being-a-fact. Every fact is embedded in some kind of theoretical context. The fact that even the most primitive human languages make use of specific concepts bears witness to this assertion.

Accordingly, when in this chapter there is question of facts, we must constantly keep in mind that, as we have seen above, the "fact" always refers to a factual *aspect* of a whole datum and includes also a theoretical aspect. Especially on levels where the factual aspect seems to predominate we are much too easily inclined to forget the theoretical aspect. Nevertheless, the theoretical aspect is clearly present, even if it is understood in the sense of being an explanatory aspect. For, even when we have not arrived at a chemical explanation in the scientific sense of the term, the discovery that a certain substance is present may contain a kind of explanation. Let us assume, for example, that an explosion occurs somewhere in a house. It takes us by surprise, for houses are not in the habit of exploding. We do not understand why this one did until we discover that a gas pipe was leaking and that someone close-by struck a match. Now the explosion suddenly is intelligible, for it happens to be a property of gas to be explosive if it is mixed with air. Accordingly, there is an explanation here, but this explanation does not remove the aspect of being-so-in-fact, for it merely shifts this aspect to a different level. That a mixture of gas and air can explode is something we know only from experience. It appears to be so, even if we do not understand anything of it. As we say, the explosive nature of such a mixture is a fact.

Fact and Explanation. In this shift from one fact (the concrete explosion) to another (the explosive nature of the mixture) there is a twofold theoretical aspect. This aspect expresses, first of all, the general datum that substances act always in a fixed, general, recurrent fashion and, secondly, that the substance in question—the gas—is explosive. Thus there is an explanation here because there is an implicit appeal to our knowledge of something which we may call the order of nature and of previously acquired details about this order. This theoretical aspect, however, does not at all exclude the factual aspect, but merely changes its position. For we may now ask, why is gas explosive? The chemist will reply that gas is a mixture of CH_4, H_2 etc., all of which are combustible substances, because they consist of elements which have a great affinity for oxygen. This explanation brings us a step further, but the factual aspect still remains. It is now on a still more general level, for we no longer appeal directly to our knowledge of gas, but to a more general knowledge concerning the chemical elements of carbon and hydrogen. However, even on this new and more general level, the affinity of these elements for oxygen itself is a fact which stands in need of an explanation.

The chemist is capable of supplying this explanation by referring to Kossel's theory about the tendency to the configuration of noble gases. Here the level becomes still more general, for the tendency to the noble gas configuration is not specific of carbon and hydrogen but applies to all elements. Yet a factual aspect remains present. In this way the process continues all the time. The formerly observed fact that there is a tendency to noble gas configuration in its turn finds an explanation in quantum mechanics, but quantum mechanics itself makes use of the fundamental qualities with which elementary particles happen to be endowed. The factual aspect never disappears, and for this reason physical science is and remains an empirical science.[1] However, because of the theoretical aspect, the physicist or the chemist manages to reduce to a few fundamental properties the many properties of diverse substances which first were simply juxtaposed as separate factual data. All these properties of the various chemical substances which first were only established from without, i.e., through the senses, become now intelligible from within as consequences of the structure of these substances.

Knowledge and Model. The process of thought described above shows what is meant by knowledge. According to a famous description of Aristotle, to know is to become the other. Somehow the intimate essence of the object known comes to be present in the knowing subject. The knower forms an image, a model of the object known. In the vision of this image, qualities which at first stood separately alongside one another now delineate themselves as a unit for the knower. He sees them now as flowing from the essence of that which he has made his own in the act of knowing. Theoretical knowledge does indeed possess something of the character which Aristotle stated so profoundly in the expression "becoming the other." Many other expressions of human language point in the same direction: e.g., "to assimilate something," "to absorb something," and "to make something one's own."

True knowledge means that what was first exterior becomes interiorized and is no longer known from without but from within. Thus the above-mentioned expressions have a profound meaning. At the same time, however, they are also somewhat deceptive, especially with respect to the knowledge which is physical science. For they seem to imply that the element of exteriority can be fully removed from knowledge, that once the human intellect is actuated it is capable of producing everything of itself, and that a real and complete unification of the object known and the knowing subject can be reached in which the object loses all its strangeness and otherness.

---

[1]As should be clear, mathematical intelligibility plays an important role in this ever-increasing theoretical explanation. From the mathematical formalism of quantum mechanics it is possible to derive, at least in part, the behavior of chemical elements. Nevertheless, the factual aspect remains. For it is a datum of experience that the mathematical formalism used in quantum mechanics can be applied to chemistry.

However, as we have pointed out in Chapter III, physical science must be characterized as knowledge by means of external sensitivity. Hence there will always remain a certain strangeness, a certain distance with respect to the object known. The abstract-analytic character of physical science also is connected with this dependence upon the senses. It accounts for the fact that physical science is always only partial knowledge. Concrete reality itself is not known in its full concreteness, but only reality as it has been taken apart into various abstract aspects. Thus every image of reality is always an image which man synthetizes from these aspects, it is always a model projected from and by man.

The model, however, is an attempt to *conceive* and *com*prehend the various aspects in their interconnection. It is never a direct intuition of reality in its own intimate unity. Although the model is oriented to reality, it *is* not reality itself but an image of reality projected in man. In other words, the image is a construct, composed of perceptional elements with which we are familiar. It is an effort to appropriate and unify something which is approached only distantly and through onesidedness.

The Inner Tension of Knowledge: Ideal and Limitation. Nevertheless, this subjective aspect of human knowledge never completely eliminates objectivity, understood as orientation to reality as it is in itself. The truth of this assertion reveals itself, e.g., in the awareness man has of the limitation inherent in his knowledge. For in a sense such an awareness breaks through the limitation, because by knowing about his limitation man to a certain extent looks beyond his limits. Man knows about the ideal of knowledge, in which the mind makes the object known entirely its own and is capable of contemplating within itself the intimate ontological and dynamic principles of this object.

For this reason he is never satisfied in physical science with the factual knowledge of the present. Knowledge has its own inner dynamics which constantly urges man on, because he realizes the relative character of his knowledge. It is this inner awareness of what knowledge should really be and of what human knowledge *de facto* is which constitutes the grandeur of man's knowledge and confers on it the mobility and dynamism that is found in all sciences in their own appropriate fashion. In physical science this dynamism reveals itself in the constant urge to go forward and find more general explanations.

The same dynamism shows its presence in philosophy. Man is never satisfied with any philosophical system and constantly endeavors to approach the same fundamental problems in different ways. This restlessness of the human spirit flows from the intellect's internal critique of its own knowledge, because the intellect knows that its actual knowledge does not agree with the ideal. For the same reason man never permanently acquiesces in a philosophical proclamation that human knowledge is fundamentally impotent. The history of philosophy shows this point very clearly even with respect to those philosophers who thought that they had solid grounds to proclaim the absolute relativity, the fundamental impotence, or the total subjectivity of human knowledge. For, whatever grounds they have, whatever arguments they put forward for the relativity, impotence, or subjectivity of man's knowledge, ultimately the force moving them in their endeavors is the idea to throw light upon the real condition of human knowledge. This idea, however, presupposes that there is an awareness of an absolute element, something that escapes all relativity, in man's knowledge and that this element is capable of true judgments. By pronouncing a judgment about what human knowledge really is, man implicitly recognizes the true character of knowledge. It is only against the background of an ideal of knowledge that an epistemological inquiry is meaningful.

The Inner Tension of Physical Science: Ideal and Limitation. However, we are not concerned here with investigating the problem of knowledge in its universality, but more especially with the way in which this problem manifests itself in physical science. This science is not interested in the investigation of human knowledge but in that of nature. Nevertheless, although physical science does not investigate human knowledge, the awareness of the possibilities and limitations of this knowledge co-determines the way in which this science operates. This implicit awareness operates as a presupposition of physical science. Once we realize that this awareness is at work in physical science, we constantly see it operate in various forms throughout this science.

As an example we may refer here to a peculiar characteristic of physical research. It consists in this that the physicist or chemist seems to be happy when he discovers deviations from hitherto generally accepted and trusted laws. He is always in search of the abnormal, of something which does not act as it should according to the rules.

Of course, experience also plays a role here, because it has shown that the study of such deviations leads to new insights. The deviation, then, is not studied for the sake of the deviation, but because it offers a possibility to arrive at better general laws. Thus this intellectual attitude of physical science shows not only the urge to arrive at universality, accompanied by the delight in universal validity, but also the expectation of finding somewhere a deviation which will make further research possible. The aversion of the scientist for absolutizing what is generally accepted, his willingness to make constant revisions, is essentially nothing else than the awareness that every image which he forms of the events of nature is in principle insufficient. It is the realization that every image is a human project and is in principle incomplete, because it does not give perfect knowledge.

Physical science would lose its dynamic character if there were no tension between the tendency to arrive at truly comprehensive knowledge and the awareness that what has already been attained is insufficient. Without this awareness science would be stranded in self-complacency, and without this ideal there would be no driving force to progress.

The Inner Tension and the Factual Aspect of Physical Science. The awareness of the tension between the ideal of knowledge and the deficiency of all factual knowledge is rendered particularly strong in physical science by the factual aspect which is never absent from this science. For every explanation of physical science merely shifts the position of the factual aspect without ever taking it entirely away. In the theoretical picture or the model formed of nature, the factual aspect always refers to something that is only sensitively established, something that is never fully assimilated. The appropriation, therefore, which characterizes knowledge, is never complete, the cognitive object retains its strangeness. The atomic structure devised by physical science may be capable of explaining many properties of a given material substance, but the fact that the atomic structure was conceived in this way was imposed by the data of the senses. It was to explain these data and to unify them that the structure was planned.

Thus the atomic structure devised by science, which makes these data transparent, itself shares in the character of givenness, i.e., of being imposed upon our mind. In other words, the model is not solely an immanent affair of the cognitive power which in this particular fashion comprehends the data. The fact that the model is imposed by the sense data confers upon it also an intentional character, in the sense that it refers to something "outside," that it demands to be itself perceived. Accordingly, through the senses the intellect seeks a new external contact with reality to find there this atomic structure, for only when it finds this structure there does it know that it is in contact with the reality to which the model refers, and not merely with itself. What is represented by the model, however, goes beyond what is directly perceptible. The earth, for instance, as a sphere, cannot directly be perceived. The same is true also of atoms. For this reason we search for such consequences from the model as are directly perceptible, or rather, consequences which can be made perceptible—the term "made" being understood here in the literal sense.

Let us illustrate the matter by means of a simple example borrowed from the sphere of the pre-scientific. For in this question also it is true that the method of physical science is essentially nothing else than an extension, a refined extension, of course, of the methods used in ordinary experiential knowledge. When we try to lift a small wooden box and discover that it is particularly heavy, we suppose that the box is filled with some heavy kind of material, i.e., we form an image of the interior of the box. At the same time, however, we realize that this image is *our* image, that it is built upon previous experiences with wooden boxes and other objects and upon the present experience of the little box which appears to be unexpectedly heavy. Whether the box is really filled with something heavy or not we do not know. There is only one way to find out, to verify our image of the situation, and this way is to look inside the box. But looking into it becomes possible only if we open the box and make the interior visible. Let us assume now that the box appears to be empty. In that case we will suspect that, e.g., the sides and bottom are not of wood but of lead or iron covered with wood. Sense verification of this suspicion requires that we first do something, e.g., knock against the wood, pierce it, or cut it open, to enable our ear, our sense of touch, or our eye to perform the perception which we desire.

There is an intimate unity between *thoughtfully* forming a picture of reality and concluding from this picture what we have to *do* to make it possible for the sense organ to perform crucial *perceptions*. This same unity is found also in the experiments of physical science. The theoretical model which endeavors to make data transparent to us is always *our* model and never the reality itself which we have appropriated through the model. We therefore examine first in thought how the model will operate when certain manipulations are performed with it. Next, we perform these manipulations with sensitively given reality itself and observe it to establish sensitively whether or not what really happens agrees with what should happen according to the model.

Interdependence of Theory and Experience. Accordingly, what is decisive in all this is sense experience. In this respect the knowledge of physical science has a passive character, in the sense that it has to wait for what happens in reality. On the other hand, it is true also that this passive registration is prepared by a preceding intellectual activity and that to a certain extent the intellect may be said to let the senses register what the intellect wants to be registered. Of course, we do not mean that the intellect can make the senses register whatever it wants, but it is the intellect which determines what is relevant in the registration of the senses. For without the theoretical guidance of the intellect an experiment does not produce any results, the established data do not reveal anything to us. Thus we are faced here with the paradoxical situation that we are fully dependent upon what is taught by sense observation in our attempts to arrive at a scientific concept of nature, but at the same time sense observation itself is dependent upon this scientific concept. The theoretical model depends upon the experimental data, and these data depend upon the theory. Thus the truth of the empiristic adage: "nothing is in the intellect which was not first in the senses" finds its counterpart in the Hegelian axiom: "nothing is in the senses which was not first in the intellect." It is hardly surprising, therefore, that physical science needed such a long time before it could develop, if we consider that its philosophical foundations reveal such a paradoxical character.

2. *The Operational Aspect of Physical Science*

Interdependence of Knowing and Doing. Meanwhile the analysis of what happens in an experiment teaches us, as we have seen, that there is an intimate interdependence not only between sense knowledge and intellectual knowledge but also between knowing and doing. For the possibility of the senses to register something in the experiment depends upon a previous intervention of man in reality. Things have to be acted upon by an activity of our hands before the senses are enabled to penetrate into what we want to see. This operational activity, however, itself depends again upon our knowledge. Here also, therefore, there is a mutual dependence. At the same time it follows that physical science and technique are essentially related. There is no physical science which is a purely cognitive activity, just as there is no technique which is purely a manipulation of reality.

Generally the dependence of technology upon physical science is more easily grasped than that of physical science upon technology. For this reason technology is sometimes called "applied science." This term, however, is just as correct or incorrect as is that of "applied technology" for physical science. Both terms are correct insofar as the knowledge of physical science can be obtained only by technical means and insofar as technical achievements are only attainable through the application of physical science. Both are incorrect insofar as the meaning of technology does not lie in the application of physical science or that of physical science in the application of technology. We will see more about this point later.

Meanwhile it should be evident that in man's activity upon matter, whether his purpose be knowing or doing, both forms of activity, knowing and doing, are inseparably connected. This interconnection is a result of the bond between intellectual and sensitive knowledge. Because sense knowledge is always limited and dependent on one's standpoint, in the literal sense of the term, material reality has to be manipulated to be fully perceived. The object which I take into my hands and turn around to look at it from all sides expresses the same intimate bond between the operational and the cognitive aspects which constitutes the heart of physical science as an experimental science. The interconnection between making and knowing, therefore, is not at all specific to physical science, but is typical of all human activity. At the same time, however, the remark must be made that in the old philosophy of science which we have inherited from the Greeks this interconnection was viewed more from the side of making than from that of knowing (in the sense of scientifically knowing). This way of viewing the relationship in question was, of course, conditioned by the state of development reached by Greek science.

The Early Development of Mathematics, Logic, and Philosophy. As has been pointed out repeatedly, the conditions that must be fulfilled before physical science can be born resemble somewhat a vicious circle. The theory has to be based upon experimental data, but these data themselves have to be acquired by means of the theory. For this reason it is not surprising that the first sciences to develop were those in which the separation of the relevant from the irrelevant could be accomplished by means of thought alone. This was the case with mathematics, logic, and philosophy. Thus it was possible to formulate principles covering these realms by virtue of which the interconnections existing in these realms could be deductively rendered accessible to insight.

The best example of all is provided by Euclid's mathematics. In it, the classical ideal of science came closest to realization. Somewhat less comprehensive from a modern point of view, but still surprisingly pure was the case of Aristotle's logic, in which the various forms of reasoning were seen in the light of a few fundamental ideas and shown to be interconnected. The same was true also of astronomy, in which all celestial movements were explained by means of the theory of circle movements. In these realms, therefore, the Greeks managed to reach the level of science, to unify and explain the variety of forms, shapes, movements, and phenomena.

With respect to explanations of nature, however, to the extent that such were given, they remained largely on the philosophical level. They were mostly considerations regarding change in general, but hardly about specific processes of particular changes. Of course, particular changes also were mentioned and described, but their specific development was not explained in its details by means of general principles. Explanatory theories, such as the matter-form theory of Aristotle or the atomic theory of Democritus, aimed at the possibility and nature of change in general. In the Greek phase of science it was not yet possible to connect the detailed items of knowledge about material things and their properties by means of scientific interrelationships. Physical science remained limited to practical experimental knowledge, especially knowledge that was important for the use and the shaping of the various materials. Thus, as far as technique was concerned, there was an intimate connection between knowing and doing, but there was no knowledge rising to the level of general science. Whatever detailed knowledge there was regarding the various materials continued to consist of disconnected items.

The Greek Concept of Pure and Disinterested Science. As could be expected, the philosophy of science of the Greeks corresponded to the actual status of their science. Science consisted in disinterested contemplation, in knowledge for the sake of knowledge, because in such knowledge man as a spiritual being attained his own perfection. Knowledge served to enrich the knower himself and not anything outside the knower. Thus there are two striking aspects in the Greek concept of science: it is contemplative and disinterested, i.e., not directed to practical application. The contemplative character of science, however, did not exclude the empirical element. Aristotle especially emphasized the empirical character of knowledge. Nevertheless, what he considered as the empirical element of science is not quite the same as what constitutes the essence of contemporary experimental science, in which the theoretical, operational, and sensitive elements are intimately united.

Surprisingly, there is a text in which Aristotle shows that he was struck by the importance of the operational element in pure science. Speaking about the value which the drawing of auxiliary lines in a mathematical figure has for seeing the demonstration of a particular thesis, he says: *"poiountes gignoscousin,"* i.e., "by making one arrives at understanding."[2]   However, this is an isolated text. There are no indications that Aristotle utilized the idea it contains in his considerations regarding theoretical science. The reason is not far to seek. Where making was closely connected with knowing, as in various arts and skills, in the technique which was based upon practical experience, making led to knowing, but not to theoretical science, at least not yet in the time of Aristotle.

The second aspect of the Greek idea of science—its disinterestedness—is likewise easily explained through the actual status of science in ancient time. Philosophical knowledge could not contribute to the increase of detailed knowledge, because it abstracted from details as such. Greek philosophy of nature made change intelligible, but it did not explain the distinct nature of the various changes in detail. As we have seen in Chapter I, this restriction does not mean that Greek philosophy must be denied any value with respect to the physical science which arose later. It does imply, however, that this value did not lie in its ability to supply a theory on the level of physical science.

So far as mathematics as a science was concerned, it too did not offer many opportunities for practical applications. Of course, mathematics did have applications—the very name "geometry," the measuring of the earth, points to this. However, what the Greeks accom-

---

[2]*Metaphysics,* bk. 8 (Theta), ch. 9, 1051a 21-33.

plished here was precisely to lift mathematics from the sphere of applications to the level of science and to axiomatize the mathematical relationships. But this achievement was of little immediate value for practical life. Here also a long time had to pass before the accomplishment would bear fruit. It had to wait until the knowledge gained from the practical experience of natural phenomena had developed sufficiently to be ripe for mathematical treatment. Only then could it lead to scientific systematization.

The Importance of the Greek View. Meanwhile the Greek concept of mathematics as a pure science offers an impressive argument showing that their notion of the disinterestedness of science was not inspired solely by the limited possibilities of applying science that existed in their time. For mathematics could be applied and was *de facto* applied. If the Greeks had dwelled on its applicability, mathematics would not have been born as a science and, consequently, neither the physical science and scientific technology of later times. Later we will have to return extensively to the relationship between theory and practice. Although this relationship nowadays is, of course, different from that in the time of ancient Greece, at least this much is certain: precisely by emphasizing the disinterested character of scientific endeavors, the Greeks opened a road to the development of a culture in which at the proper time technique would be drawn into the sphere of science.

How correct the Greek view was is shown, moreover, also by the contemporary situation. Great and really new possibilities in the realm of technological applications continue to be disclosed not by scientific research which is directed to the application of science, but by the pursuit of science for the sake of knowing. Nuclear energy, for instance, was discovered not because a deliberate search was made for new sources of energy, but through purely speculative thinking about the data which led to the theory of relativity and through the search for an atomic structure which would explain the phenomena of radio-activity.

Accordingly, the fact that the operational aspect of scientific knowledge was at first perceived only in a dim way did not have its basis only in the undeveloped status of science. It had also a different and more general ground, which was closely connected with the reason put forward above for the priority of the theoretical element. No matter how much now, after the development of physical science, we are convinced of the value which must be attributed to its operational aspect, nevertheless even nowadays we are still inclined to see the experiment in the service of the theory rather than the theory in the service of the experiment. If it is true that the theory also serves the experiment, the reason is precisely that the theoretically guided experiment itself increases our theoretical insight. The operational factor is indispensable in the acquisition of knowledge for no other reason than that our senses are limited. Thus the operational aspect, together with the sensitive aspect, serves the theoretical aspect. It seems to play a subordinate but indispensable role. Accordingly, the priority which the Greeks attributed to the theoretical factor was not based solely upon the primitive status of their science, but also on the clear realization of the hierarchy to be assigned to the various aspects. We will have to return to this point later when we will speak about technology.

Undoubtedly, the Greeks underestimated the operational aspect of science, just as they minimized its applicational possibilities. Yet this was a *felix culpa,* a fortunate fault, which enable them to discover the essence of science where it could be discovered most easily— namely, in mathematics, logic, astronomy, and philosophy. Knowledge of nature, however, had still to travel a long road before it could attain a scientific status.

3. *Physical Science as Human Knowledge*

Ancient Physics. As we have seen above, the intimate connection between the rational, the operational, and the empirical aspects of physical science is a natural extension of ordinary human knowledge. True, in the forms of science which were first discovered and pursued the rational element stood prominently and fairly exclusively in the foreground. It could hardly have been different. For science is first of all an intellectual affair, the data have first to be brought into the sphere of the intelligible. Immediate success in this matter can be obtained most readily with respect to those aspects of reality on which the intellect has, as it were, a direct grip—namely, the mathematical and philosophical aspects. Thus at first much was left out of consideration, at least in the formal sense, for materially speaking nothing remained unconsidered. The reason is that the whole of nature was raised to the level of an intellectual consideration in the philosophy of nature, but this mode of considering was and remained a special kind of intellectual pursuit.

The Birth of the New Physics. Maritain remarks somewhere that the essence of what happened in the seventeenth century in which the new physics was born consisted in this that the role which hitherto had been played by philosophy was taken over by mathematics.[3] This remark contains a large amount of truth. Until the seventeenth century it was especially the philosophical sphere of thinking which raised the consideration of nature to the level of scientific knowledge, while from that time on this function has been fulfilled by the sphere of mathematical thinking. The proper specific form of rationality which has made the interconnections studied by physical science transparent is really the rationality of mathematics.

At the same time, however, it is interesting to note that even the Greeks made use of mathematics to understand natural phenomena, especially in the realm of astronomy. For in astronomy the quantitative aspect of movement imposed itself so strongly that the mathematical description appeared to be most appropriate. In this way astronomy received a status that differed widely from that of ancient physics, for ancient physics was primarily a *philosophy* of nature. This difference revealed itself in the view that the nature of earthly things, subject as they were to coming to be and passing away, to qualitative and substantial changes, was wholly different from that of the nature of celestial bodies, which knew only quantitative changes in the sense of movement.

Of course, this view was wrong, but it becomes comprehensible if we take into consideration that ancient physics and astronomy differed so much in their actual status. We may even say that they had of necessity to differ widely because celestial motions lend themselves so much more directly to mathematical analysis than do terrestrial phenomena, which impress our immediate experience as far more varied. It is not without reason that in the seventeenth century the correct insights into the mechanics of terrestrial phenomena were obtained in part also by means of the mechanics of celestial bodies. It is for this reason that the discovery of the principles of inertia and of universal gravitation by Newton and Galileo, which they used to explain both celestial motions and earthly falling motions, was such a portentous discovery.

This discovery did not only open the era of the universal mathematical science of nature, but also disrupted the entire contemporary worldview. The blow was especially hard because it meant at the

---

[3] *The Degrees of Knowledge,* New York, 1959, p. 41.

same time a break with the existing scientific-philosophical tradition. It was a real revolution. Undoubtedly, in the realm of science the Copernican discovery, according to which the earth no longer constituted the center of the universe, was the most spectacular event of the century because of its exegetic and theological connotations. *De facto,* however, something much more important was at stake— namely, the discovery of a new scientific method for the pursuit of physical science, the change from philosophical rationality to mathematical rationality. Provisionally the operational element remained somewhat in the background. Galileo and his contemporaries experimented far less than is usually assumed to have been the case, for part of their experiments were mere thought experiments.

Nevertheless, the decisive step was taken. It consisted in the universal application of the mathematical method to all empirical data. For this method forced man to make measurements. Thus in principle the operational element had entered into the picture, for even a simple measurement is a kind of operation. Moreover, measuring often requires that the object be placed in conditions which are adapted to the taking of certain types of measurements. In addition, the analytic-inductive method of the physical sciences requires that the various aspects be isolated, so that their interconnections can be studied. This also demands operational interference in the natural order. For in ordinary experience these aspects are too interwoven to permit man to penetrate into their interconnection. Finally, the bond of the sense organs with external contact forces us to make what is internal external, and this again means interference and manipulations.

Physical Science and "Ordinary" Human Knowledge. Thus the whole development of physical science may be viewed as the constantly increasing integration of new elements of human activity into the sphere of science. In a certain way physical science mirrors the unity of human activity. For this reason it was not surprising that in this and the preceding chapters we could repeatedly point out how the specific method of physical science is a natural extension of man's "ordinary" way of knowing and of the activities which are connected with knowing. While it may be true that the operational element played a relatively much more subordinate role in the earlier phases of scientific thought than in daily life, in which things are constantly handled for the sake of knowing, nevertheless it is true also that this operational element is accorded its full function in the well-developed physical science of our time.

In this way one can easily see that the various aspects of physical science, which in their combination are specific to the scientific method are essentially nothing else than systematically and universally developed aspects of something which is a general human characteristic and which occurs as a unit on the level of ordinary life.

The Paradox of Physical Science. Thus we arrive at the somewhat paradoxical conclusion that the features exhibited by physical science are the natural extension of the ordinary pre-scientific way of man's acting. We call this conclusion paradoxical, because there are, on the other hand, many reasons for placing physical science in sharp contrast with man's ordinary way of acting and with his ordinary way of experiencing reality. Perhaps the situation may be formulated in this fashion: although physical science contains all these ordinary aspects, it develops them methodically in a very onesided way. The exact character of physical science illustrates this point most clearly, for sense experience is reduced to purely abstract measuring registrations. In physical science nothing else remains of the original qualitative wealth of experience than pointer readings.

What is especially peculiar in this paradox is that, on the one hand, during the course of its development physical science has constantly integrated more aspects of human activity into its sphere, but, on the other hand, it has also become more and more abstract. For, after the strongly contemplative rationality of the old philosophy of nature, experience was gradually given a greater role and in a later phase of development, the phase of the experiment, the operational element also was directly incorporated into science. On the other hand, despite the gradual integration of all human faculties, we see physical science become more abstract and nature shrivel away to a system of abstract mathematically formulated relations between magnitudes that are "artificially" obtained. It is this paradox which makes the penetration of physical science into the whole of life such a controversial subject. Unfortunately, the discussions often run their course without much understanding of the character that is proper to physical science. For this reason it will be necessary to investigate this character somewhat more profoundly.

The Onesidedness of Physical Science. In the preceding chapters we have considered physical science especially with respect to its methods. We discovered that these methods are not specifically proper to this science but are a general characteristic of man. These methods, then, throw light in a certain way on the cognitive situation of man, on the spontaneous non-reflective character of ordinary knowledge, its abstract-schematic character, its passive-active character, as well as its cognitive-operational character.

At the same time all these characteristics seem to be distorted as they reveal themselves in physical science. They seem to be projected against a background which makes us see physical science more as a caricature of genuine human knowledge than as its faithful picture. Thus, to all appearances, while physical science reveals all the aspects of human knowledge, it uses them in a very onesided fashion. To discover this onesidedness, it will be necessary to delve somewhat deeper into the object of physical science, material nature. Perhaps a philosophical analysis of the nature of matter may be able to show us why the method of physical science is as it is. We will dedicate the remaining chapters of Part One to this analysis.

CHAPTER SIX

THE FUNDAMENTAL STRUCTURE OF
MATERIAL REALITY[1]

1. *Introduction*

In speaking here about the fundamental structure of material reality, we do not intend to take this term in the sense in which it is used in physical science. For this book is not a treatise of physical science but a study about physical science itself. In a treatise of physical science the first chapter dealing with the fundamental structure of material reality would probably speak about atoms and molecules, the second about atomic nuclei and electrons, the third about protons and neutrons, etc. It would thus give us a progressively more profound analysis of the structure of matter, as it reveals itself in physical research. Accordingly, atomic and sub-atomic structures are, as we noted in Chapter 1, *results* of physical research, but not structures which condition this research itself.

What interests us is a philosophical consideration of matter, and this means here that we ask ourselves in what way matter must be constituted if it can be at all object of the method used by physical science. For, as we have seen, this method is a very special kind of approach to reality, one that has been established, through prolonged familiarity with, and study of matter, as a refined application of man's cognitive possibilities. The method of the physical sciences, therefore, on the one hand, reflects something of man's cognitive possibilities and, on the other, something of matter itself. It is only for one who considers physical science and its method as the universal science and the universal method that the consideration of these two aspects is identical. Such a person, however, will have very little to consider, because every consideration of physical science and its method is a reflection and therefore itself lies beyond the realm of physical science.

To investigate what the specific aspect of matter is which makes it accessible to the method of physical science, it will be best to start

---

[1]For a more complete analysis of this point, see the author's *The Philosophy of Nature*, Pittsburgh, 2nd ed., 1954 (reprinted 1959), Ch. IV.

again from an analysis of this method, viewed this time especially in reference to the object considered. As the paradigm of this method we will select the experimental investigation. In doing so, we will connect our considerations with certain ideas that were mentioned in the first chapter, when we spoke about a peculiar presupposition of physical science—namely, the presupposition by virtue of which material nature is seen at the same time as both changeable and immutable. We must now penetrate somewhat more profoundly into the experimental method to see what else it presupposes in its object if this object is to be accessible to experimental research.

2. *The Species-Individual Structure of Matter*

A Presupposition of Experimental Research. To illustrate our analysis of the experimental method, we will use a simple example of an experimental investigation. Let us assume that we want to know which factors influence the rusting of iron. In that case we will expose iron to all kinds of influences, e.g., humid air, dry air, oxygen-rich water, carbonated water, distilled water, varying also the range of temperatures. During a fixed lapse of time the iron will not rust in some of these cases, in others it will rust only a little, and in others again it will be strongly affected by rust. It would even be possible to determine quantitatively to what extent iron is affected by rust.

What interests us here is not the chemical result but something else—namely, the fact that the various pieces of iron, say, nails, are presupposed to be of the same nature. They are assumed to be representative of the matter which we want to investigate and which we call "iron." It is because of this presupposition that we are able to use the various data, obtained by means of different nails in different conditions, for the purpose of drawing conclusions regarding the rusting of iron. If one nail had been iron, the second copper, and the third gold, they would have been useless for our inquiry into the rusting of iron.

Accordingly, the whole experiment is based upon the presupposition that all nails are interchangeable representatives of iron. If this were not so, if there were no nature of iron with its specific properties, then our research would have been meaningless. How much the experimental method is based upon this presupposition becomes even more evident when we raise the following obvious difficulty. It belongs, we may say, precisely to the requirements of a good experiment first to make certain that all our nails really consist of the same material—namely, iron, and exactly the same kind of iron, for one technical kind of iron differs from another. Of course, it is quite true that we must make certain of this matter, for instance, by means of a chemical analysis of its composition.

What is remarkable here, however, is that this chemical analysis itself makes use of the presupposition that the chemical element "pure" iron, like any other pure chemical element, always reacts in the same way and therefore can be recognized by means of its reactions. In other words, although it belongs to the domain of physical research to determine whether or not concrete objects have the same nature, this research is possible only if we tacitly accept that individual objects in nature can be classified according to specific kinds of matter having specific properties.

What we mean, then, by the species-individual structure of matter is the peculiar fact that every concrete material thing alongside its concrete individuality at the same time represents a certain species. For this reason we could even say that two exactly similar nails are both wholly identical and wholly different. Wholly identical, because they are specifically the same, wholly different, because one individual is independent of the other and one could be destroyed without harming the other.

The species-individual structure is not limited to material objects in the sense in which we usually speak of *things,* but applies also to properties and processes. Every concrete fall, for example, represents the process of falling; hence by dropping many objects under different conditions we can make a study of fall. Likewise, the same property redness may be studied in many concrete objects. In this way the species-individual structure pervades the whole of reality. If we want to study this structure, we have of course to make use of concrete things. We are never able to experiment with *iron* as such, but only with concrete iron objects; we can never study *fall* as such, but only this or that concrete fall; we cannot observe *red* as such, but only this or that concrete red object or red bundle of light. Everyone of these concrete items, however, represents at the same time something specific. Because they are *concrete, individual,* we are able to perceive and handle them, and because they represent something *specific,* we are able to derive something general from these individual perceptions.

Repeatability and Species-Individual Structure. To explain the species-individual structure, we spoke above about two concrete but specifically identical things, such as two nails. Evidently, this specific identity refers only to the being-iron of the nails and not, e.g., to their weight or shape. Although technology tries to fabricate concrete things which are practically identical in all respects and therefore interchangeable, the efforts will never be successful. Equality can be reached only with a certain tolerance, i.e., the differences in composition, weight, form, etc. must remain within accurately determined limits prescribed by the function assigned to such technical products.

Thus the real existence of two wholly identical individuals is not likely ever to occur. However, such an identity is not at all required by the species-individual structure as the foundation of the experimental method. The specific similarity that is required refers in principle only to a single aspect. For instance, in the experiment about the rusting of iron the important point is that the concrete objects used in it are made of iron. Whether or not their weight and shape are the same does not matter, as long as they consist of iron. Even with respect to their being-iron, it is supposed—but not *pre*supposed—that the concrete nails are exactly identical as far as their being-iron is concerned. This is supposed, because otherwise the experiment in question would lead to faulty results. Accordingly, the experimenter must take great care that his nails represent as purely as possible the iron which he wants to investigate.

We speak here explicitly of supposition and not of *pre*supposition to emphasize that the point in question is something pertaining to the realm of physical research itself and could be contradicted by a physical investigation. The presupposition, on the other hand, refers to the fact that being-iron is not in principle limited to a single instance, but can be repeated over and over again. The term "species-individual structure," therefore, indicates also that we have here a repeatable structure, i.e., in more technical language, every magnitude and every relationship between magnitudes is in principle reproducible. Thus the species-individual structure does not mean that every concrete object with all its properties will be repeated as such.

In this connection we may mention that physical science itself assumes the exact repeatability of the entities which in its view are the building blocks of material reality. Molecules and atoms of water, electrons, etc. are supposed to repeat themselves always in exactly the same fashion. Of course, physical science knows very well that the situation in which a concrete molecule of water finds itself cannot be strictly repeated in its concreteness. However, in its abstract considerations and definitions physical science disregards this impossibility. All molecules of water, as molecules of water, are exactly alike with respect to all their inherent properties and with respect to their ability to enter into all kinds of situations. For instance, a water molecule as crystal water of a crystal of copper sulphate is in another situation than a water molecule in the sea or in an animal organism. Nevertheless, they are all the same water molecules and therefore interchangeable; in principle they are absolutely equal. The same applies to all kinds of molecules, atoms, and subatomic particles. The exclusion principle of Pauli, for instance, teaches that no two electrons in a particular atom can be in the same situation, but this principle does not exclude that, in principle, each of these electrons may find itself in each of these distinct quantum situations. In principle, the electrons are equal.

Physical Science Sees Concrete Realities Primarily as Instances of Specific Structures and Properties. We have to delve somewhat deeper into the assertion that in its study of concrete reality physical science is hardly interested in this concrete reality itself, except insofar as this reality is an instance of a certain kind of matter, of a certain type of property, of a certain type of process, or of a certain kind of magnitude. A result of this attitude is that for physical science concrete things always evaporate into being mere representatives of certain magnitudes. To use a term which we have used before, it is always a question of analyzing the concrete in its abstract aspects. Concrete things are seen as instances of many magnitudes which, as it were, happen to meet in these concrete objects. The concrete nail, as an instance of iron, is lined up with other iron things; as being of a certain weight, it receives the same label as other objects having that weight; as an example of something hard, it is classified with other hard objects, etc.

The typical abstract scientific concept of "nature"[2] is closely connected with this situation. Nature is not the internal principle of being and of operation of a natural whole, which appeals so strongly to us especially in living nature. For physical science nature is the sum total of the aspects and the totality of the way in which these aspects

---

[2]Strictly speaking, it is not correct to speak of a scientific concept of nature, for nature is not one of the concepts which play a role *within* physical science itself. What is meant here is the concept of nature which implicitly plays a role in physical science, i.e., the concept of nature which is obtained through reflection upon the way in which physical science methodically goes to the encounter of "nature."

are interconnected. For example, as viewed from physical science a horse is an instance of certain biological, chemical, and physical structures, but not a unique individual having a certain nature which determines the being and acting of this unique individual.

As has been mentioned several times, the viewpoint of physical science which sees only instances of certain magnitudes agrees in some respects with the way things go in ordinary life. In daily life also we see a nail now as a nail, then as an iron object, then as heavy, etc. This situation is an inevitable consequence of the abstract nature of our concepts. The difference, however, between the viewpoint of ordinary life and that of physical science lies in this that in life we continue to see weight, form, color, etc. as properties of the concrete thing which we call a nail, while in the abstract consideration of physical science it is precisely this concrete thing which has lost its meaning and importance. In principle, there is no difference between the thing itself and its properties; in other words, the philosophical categories of substance and accident do not play any role within the confines of physical science.

Physical Science Does Not Deny the Substance-Accident Structure of Material Reality. On the other hand, it would be wrong to claim that concrete reality has disappeared entirely from physical science. It is not true that in every respect a concrete object resolves itself in physical science into being an instance of many magnitudes which happen to meet, as it were, by accident in this object. Being-iron, for example, is not a wholly isolated magnitude in a physical or chemical consideration, for a totality of other properties is connected with it. On the macro-scale iron has a specific gravity, a specific color and all kinds of accurately determined chemical properties. On the micro-scale, i.e., considered as an atom, being-iron is connected with other properties which constitute the basis of the properties pertaining to iron on the macro-scale. Thus it is not by accident that all these properties meet in iron, for they belong together. On the other hand, there are other qualities which merely happen to be together with iron, such as the shape of a nail or its size, for sometimes iron has these qualities, and sometimes it does not have them.

In this way we still find something corresponding more or less to the distinction between substantial and accidental properties. It is important to note here that the distinction which physical science makes between properties belonging together and properties which do not belong together is not merely the *result* of physical research but also in a certain respect a presupposition of this research. The fact that pure iron has this specific gravity and color is known, of course, only as the result of scientific research. On the other hand, that there is something like a substance-accident structure, or in the language of physical science, that there are certain fixed complexes of magnitudes in concrete objects, is again something without which the experimental method would not be able to do anything. In our experiment there would be nothing which could be grasped firmly. Let us assume, for example, that we call something "iron" because it is attracted by a magnet. If we were to imagine that this attraction were a wholly isolated property, what would be the sense of experimenting with iron? For the experiment wants to investigate precisely the properties or behavior of iron, i.e., what is inseparably connected with being-iron and what not.

Considered in this way, the difference between man's spontaneous familiarity with things and his scientific knowing and handling them is not as great as it may appear. The difference here again is that physical science in its abstract way of viewing things develops and pursues certain aspects of spontaneous knowledge in a onesided way, without doing violence to reality. However, it may happen that a person who is not aware of the abstract and onesided character of the method used by physical science disregards the specific approach pursued by this science. Thus he may be led to think that physical science denies certain fundamental matters because it does not explicitly mention them. Such a person is a victim of what Whitehead calls the "fallacy of misplaced concreteness." A close philosophical analysis of the physical method, on the other hand, shows that this very method implicitly contains a much broader vision of material reality than appears at first sight.

The Reason for the Viewpoint of Physical Science. The proper reason why physical science in its analysis of concrete material reality sees this reality primarily as an instance of many magnitudes and not as an entity having a determined nature lies in its character as a science. As a science, physics wants to make reality transparent. In the prescientific attitude of mind the last word is an appeal to the fact that something belongs to the nature of the object under consideration. For iron it is natural to rust, but not for gold. The medieval Aristotelians would have said that the reason for the difference lies in the nature, the *forma,* of these two metals. This type of explanation has often been ridiculed as devoid of meaning, as a pure playing with words. Fundamentally, however, it expresses profound wisdom—namely, that our knowledge of material reality will always come face to face with the fact that things are as they are, with their nature as the principle of their being and operation, and that our knowledge has to take this nature as it is.

Accordingly, the fault of the Aristotelian view should not be sought in its reference to the nature of things in general as the ultimate cause of their way of acting. Considered in itself, this view is philosophically not incorrect. However, it is a view which as such does not give scientific knowledge of nature but rather acts as a condition making this knowledge possible. The fault of the Aristotelian view, then, should be sought elsewhere—namely, in the conviction that the natures of different matters were, as it were, simply juxtaposed without there being any possibility of viewing them as originating from a more general nature.

It is precisely the last-named possibility which physical science endeavors to exploit, for it attempts to reduce the actual natures of iron, gold, water, etc. to more general principles of nature. Physical science, then, does not take the nature of iron with its inherent properties as a single total givenness, but also undertakes to analyze this givenness. For it is not at all open to immediate understanding that a substance which becomes rusty will produce hydrogen when it comes into contact with muriatic acid. For this reason a piece of iron is in principle considered as an instance of different properties, and by viewing iron in this fashion the concurrence of these properties in this one instance becomes a problem. Although the solution of this problem ultimately refers again to the nature of the component "parts" of iron, nevertheless it remains true that various properties of iron have become somewhat transparent in the process.[3]

Accordingly, it is not at all because it denies natural wholes that physical science institutes this analysis. The purpose of this analysis is to acquire some understanding of the interconnections which the different aspects of a natural whole exhibit. For this reason physical science attempts to formulate *general* laws of nature, fixing the relationship between magnitudes which physical science has learned to consider as universal magnitudes characterizing matter. Through

---

[3]This reference to a more profound nature is made by stages. Cf. what has been said above (p. 77) about this point in a different context.

these general laws of nature science next attempts to render the specific behavior of every type of matter transparent. In this attempt such a species of matter seems to be the meeting-place of these various magnitudes in certain quantitative proportions. In the perspective of physical science, therefore, iron and gold do not differ in this that they have entirely different qualitative properties which are irreducible, but their difference arises from a quantitatively different participation in the same fundamental properties.

Prescientific and Scientific Knowledge of Material Reality. This tendency to reduce everything to quantitative differences at first sight seems to differentiate physical science basically from prescientific knowledge. For, alongside properties which all or at least many substances have in common, as e.g., weight, prescientific knowledge knows other properties which belong to one substance but not to another as, e.g., transparency or redness. However, the fact that prescientific knowledge is already in possession of properties which are general or fairly general indicates how much here too physical science lies in the same line as ordinary experience. Physics merely attempts to penetrate more deeply into the plurality of experience.

An interesting example is that of weight. Aristotle divided material substances into heavy and light. Heavy were those which moved toward the center of the earth, and light those that moved away from this center. Thus heavy and light were irreducible properties. But the mechanics of the sixteenth and seventeenth century, through a careful analysis of all factors which appear to play a role in the fall, discovered that in principle all substances are heavy and that this rule applied even to celestial bodies which, according to ancient thought, were supposed to be essentially different from earthly matter.

Two points should be noted here which reduce somewhat the striking difference revealing itself between ancient thought and later physical science. First of all, it should be kept in mind that classical physics did not attribute gravitation in a wholly universal way to all matter. Only so-called ponderable matter was heavy; light did not have any demonstrable weight. Only in the twentieth century, when the difference between the phenomena of matter and those of light were bridged, was weight attributed also to light. Secondly, it is worth while to consider how Aristotle accounted for the difference between "heavy" and "light" substances in the scientific system of his time. According to his view, both kinds of matter tended to their "natural place." For heavy matter this place was the earth, and for light matter it was one of the spheres around the earth. Thus the different properties were somehow reduced to unity, they were seen as different ways of sharing in the *same* tendency.

Moreover, there are many other points in Greek thought which indicate that the Greeks sought to bring unity into the diversity of phenomena, not only in the philosophical sense but also more or less in the sense of physical science. An example is Empedocles' theory of four elements, especially as developed by Aristotle. No matter how faulty the theory was, it was a definite effort to reduce the multiplicity of perceptible material qualities to a few fundamental properties. To give another example, the direction taken by the atomic theory of Democritus was a brilliant stroke of genius, especially because of its emphasis on the quantitative aspects. For what characterizes the scientific reduction of the various qualities is precisely that physical science performs this reduction by means of a quantitative analysis, thus making mathematics the typical rationality of physics. We must investigate now why the mathematical method could be so enormously successful in physical science and why this method is so suited to the fundamental structure of matter.

3. *The Species-Individual Structure and Mathematics*

That mathematics has a limited application in our knowledge of matter does not constitute a problem, but there is a problem in its *universal* application. A limited applicability is easily accounted for, because the original forms in which mathematics was pursued— arithmetic and geometry—aimed precisely at the directly visible quantitative aspects of material things, i.e., their numerability or discrete quantity and their extension or continuous quantity. These aspects could be considered in themselves, apart from qualitative properties, through a process of formal abstraction. Thus it was readily evident that the results attained by mathematical thinking were applicable to the quantitative aspects of matter, for these aspects themselves were the object of mathematical thought.

Less evident, however, was the applicability of the mathematical method to qualities, for these were exactly the aspects from which mathematics made abstraction. The rectilinear progress of a light ray, its reflexion and refraction lay immediately within the reach of geometric optics, because such a ray could easily be schematized as a line. But it was an entirely different question to express the qualitative difference between green and red light in a quantitative fashion. Yet what would make physical science so important was precisely the quantitative approach to qualitative differences, the use of a method oriented to the quantitative in a realm which was not at all quantitative and which therefore at first offered but few possibilities for a quantitative approach.

The Development of Mathematics. Accordingly, the qualitative aspects, as distinct from the quantitative aspects, of matter did not seem to offer much scope for the use of mathematics. Likewise, a first acquaintance with the development of mathematics would not give rise to the suspicion that mathematics would ever be able to become such a universal auxiliary science of physics. For the development of mathematics shows us a science which recedes more and more from its original object. Alongside Euclidean geometry there arose non-Euclidean geometry, whose axioms did not express idealized relations corresponding to what seems to be intuitively given in sense experience but relationships which deliberately deviated from this experience.

Somewhat later in history we find an abstract mathematics. It no longer cares at all about what its symbols express, but seems to be wholly absorbed by a free play with these symbols. The properties of what is represented by the symbols are no longer determined by a reference to reality, but by rules of operation developed in the system itself.

In ordinary arithmetic $+$ and $\times$ mean adding and multiplying, i.e., operations which express what can really be done with things. The algebraic formula $a + b = b + a$, therefore, corresponds to the fact that it makes no difference whether I add three apples to four apples or four apples to three apples. Likewise, $a \times b = b \times a$ expresses that three heaps of four apples each are equal to four heaps of three apples each. The algebraic formulae express such realities in an abstract way and therefore apply not only to the numbers three and four, but to all numbers.

Their abstractness, however, does not sever the bond with reality, so that certain formulae are valid but not others. For instance, $(a + b) \times c = (a \times c) + (b \times c)$, but $(a \times b) + c$ does not equal $(a + c) \times (b + c)$. For three heaps of four apples added to five apples give another result than $(3 + 5)$ heaps of $(4 + 5)$ apples. In abstract algebra, however, there is no objection against defining $+$ and $\times$ and fixing them in the rules of operation in such a way

that $(a \times b) + c$ equals $(a + b) \times (b + c)$. The fact that now
the result no longer agrees when I use apples does not matter in the
least, for the system has no intention whatsoever to express possible
manipulations of apples or other material objects.

All an abstract system determines with respect to the meaning of
the symbols it uses is their so-called "operative meaning," i.e., it
determines how the symbols may be used within the system and which
relations they have with one another within the system. The abstract
system does not say anything whatsoever about the so-called "eidetic
meaning" of the symbols, i.e., their possible reference to existing or
thought realities. Thus it is not a possible eidetic meaning but only
the operational meaning which determines how the symbols are interrelated. Whether or not, therefore, $(a \times b) + c = (a + c) \times$
$(b + c)$ depends not on a possible eidetic meaning which we may be
able to attribute or are desirous of attributing to the symbols, but on
the operative meaning of the symbols. Of course, once the system has
been formulated, one may investigate whether or not it may be given
an eidetic meaning and what this meaning could be, but this is an
entirely different question.

Thus we see with respect to the above-mentioned formula that
we cannot give it an ordinary algebraic interpretation; *a, b,* and *c*
cannot represent numbers, and $+$ and $\times$ cannot mean addition and
multiplication. On the other hand, it would be possible to interpret
the formula as a relation between logical magnitudes. If *a, b,* and *c*
represent propositions or judgments, the sign $\times$ the logical connection between judgments which we express in English by the particle
or, and $+$ the connection expressed by *and,* then the formula may
have an eidetic meaning. If, for instance, for a certain function the
requirements state that the candidate should have a B.A. or a B.Sc.
and twelve credits in Education, then these requirements may be
formulated also as B.A. and twelve credits in Education or B.Sc. and
twelve credits in Education.

Of course, it may be possible that in the construction of an abstract
system the relationships between the symbols are chosen in such a
way that they are open to a certain interpretation. For instance,
mathematical logic is constructed in such a way that it can be interpreted as logic, its operative meaning is chosen in view of the desired
eidetic interpretation. However, even in such a case the mathematician will tend to develop the system without making any direct appeal
to the eidetic meaning, but will appeal only to the operative meaning,

just as in mathematics we do not let ourselves be guided by intuition but by the proof of a theorem from the axioms.

Accordingly, it should be evident that for mathematical activity as such it is indifferent whether or not we have an eidetic meaning in mind, whether or not such a meaning can be discovered later. The only relevant point is the construction and investigation of the abstract system itself.

The Paradox of the Applicability of Mathematics to Physical Reality. What remains remarkable here is that mathematics, after going entirely its own way, free from encumbrance with material reality, has found such a broad universal possibility of application in physical science. How strange this really is is best seen when one pays attention to other examples of systems in which the elements composing the system are chosen in full freedom through the operative rules assigned to the system. This happens, e.g. in chess. What a king, a knight, a castle, or a pawn are and which moves these chessmen may make are not at all determined by what real kings, knights, castles are, but solely by the rules of the game. The game was originally more or less related to military strategy. It would, however, have been extremely strange if the development of the game of chess, which disregarded reality, would have determined the evolution of military strategy. Yet something like this seems to have happened with mathematics. Free mathematics, which has disregarded entirely the quantitative properties of material reality as they are intuitively experienced, reveals itself as the rational means *par excellence* to solve the problems of physical science which arise wholly from experience. How, we must ask, is this possible?

A Nominalistic Reply. This intriguing question receives a variety of answers, going from a Platonic description of the object of mathematics to extreme nominalistic views. The Platonic view describes the object of mathematics as the realm of subsistent essences which man discovers but cannot create. Extreme nominalistic views conceive mathematics purely as a means of description and regard mathematical theorems as tautologies which, consequently, can never express anything new. In the nominalistic view mathematics is concerned exclusively with our way of speaking about the things which we experience and with the way in which we summarize these experiences. No matter how much truth there may be in this view, if mathematics were really nothing else than description and summarizing without any other relationship to material reality, then it would remain unexplained why mathematics as a rational-theoretical means leads us to really *new* experiential knowledge. Of course, it remains true that structures of reality which have been theoretically deduced are accepted as structures of *reality* only when they have also been *experienced*. However, such experiences are not at all chance experiences. Yet they would be pure chance if the theory were merely a summary of previously acquired experiences.

The Platonic View. In the Platonic view the world of ideas served as an exemplar to the demiurge in creating material reality from the chaos. There is no problem here with respect to the application of mathematics to this reality. However, against this view one may point out that it neglects too much the element of freedom in choosing axioms. For this freedom goes so far that what is an axiom or theorem in one system simply is untrue in another. In a Platonic view the axioms always refer to some kind of "transcendental" reality. Hence they do not seem to leave room for mutually contradictory systems or even for a mathematics which has been formalized to such an extent that it pays attention only to what is formal and not to any extra-formal object. Of such a mathematics we may say with Russell: "Mathematics may be defined as the subject in which we never know what we are talking about, nor whether what we are saying is true."[4]

The Applicability of Mathematics to Material Reality. However, we are not concerned here with the philosophical evaluation of mathematics in its modern form as abstract mathematics, but will limit ourselves to a problem pertaining to the philosophy of nature. This problem is, how is it possible that a freely created mathematics, i.e., a system that is not based on data abstracted from experience, remains applicable to material reality, not only insofar as it can be used to embody the knowledge of experience in a refined system of description, but also and especially insofar as it serves to develop this knowledge and to discover new data of experience? Whence comes this obviously very intimate bond between physical science and mathematics, by virtue of which these sciences in spite of their inner distinction, continue to fertilize each other? That there is, indeed, a reciprocal fertilization is made apparent by history. For this history

---

[4]For a general survey of the various views taken with respect to the philosophy of mathematics, see E. W. Beth, *The Foundations of Mathematics*, Amsterdam, 1959.

is far less rectilinear than one would perhaps infer from the preceding pages in which we spoke about the development of mathematics into abstract mathematics.

Historically speaking, this is what happened. From the pre-Greek knowledge of mathematics, which was strictly an auxiliary science used for astronomical calculations, the surveying of lands, architecture, and similar endeavors, there arose in the Greek era pure mathematics, cultivated for its own sake. This picture changed again somewhat in later times, for with the rise of physical science mathematics assumed again preponderantly the role of an auxiliary science. Even its further development was largely determined by the problems raised in the evolution of physical science. These problems led to a large-scale development of mathematics, as is exemplified by analytic geometry and infinitesimal calculus. However, this huge expansion of mathematical knowledge irresistibly forced the mathematicians back to the ideal of Euclid and thus gave rise to the desire of rigorous axiomatization also in non-geometrical realms. As a result, the axiomatic system as such began to occupy the focal point of attention, which led to the development of abstract mathematics. Since the structure itself of the mathematical system became important, regardless of the object, the primary object of mathematics—the quantitative aspect of the world of experience—began to lose its importance. This led to a vigorous blooming of pure mathematics. Surprisingly enough, however, the results attained by it revealed themselves applicable to material reality.

Species-Individual Structure as the Foundation of Mathematics. Accordingly, there has to be something which continues to bind mathematics to the world of experience, no matter how much mathematics goes its own way, no matter how much it cuts loose its bonds with this world of experience. What this something is will become clear when we take into account that the species-individual structure, which we have learned to recognize as the fundamental structure of material reality, is also the foundation of all mathematical thinking. No matter what may be the object of a mathematical system, this object has certain properties. One of these properties is that a given entity, indicated by a recognizable symbol, is always exactly the same whenever it occurs in the system. Otherwise the system would not be a system. In arithmetic the symbol 5 always indicates the same number; in algebra the symbol a always refers to the same magnitude

—namely, an arbitrary number; in an abstract system a given symbol, e.g., *p,* constantly signifies the same—namely, a magnitude with which certain particular operations may be executed.

All this is precisely what is indicated by the species-individual structure. The symbol which appears here and now in this particular place means specifically exactly the same as what "the same" symbol means in a different place. It is, moreover, because of this loyalty to the species-individual structure that the mathematical entities can be expressed by material symbols. Thanks to the fact that each symbol, whenever it occurs always means exactly the same, mathematics has, as we have seen above, the character of exactness. Mathematics is exact, because the meaning of what the symbol indicates is repeated in a strictly univocal way. For this reason mathematics is the ideal form of univocal reasoning, in which from axiomatically established relationships new relationships (theorems) are deduced. In this reasoning process it is irrelevant whether or not an eidetic meaning is assigned to the symbols. Whether it is done or not does not change anything in the exactness and univocity, because the reasoning process is determined exclusively by the operative meaning attached to the recognizable symbol.

It goes without saying that the applicability of mathematical reasoning can admit only eidetic meanings which themselves also are univocal. This means, therefore, that mathematical calculus is most properly attuned to material data. For the fundamental structure of matter is the species-individual structure and, therefore, all relations between material data remain in principle within this structure, so that they are in principle also capable of mathematical description and treatment. Certain conditions, however, have to be fulfilled to make them also actually capable of such a description. Let us examine these conditions.

What is Required for the Mathematical Description of Empirical Data? First of all, the empirical data must be presented in such a form that they can be handled in a strictly univocal fashion. This requirement has gradually led to the reduction of the sensitive aspect to the simple registration of certain instrumental data. The content of a physical concept is univocally determined in an ideal way in the instrument. Thanks to the instrument, whether something is red or not does no longer depend upon the appreciation and evaluation of the color by a sense organ exposed to all kinds of variable influences, but only upon the appearance or non-appearance of certain lines in the spectrometer. Even when no use is made of instruments in the physical sense of the term, as in classical chemical analysis, the chemical concept of the substance that is being examined remains unchangeably rooted in the whole of the established analytic procedure. Whether or not, for instance, a certain alloy contains silver is determined by a series of chemical experiments which produce or fail to produce a white precipitate. Whether there is more or less silver is determined, after the necessary analysis, by means of a scale whose pointer indicates a certain position.

Accordingly, all observations of physical science take place in such a way that in the instrument and the procedure the physical magnitude in question is univocally determined. Hence to see whether or not the content of a given physical concept is applicable to a concrete empirical reality, it is sufficient to read the instrument. The qualitative differences, then, of the data are anchored in the qualitative differences of the instruments, and the quantitative differences of the same quality are anchored in the differences of the quantitative effects. A particular motion of the amperemeter, for example, means, because it is an *ampere*meter, that there is question of an electric current, and the pointer reading expresses a quantitative measure of this magnitude. The relations between the various magnitudes can be determined in a similar fashion.

Because of this mode of operation, the physical data are univocally determined. Consequently, one or the other system of abstract mathematical formalism can be applied to them. Sometimes there will be no difficulty in finding the appropriate system—namely, when a particular mathematical system has been developed especially in connection with certain empirical data, as is the case, for example, with elementary arithmetic and geometry. Such a connection, however, is lacking in the abstract system, because these systems have been developed precisely for their own sake.[5] In their totality these systems express, as it were, formally which relations are possible within structures that, despite all their differences, have the species-individual structure in common.

Accordingly, abstract mathematics investigates the possible wholes of relationships within the species-individual structure. To determine

---

[5]It is, of course, impossible to draw a sharp dividing line between abstract and non-abstract systems. For once the non-abstract systems are mathematically formulated, they too operate with idealizations and tend to pursue their own interests.

which of these wholes, which axiomatic system applies to certain empirically discovered relationships between the various magnitudes occurring in a given realm of phenomena is a task which does not concern the mathematician but the physicist.

The second condition, therefore, for applying a mathematical system to empirical data consists in determining which particular axioms mirror certain aspects of empirical reality. In this determination an important role is played by the model, of which we have spoken in a preceding chapter, for in the model all kinds of irrelevant aspects are omitted and the image of the material process is constructed in such a way that especially the mathematical aspects occupy the center of attention. Thus the discovery of a suitable model means at the same time the discovery of a suitable axiomatic system of mathematics. This system, however, is really more fundamental for physical science than is the model itself. The model merely acts as an intermediary in finding the suitable system. Thus it is not surprising that in the course of the evolution of physical science we see a decrease in the importance of physical models and an increase in that of the mathematical element.

4. *Quality and Quantity*

Quantitative Aspects of Qualities. The universal application of mathematics has become possible only because of the concentration upon the quantitative aspects of material phenomena, or as it is also expressed, the reduction of the qualitative to the quantitative. This last expression especially must not be misunderstood. As we pointed out before, physical science as an *empirical* science always presupposes a qualitative aspect. Even measurements as such are based upon something qualitative.[6] Moreover, we have seen that the application of mathematics in physical science does not depend only on the possibility of expressing certain magnitudes in quantitative values, but also on fixing these magnitudes sufficiently by means of appropriate instruments or procedures, i.e., by means of qualitative aspects.

There is, however, still another aspect which demands our attention—namely, an aspect which lies in the development itself of mathematics. The evolution of mathematics has divorced this science more and more from the numerable and measurable, in the original sense of these terms. Mathematics now studies also relationships which cannot be properly classified in these original quantitative categories.

---

[6]Cf. Chapter IV, pp. 53 ff.

By means of this generalization of the mathematical object mathematics has become also more suitable for the study of what formerly as the qualitative was opposed to the quantitative and what, consequently, seemed in principle not capable of mathematical treatment, because this treatment was attuned to quantitative elements. The quantitative treatment of qualities remained, as it were, on the periphery of qualities as such. Nevertheless, the possibility of such a peripheral treatment was admitted. For every quality is always a quality of something material which, as a material being, has extension, so that qualities were indirectly quantified. Because, for instance, a red object has a certain surface, the redness also is connected with a certain extension.

Moreover, this indirect extension is not the only quantitative aspect of qualitative elements. Even on the prescientific level, qualities reveal something else which invites quantitative consideration. We mean so-called "intension." An object may be more or less intensely red, green, warm, or hard. True, this intensive character cannot be immediately classified under the heading of quantity in the sense of the extended or of the discrete and, therefore, is directly neither measurable nor numerable. Nevertheless, something extensive appears to be connected with the intensive. For instance, more intense heat can be felt at a greater distance than less intense heat, and objects expand more according as they are hotter. In other words, the intensive has extensive effects. Even at an early stage in its development physical science put this property to good use for measuring the degree of heat by means of the expansion heat produces in gases and liquids.

This point has been mentioned before when we considered the sensitive-empirical aspect of physical science.[7] We indicated there that physical science sometimes has wholly divorced the perception of the various qualities from the senses to which they originally referred, but also that this procedure was entirely in line with the pathway laid out in prescientific experience. Even in prescientific experience we do not only *feel* heat but we *see* it also. Something similar applies to the above-mentioned example. The quantitative measurement of the degree of heat by means of the expansion of gases and liquids is merely a systematic development of a procedure which was known even in prescientific experience.

---

[7] Cf. Ch. III, pp. 40 ff.

Quantification of Relationships Between Qualities. Physical science, however, has gone beyond this. It did not limit itself to systematically measuring the intensities of the various qualities by means of their extensive effects, but proceeded also to the quantification of the relationships existing between these qualities. This quantification goes far beyond the original simple measurement of intensities, which remained within the confines of a single quality. More or less intensely red is and remains something wholly different from more or less green, and this in its turn differs entirely from more or less warm in the qualitative sense of the term. In the wave theory of light, however, the difference between green and red itself is connected with a difference of frequency, which is a quantitative magnitude. Upon closer inspection physical science here also appears to be less revolutionary—or less "unnatural"—than it seems to be at first. For even in prescientific experience the gradual color differences resulting, e.g., from the heating of a poker indicate the fact that the intensification of the quality "heat" is accompanied not only by the intensification of a certain color but also by qualitative changes in color.

Physical science undertook the systematic study of all these interconnections between changes in intensity, qualitative modification, and extensive effects. Thus it opened also qualities themselves for quantitative investigation. It remains true, of course, that experimental measurements are always directly concerned only with extensive effects. Nevertheless, these extensive effects teach us something not only about the relationships of intensities but also about those of qualities. The possibility of progressing in knowledge in this fashion arises from the fact that the object of mathematics itself is no longer restricted to the measurable and the numerable, but has become much more universal. Its object now is all formally possible relations within the species-individual structure. Since the qualitative as a property of material being belongs to the species-individual structure, it too can be treated mathematically.

Accordingly, contrary to what an earlier, more limited view of quantity suggested, the qualitative and the quantitative are not simply juxtaposed aspects of matter. For quantity pervades the whole of matter in all its aspects, and quality does the same with respect to quantity. This assertion is not a vague kind of metaphor but indicates something real, as appears from the character of physical science. In this science the qualitative and quantitative aspects are interwoven to such an extent that its method in dealing with any material phenomenon presupposes both aspects. The qualitative aspect is presupposed because physical science deals only with *observable* phenomena; the quantitative aspect is presupposed because all empirical data must be open to mathematical analysis. In other words, exactly the *same* data have to be both observable and open to mathematical analysis.

5. *The Determinism of Matter*

Determinism and the Experimental Method. If we want to pursue still further our reflection on the nature of matter, in order to understand why matter is accessible to the methods used in physical science, it is the determinism of matter in all its operations which will impress us as one of its most striking characteristics. Everywhere we find this determinism. Man's entire technology is based upon it. By necessity of nature, certain dispositions of matter result in certain operations. The concept of determinism, moreover, has traditionally always been intimately connected with the way in which a mechanical system operates. This connection caused considerable difficulties in modern physical science when it became clear that not every natural event could be reduced to mechanical models. Some went so far as to reject not only mechanicism but also determinism.

Nevertheless, such a rejection is not justified. True, a mechanical system presupposes determinism, but we may not reverse this proposition. It is quite possible that there exist determined systems which cannot be represented by mechanical models. However, we will not enter into details concerning this matter, because it possesses only an incidental interest for the problem of determinism from the viewpoint that is to be considered here.[8]

The best idea of what the determinism of material activity means is obtained by considering how this determinism is the foundation of the experimental method. This point has been touched on in passing in Chapter I when we spoke about the question of the mutability and immutability of matter. For determinism is nothing else than a certain way in which mutability and immutability go together. Determinism states that the different operations which a material object exhibits in varied conditions are fundamentally expressions of an unchangeable

[8]The interested reader may be referred to our work, *The Philosophy of Nature*, Ch. VII.

pattern of operation which is given with the nature of the matter in question and reveals itself in the experiment. For, precisely because these operations are expressions of an immutable pattern, the experimental method is so fruitful in making us know this pattern from many different angles. Through its different expressions we are enabled to discover this pattern.

Species-Individual Structure and Determinism. This reply, however, does not yet go to the very heart of what exactly determinism is. We have still to consider the question of why there exists an immutable pattern of operation. The answer to this question becomes clear when we connect the determinism of the material operation with the fundamental structure of material reality, the species-individual structure. This structure indicates that every concrete material being is at the same time something individual and something specific, in such a way that the individual disappears, as it were, in being an instance of a particular specificity, or rather in being an instance of many specificities. With respect to the operation of such a material entity this situation means that the operation does not proceed from the individual, save insofar as this individual is an instance of the specific.

Accordingly, it is not so much this *concrete* magnet which attracts iron as magnetism operating in this magnet. It is not so much *this* muriatic acid which dissolves iron as the being-muriatic-acid of this liquid. It is true, of course, that magnetism and muriatic acid are abstractions. Only concrete things exist, and for this reason it is correct to say that this magnet attracts iron, for only concrete things act and only from concrete things can operations proceed. However, what we want to emphasize by using the term "magnetism" is that what is done by a concrete magnet is wholly determined by the fact that this thing is an instance of magnetism. The concreteness of the magnet as an individual neither adds nor subtracts anything from the magnetism.

This point becomes even clearer when we raise the objection that the working of one magnet may differ considerably from that of another. This kind of "individual" differences, of course, cannot be denied, but they do not arise from the individual as individual, but from the fact that one magnet is bigger or heavier than the other, or perhaps differs from the other in composition or structure. In other words, the reason is that one and the same concrete individual is an instance of many specificities. What the individual does, it does not do because of itself but because it unites these many instances in itself. Strictly speaking, moreover, there is no "self" here, for selfhood means precisely that the individual is not reduced to being an instance, that the individual as individual has meaning because it is present to itself, knows about itself, determines itself.

It is this self-determination which as human freedom stands in contrast with determinism. If, then, we want to penetrate more profoundly into the meaning of determinism, we have to take into consideration also the meaning of freedom. For these two concepts evoke each other and, therefore, a better understanding of freedom will logically result in a better concept of determinism, and vice versa.

Moreover, the purpose of this book is to reflect upon the value of physical science for man and his culture. It, therefore, demands that we endeavor to penetrate into the relationship between material determinism and human freedom. For this reason we will dedicate the next chapter to this problem.

CHAPTER SEVEN

THE BEING OF MAN AND OF MATTER

1. *Freedom and Determinism*

a. The Difficulty of the Problem

Why Philosophers Differ in Their Views of Man. What is striking about man's being is that man experiences in himself both determinism and freedom. This situation contributes to the clarification of these concepts, insofar as we are internally present to both determinism and freedom but, on the other hand, it also makes these ideas more obscure, because in the spiritual-material being which man is determinism and freedom are closely interwoven. The fact that our experience gives us at the same time a clear distinction between freedom and determinism as well as their intimate interconnection makes it clear why there are different philosophical views regarding man.

If attention is concentrated upon the distinction between what is experienced as a free and responsible action and what is experienced as a working of nature, one will easily arrive at a dualism in which spirit and body are sharply separated (Plato, Descartes). The body is seen as a determined, purely material thing, which is guided and directed by the free and immaterial spirit.

If, on the other hand, one refuses to accept this dualism because of man's unity, it becomes difficult to do justice to the elements of both freedom and determinism. Their intimate interconnection induces some to sacrifice freedom and others to negate determinism. In the first case man's activity is viewed exclusively as the result of very subtle mechanisms which, because their complexity is not understood, seem to reveal an apparent freedom that does not really exist. This view is held by many forms of materialism. In the second case determinism is denied or at least disregarded. Man's existence is seen as absolute freedom, man is not bound by the possibilities of his nature, but realizes himself according to his own project.[1]

---

[1]"L'homme est seulement, non seulement tel qu'il se conçoit, mais tel qu'il se veut et comme il se conçoit après l'existence, comme il se veut après cet élan vers l'existence; l'homme n'est rien autre que ce qu'il se fait." Jean-Paul Sartre, *L'existentialisme est un humanisme,* Paris, 1946, p. 22.

116

Thus it appears that it is not easy to maintain both freedom and determinism without falling into a kind of dualism. The reason is that freedom and determinism appear to us always in different perspectives, they are known in different contexts, and therefore it seems either that they belong to wholly different worlds or that, when attention is paid to one, the other hardly appears at all.

Physical Science and Freedom. An investigation of man according to the method of physical science does not reveal man's freedom. Such an investigation may find perhaps inexplicable things, but they will be ascribed to the complexity of the object and the imperfection of the knowledge attained by the scientist. In a science such as physics which works with the means of exteriority freedom cannot be observed. Freedom makes its appearance only in self-reflection, when man reflects upon his own actions, when he experiences himself as a self. This does not mean, of course, that to know freedom it is necessary explicitly to reflect upon freedom in a philosophical fashion, but it does mean that a certain degree of self-experience is needed. Freedom, therefore, is known only from within, i.e., only in combination with self-knowledge. Nevertheless, if we limit ourselves to these observations, it will not be possible to arrive at a clear idea of both the distinction between freedom and determination and their intimate interconnection. Although, strictly speaking, these observations are true, they suggest something which is not true. They suggest, for instance, that physical science is able to establish determinism, and this is not the case. They suggest also that freedom in no way would appear within physical science, and this too is a mistake. Let us begin with the first suggestion.

Physical Science Presupposes Determinism. Above we introduced the determinism of matter as a presupposition of the experimental method. The fact that it is a presupposition indicates that the concept of determinism is not a concept of physical science, although it constitutes the foundation of the thinking and doing of this science. Physical science does not *observe* determinism, but presupposes it. It may *seem* to observe it because it always sees its data in the light of this presupposition, but this is not the same as observing determinism. For example, it is certainly not true that the observation of an immutable pattern of behavior in natural events points immediately to determinism.

The reason is that immutable behavior may be the result of either a determined pattern or of a freely chosen pattern. A man who leaves his house every morning on the stroke of eight o'clock makes just as deterministic an impression as the clock itself, although his behavior has an entirely different basis. Of course, even in man such a behavior may express a kind of determinism indicating that he is "being lived" rather than living, but it does not have to be so. Punctuality may also be a virtue, i.e., the result and expression of self-discipline. A punctual man may be much more free than one who disregards the clock. In other words, freedom should not be confused with arbitrariness. Behavior which for the outside observer is constant may be either free or deterministic, just as what appears to be arbitrary to such an observer may be free or deterministic. For arbitrariness may be an effect of the many chance factors which influence the behavior in a deterministic way, but it may be also the expression of man's free adaptation to such factors.

This remark leads us to a second misunderstanding. We will merely indicate it here and revert to it later in greater detail. Freedom does not mean the lack of determination, but the absence of *automatic* determination. For self-determination also is determination. Thus we arrive at the conclusion that, strictly speaking, whether we have to do with freedom or determinism is something which cannot be observed externally but only judged internally. We experience freedom in ourselves and also in our fellow men, because they reveal their interiority to us in their external words or gestures, which—and this is another sign of freedom—can reveal as well as conceal their interiority.

The Physicist and Human Freedom. Material things do not reveal any interiority. For this reason the pursuer of physical science tacitly assumes that their exteriority is not based upon any interiority and that, therefore, the externally visible material pattern of activity is not based upon free self-determination but determined by the nature of the things in question. Physical science thus connects one actual characteristic of nature with the other and in this way formulates laws. What is remarkable here is that physical science in principle does the same with the external expressions of man, insofar as these expressions are materially perceptible exteriorities and thus fall under its methods of perception. In doing so, physical science on its own level knows how to distinguish between data which lie wholly within its reach and, therefore, have to be interpreted deterministically as expressions of nature and other data which do not fulfill this condition.

"Within its reach" means here that the observed facts to be explained can be fully accounted for by more fundamental facts, which themselves have to be in principle observable. For instance, the behavior pattern of salt, i.e., its physical and chemical properties, can be explained by means of the molecular and atomic structure of salt, and these structures themselves are in principle subject to observation. If, however, physical science does not succeed in making such a reduction, it finds itself at the limits of its possibilities. It is faced with a vacuum.

On the other hand, physical science is never an abstract science in the sense that it is pursued, as it were, by an impersonal subject. No matter how abstract it may seem, it is pursued by a living human being who knows other things and other aspects than those of physical science. For this reason the physicist and the chemist also *know* the boundaries of their science, they know about freedom and determinism. Because they know about both, they are capable of applying the method of physical science to other realms, in which, however, it plays only a secondary role. For instance, the historian of art may make use of chemistry to determine who has painted a certain picture. In such a case chemistry is integrated into a wider and broader framework, because man's broader knowledge breaks through the abstraction of chemistry. As a human being, the chemist knows about paintings, but he knows nothing about them as a chemist, i.e., as standing on the abstract viewpoint of chemistry.

The Problem of Freedom and Determinism is Not a Problem of Physical Science. Accordingly, the method of physical science is always handled by man, whose knowledge goes beyond the aim envisaged by the abstract method of physical science. Thus, although physical science starts from the assumption that its objects are determined, the problem of freedom and determinism is not a problem of this science. It is not a problem that can be solved through the methods of physical science, but is a philosophical problem. We do not mean to say that what is observed by physical science is irrelevant to establish whether a particular behavior is free or deterministic, but merely want to express that these physical data have to be interpreted within a broader framework than that of physical science itself.

In practice, there is always such a broader interpretation, but its presence is not always recognized as such. For instance, the nine-

teenth century belief in the determinism of the entire cosmos, including man, was not at all based on physical science. It was founded
on philosophical considerations which, despite their inspiration by
physical data, were not established on these data. It may be worth while
to enter into greater detail here because, carefully considered, the
situation is still the same as it was in the nineteenth century. True,
there are differences, but these differences are more psychological
than physical. They arise from a difference in appreciation of the
status attained by physical science.

The nineteenth century thought that theoretically its scientific
explanation had reached its apex. Although many things remained
unexplained, it was thought that in principle the correct theoretical
framework had been discovered within which everything could be
explained. The whole universe was a giant mechanism, so that in
principle it could be explained by means of the laws governing mechanisms. All that remained to be done was to arrive at the correct
understanding of the various detail mechanisms, including those
which constituted man.

At present, however, there is every reason to suspect that the
micro-structures which were supposed to be the basis upon which all
macro-events were to be explained cannot be integrated into such a
mechanistic framework. Thus there seems to be more room for what
is in principle not explainable, for the non-determined, and for freedom. The remarkable point, however, is that despite this change in
the thinking of many physicists, nothing much has really changed.
For freedom continues to be put on the same line as the non-free.
While formerly everything seemed to be determined, now everything
seems to be undetermined. Thus before and after this change of view
there is no question of distinguishing between freedom and determinism. Nevertheless, they are distinct. Let us examine this distinction
in order to arrive at a better understanding of freedom and determinism and their interplay.

b. The Interplay of Freedom and Determinism

The Nineteenth Century Dilemma. We will take as our starting
point the considerations which led the nineteenth century scientists to
the denial of all human freedom. Their principal reason was that man
is a material being and as such wholly subject to the deterministic
laws of matter. The more became known about the human body, the

more it became clear that this body was subject to exactly the same laws which physics and chemistry had formulated for matter. How, then, could there be question of freedom in man? Once a particular material constellation of factors was given for man and his surroundings, did not other constellations have to follow by necessity of nature, i.e., deterministically?[2] Such a chain of thought leaves no room for freedom. Therefore, either this scientific reasoning process is not correct or our freedom is merely apparent freedom.

The question, however, which has to be raised here is whether the dilemma does not arise from a misunderstanding of both determinism and freedom. Such a misunderstanding would seem to make the interplay of freedom and determinism and their simultaneous presence in man impossible. For this reason we will first endeavor to obtain a measure of understanding of the possibility of their interplay, for this understanding will be an important contribution to the clarification of both concepts. Unfortunately, the understanding of the interplay between determinism and freedom in man himself as a material-spiritual being is obscured by the fact that the material processes and the exercise of freedom are always known only in different perspectives. For material processes are known in the perspective of physical science, which works by means of external observation, and the exercise of freedom is known in the perspective of internal self-experience. We will choose, therefore, an example of the interplay of freedom and determinism in which this interplay takes place in the realm of exteriority. For in such an example it is easier to see the point at issue and, once this point has been understood, it will be less difficult to concentrate upon the arduous problem of interiority.

An Example of the Interplay of Freedom and Determinism. The construction of an airplane is a free act of man. This construction, however, can be successfully executed only when we take the determinism of matter fully into account. For this reason the materials to be used and their ways of acting have to be well known. This knowledge implies two things—namely, something positive and something negative. Negatively, it means that we must know which properties of matter prevent the attainment of flight, and positively, we have to know which properties of matter make it possible to fly.

---

[2]Although this formulation seems to be typical only of classical physical science, it is equally valid for modern science. For, with respect to our problem, it is not very important whether these constellations follow with exactness or only with great probability.

This simple observation allows at once a very important conclusion, which is this : the determinism of matter is not merely an impediment of freedom but also creates the conditions under which freedom can be exercised. For it is precisely because matter continues to retain its properties even in the arrangement made by the technical product that we are able to make use of such arrangements. Because of the determinism of matter, we can rely upon matter. An engine needs fuel which, therefore, we have to supply to it, but when it has fuel, it works. That is to say, if the engine is in good condition, but to this condition the same rule applies. If the engine is in good condition it runs, if not, then it does not run. The deterministic nature of matter restricts the possibilities of flying to a few very special forms or arrangements but, on the other hand, this same determinism causes the mechanism in question to fly of necessity once these forms have been given to matter. The free act of man which we call "flying" realizes itself by means of the determinism of matter.

Accordingly, freedom and determinism are not as irreconcilably opposed as they seem to be at first. From the viewpoint of physical science, the whole process of flying is deterministic. Once the airplane is built and the controls are placed in a given position, flying follows of necessity. But from a different viewpoint there is no determinism at all. For that the material out of which the plane is built has received this particular arrangement is not at all a necessity of nature. This arrangement arose from a purposive free act of man, who wanted to fly and therefore constructed an airplane.

Although quite a few problems still remain unsolved, it should have become evident that freedom and determinism can go together. They do not exclude each other. This insight leads at the same time to a better understanding of freedom and of determinism. With respect to freedom, as was duly noted above, freedom, as it is present in man, is effectively freedom only when it adapts itself to the determinism of matter. Man's freedom is a freedom bound up with matter, just as also man's knowledge is bound up with matter. This bond, however, is of a very peculiar nature, as we discovered when we spoke of human knowledge. For, although our concepts are bound up with matter, this bond does not mean that man can know only what is sense perceptible. Man is capable of forming analogous concepts by virtue of which he transcends matter in spite of his being bound up with matter.

Something similar occurs also in the exercise of human freedom. Man sees in certain materials and their arrangements the possibilities of an airplane, which as such is not yet realized in matter, at least not in the same fashion. In building an airplane, he realizes his own idea, but he is able to do so only in dependence upon what is materially given. Not only is the airplane itself which he builds wholly permeated with material determinism, but the activity of constructing it also takes place in accord with the laws of nature. One who builds a plane has to use the required power and the necessary tools to change the materials into the parts of an airplane and to join these parts into a plane. Thus there is a constant interplay of freedom and determinism. We will revert to this point later, after we have investigated the consequences which the preceding analysis has for the concept of determinism.

c. The Concept of Determinism

The "Closed System." Determinism apparently does not mean that, once a particular constellation is given, another constellation follows from it of necessity. Such a necessity applies only to a closed system, a material system which is not subject to any influence from outside this system. What is meant by a "closed system" is not as simple as it may appear at first.[3] Thinking about the example of the airplane, we may be inclined to consider the plane as a closed system. Strictly speaking, however, this idea is not correct. An airplane is an airplane only when it flies, i.e., when it is a thing which flies because of the surrounding air, the gravitational field, and a host of other factors. All these real physical forces existing outside the airplane have to be brought to bear upon the closed system of the airplane. For just as much as the system itself they determine what will happen.

This leads us to the important conclusion that the determinism of a system does not at all mean that the future of this system is fully determined, for what will happen to the system in question depends also upon the influences which will be exercised upon it and which are not necessarily controlled by the system. Whether the plane will fly or not, whether there is air around the plane or not, is not

---

[3]D. Bohm exercises an interesting critique upon the concept "closed system" and the deterministic causality existing in it. See his book, *Causality and Chance in Modern Physics*, London, 1957, pp. 61-62.

implied in the structure of the plane. This, however, does not mean that the plane is not deterministic. It is deterministic because, when certain buttons are pushed, the engines will begin to run, the wing flaps and tail assembly will assume a particular position, and all this necessarily implies that the plane will move forward and upward into the air.

Accordingly, determinism does mean that the activity of this system is fully dependent upon the nature of the system and the situation in which it is located. It does not mean that the conditions which fix the situation of the system are themselves deterministic. The effect of a particular external cause acting upon a particular system may be deterministic, although this external cause itself does not necessarily belong to a deterministic system. For instance, a human hand which regulates the speed of an engine by turning a handle undoubtedly exercises a deterministic influence upon the engine, but it does not follow that because of this influence the hand itself has to belong to a deterministic system. Whether or not this is the case has nothing to do with the determinism of the engine.

This clarification of what exactly is meant by determinism thus leads us to the important conclusion that material systems may be fully deterministic without implying that the universe as a whole would have to be deterministic. Such a universal determinism would be the case only if all totalities and structures existing in the universe would be deterministic. For in that case every cause which is external with respect to a particular system would have its activity wholly determined by the system to which the cause itself belongs. If, then, there would exist only purely material and consequently determined systems in the universe, their activity also would have to be deterministic. But physical science itself shows that this is not the case.

Physical Science, as a Human Activity, Reveals Freedom. While it remains true that, as we mentioned above, freedom never appears within the perspective of the *method* followed by physical science, this does not take away from the fact that physical science as a *human* activity reveals man's freedom. In this sense, therefore, freedom appears in the perspective of physical science. It is really a strange situation if one denies freedom in the name of physical science, for physical science, from both its theoretical and its experimental aspects, speaks of freedom and creativity. As far as the theoretical aspect is concerned, the matter is quite evident, because theory always means an internal assimilation of what is experienced by means of a self-projected image or model. For knowledge is not a purely passive submitting to external influences, but an active building of the known in oneself and a going out from this to the object that is known. Thus knowledge is self-determination *par excellence,* albeit a self-determination with respect to the other, intentional directedness to the experienced material reality.

It is for this reason also that this self-determination urges man to experiment. For the arrangement which natural objects receive in the experiment is an arrangement which is first conceived from within, from the viewpoint of a theory, and then executed in the order of nature through man's active interference. Accordingly, although there is an influence, originating in matter, which induces man to interfere in matter, this interference is not a determined operation which takes place, as it were, behind man's back. The influence originating in matter determines the sense organ, determines the cognitive image, and this image in its turn determines the mode in which man interferes. Nevertheless, these determinations are not at all deterministic, precisely because they are self-determinations of man, who is most intimately connected with them.

Something very mysterious is really always contained in our knowing. Man is driven to study nature by a desire which ultimately is nothing else than a longing to understand himself. For he realizes that he himself also belongs to nature. For this reason any act of knowledge, no matter what its object is, is ultimately also always man's seeking of himself. Man is so interested in the determinism of matter, because he knows that he himself is deeply involved in it. However, we are touching here a general problem which will have to occupy our attention later. We will therefore return to the problem of the interplay between determinism and freedom, as this problem presents itself in the pursuit of science viewed as man's tendency to knowledge.

Experiment and Man's Self-Determination. In the preceding pages we illustrated the interplay of determinism and freedom by means of a technical example, viz., the building of an airplane. It should be clear that whatever was said about the construction of a plane applies also to scientific experimentation. Man's experimental interference is a free act, i.e., an act in which man acts from within, from his own self-determination in his cognitive activity. Nevertheless, this interference is fully attuned to the determinism of matter, because it is directed to matter and has to be executed by material means. Here also it is true that this determinism, on the one hand, limits the cognitive and operative possibilities but, on the other, provides these possibilities. We are able to experiment, because we can count on matter, because the workings of its nature are determined. At the same time, however, these same workings of nature are the reason why we can do only what matter allows us to do. The experiment has to proceed along very definite lines. Thus we find in the experiment also an interplay of freedom and determinism.

There is another point which demands our attention here. As we mentioned before, freedom is self-determination and not arbitrariness, and the truth of this assertion reveals itself in what makes man pursue physical science. In a certain sense it may be said that the pursuit of science as well as that of technology is a natural urge of man. He simply cannot cease doing it. Or is he perhaps able to cease doing it and does this precisely constitute his freedom? For instance, is the ingenious scientist who, in order to make use of his freedom renounces physical science, the free man *par excellence,* or at least freer than his colleague who devotes himself wholly to physical science? The reply to this question forces us to delve more deeply into the essence of freedom.

d. The Essence of Freedom

Freedom and Choice. When there is question of freedom, we think first of all of the possibility of choosing, of being able to do something or not to do it. This is what we may call freedom from necessity. Nevertheless, this absence of necessity does not seem to constitute the most intimate essence of freedom. The way in which man pursues science may serve again to clarify this statement. Science justly demands freedom but, we may ask, why does it make this demand? The only reply is that science itself wants to determine what it wants to admit.

Does it follow, therefore, that, in order to pursue science freely, we reserve to ourselves the right to state anything we fancy in the name of science? If we want to be free in pursuing science, are we obliged—I almost said "forced"—to deny from time to time the law of Newton? Of course not. Freedom or to determine for oneself in science what is to be admitted, does not mean arbitrariness, but only that no power outside a science is able or entitled to determine what has to be admitted in the science in question.

Freedom, then, here also means self-determination, being-bound on the basis of what in one's own view must be held to be true. Freedom, therefore, does not exclude norms but, on the contrary, includes them. Scientific freedom means that science is normalized only by what it itself sees as scientific truth and not by anything extraneous. For science is the pathway to understanding and by understanding it creates freedom.

That the possibility of choice plays only a minor role in freedom appears also from the ordinary course of affairs in science. A physician, for instance, may have several therapeutic possibilities for treating a particular disease none of which, however, is perfect. If a non-medical power would prescribe which therapy he has to use in a particular case, he would justly consider this prescription an encroachment on his freedom, for he himself wants to determine what has to be done.[4] Let us assume now that a really effective therapy for the disease is found. Obviously, all physicians will limit themselves to the use of this therapy. Do they see this limitation, the actual disappearance of a possibility of choosing, as a restriction of their freedom? Certainly not. Just the opposite will happen. If the therapy in question is not only effective but also scientifically intelligible for them, they will feel liberated of a heavy burden. They now dominate the disease in question, both in the order of understanding it and in that of curing it. Their former freedom of choice arose really from a limitation, and the removal of this possibility of choosing meant undoubtedly an enrichment of their freedom. Freedom of choice, therefore, is not the most essential element of freedom.

Choice is Not Arbitrary Self-Determination. This statement, however, does not mean that freedom of choice as such is valueless for true human freedom. Man has to find his way by groping, as it were, in darkness. For this reason freedom of choice is an essential aspect of human freedom, although it is not the whole essence of freedom. Physical science again may serve to illustrate the point. In this science the freedom of choice will never be removed, because every physical insight is always relative, so that man's bond to a physical truth will always imply a certain reservation. Thus freedom of choice is for man the necessary road to arrive at true freedom,

---

[4]There may, of course, be non-medical grounds against the use of a particular therapy; for instance, it may be too expensive. The physician will see such a ground less as an encroachment on his freedom than as a limitation of it.

at justified self-determination. Accordingly, human freedom as self-determination is never self-determination for the sake of arbitrary determination but always self-determination for the sake of becoming human in a fuller and richer way.

These thoughts throw some light on the problem which was the starting point of this study of freedom—namely, the question whether or not the physicist who, in order to live his freedom, renounces physical science is the free man *par excellence*. We have to make a distinction here. If the decision is made arbitrarily, it has hardly anything to do with freedom. If, on the other hand, the decision is made because the pursuit of science prevents the physicist from fully developing his personality, then it may be indeed a free deed *par excellence*. Thus the question cannot be answered in a general way. There are, moreover, all kinds of social factors which imply additional aspects of responsibility. We will have an opportunity to return to this point later when we will consider the enormous material possibilities provided by technology.

Is Man Determined by His Human *Nature?* Another problem demands our attention here, because it arises from a thought which imposes itself almost spontaneously when we reflect upon what has been said above about freedom of choice and the innermost essence of freedom.

Above we considered the building of technical products and the pursuit of science as free activities. The objection could be raised that these activities may be free perhaps in the sense that we can either exercise them or not exercise them, but not in the sense that there could still be question of freedom once we have chosen to pursue them. One could say, for instance, that the ideal way of flying is, as it were, pre-fixed in the laws of nature; hence the development of aeronautics also is predetermined, although we do not yet know its future evolution. The same applies also to the evolution of physical science. In principle, its development is predetermined. We may compare it with the way in which the evolution of animal species is implied in the laws of nature, at least in its broad lines. Of course, in neither case is chance to be excluded. Both man and nature have to enter into many dead-end streets, but what will manage to survive or maintain itself lies predetermined in the nature of the things themselves. Thus there would be no question of true freedom.

We may even go further and say that, strictly speaking, there is not even a freedom of choice between building or not building airplanes, between pursuing science and not pursuing it, for man's nature happens to be such that he naturally tends to engage in these tasks, that he simply *has to* tend to them. When at a given moment it became possible to build airplanes, man simply had to build them. When at a given moment the physician hears about a new discovery in medicine, he simply has to make use of it.

Does it not follow from these considerations that, although working at the evolution of science and technology is not experienced by man as a limitation of his freedom, he nevertheless is not at all free, because his human nature forces him to exploit the new possibilities? The fact that in this connection we speak of man's *nature* is, indeed, not without significance. This term refers to the whole man and not merely to his biological nature. Man has a nature not only insofar as his material aspect is concerned—this nature is studied by the biologist—but also insofar as he is a material-spiritual being. Apparently, therefore, we see an analogy between the nature of man and the nature of material things. Does this analogy mean that on a broader level there still is determinism, a determinism of man's free activities, a determinism which cannot be studied by the methods of physical science because it is not founded on material nature, but which nevertheless is no less real because it is anchored in the nature of man?

The Analogy of "Nature" with Respect to Man. For a proper perspective on this difficulty it is necessary to recall what has been said before regarding the meaning of analogy. Analogy expresses agreement and difference, but in such a way that the two are inseparably united. The difference permeates the agreement, and the agreement pervades the difference. If, then, we speak of human nature, the term is used by way of analogy with the nature of material things, and all the implications of analogy must be kept in mind. Thus the determinateness of human nature is analogous with the determinateness of material nature. There is agreement as well as difference.

As far as the agreement is concerned, enough has been said about it in the preceding pages. There is in both natures really a being-determined. The difference, however, is that in man it is precisely the individual man himself who corresponds to his nature. While individuals of material nature occur solely as instances of the specificities which determine them, the human person is not solely an instance, precisely because of his self-knowledge and self-possession. When man develops his human nature, he does so because he has discovered who he himself is and what his task is. Being-man is the task of having to be human.

Reverting to the parallel between the development of things and that of human activities, the great difference is this: things develop spontaneously, while man must first learn to know himself as man, as a knowing and creative being, he has first to assimilate nature internally and actively in his science before there can be question of technical development, he has first to realize his ethical value before there can be question of social development. In other words, man has to be constantly present to his development. He is internally involved in it, he develops himself, he determines himself.

This is precisely what we have called "freedom." The fact, therefore, that there is a human nature does not at all exclude freedom. It does make clear, however, that human freedom is not absolute. This freedom is not absolute, of course, insofar as it has to make use of the determinateness of matter, which renders it essentially limited. But it is also not absolute because human nature, which is normative of what man recognizes as his task, is not a project of man himself.

e. Freedom and Determinism in Man

A Fundamental Difference. For the scientist who pursues the study of man, as happens, e.g., in the various branches of medical science, there is still another problem which differs from the problems that were considered in the preceding pages. We mean the problem of the interplay of freedom and determinism *in* man himself. This problem was mentioned at the beginning of our study of freedom, but it remained as yet unanswered. Hitherto free self-determination and determinism were placed outside each other—freedom in man, determinism in material nature—and we investigated how the two could interact. True, a certain analogy was discovered between human freedom and the determinism of nature, but the two remained simply juxtaposed. Thus we denied that the material universe is deterministic, because in this universe there is also man who is the bearer of freedom. Man as a *whole,* therefore, was considered to be a free being.

The difficulty, however, is not so much that in the universe free and deterministic beings are juxtaposed as that in one and the same being, in man, freedom and determinism are together. The material components of the human body obey, as far as we know, exactly the same laws as all other matter. If, then, all material activities outside the human body are deterministic, how is it possible that these same laws of nature, operating in the human body, do not have the result that human activity is likewise deterministic? How can man have a free will, if all its activity is at the same time the activity of a deterministic bodily being? A wealth of empirical data could be adduced here to show that influencing bodily being is at the same time influencing the spirit.

Dualism. It is not surprising that reflection upon the concurrence of freedom and determinism *in* man has led to a kind of dualism. In such a dualism the spirit or the soul is considered as a separately existing entity which dwells in the body and, as it were, guides this body. The ideas developed in the preceding pages about the interplay of free and deterministic beings are simply extended to man himself. Man *seems* to be, but is not a unit—no more than the pilot is one with his plane. In other words, there is only an accidental unity of two subsistent entities.

We would not like to claim that in thinking and speaking about the unity of man it is possible to avoid all dualism. Dualistic expressions are inevitable, if only because we have to make use of two modes of knowing and, in a sense, also of two analogous terminologies to express the spiritual and the material aspects of man. Nevertheless, even though a certain dualistic way of conceiving man is inevitable to do justice to the material-spiritual being of man, we must clearly realize the limitations to be imposed on this dualism because it detracts from man's unity. This unity manifests itself in manifold ways. It reveals itself in our knowledge through the mutual interpenetration of intellectuality and sensitivity. It manifests itself also as genetic unity, insofar as man's intellectuality awakes only with the body's development and is lost again when the body degenerates. The dependence of the mind on matter is not simply like the dependence of a craftsman upon his tools.

Man as a Bi-Unity. There are other points which give food for thought. The dualistic conception of man really only delays the difficulty. For what makes it possible for man to build and operate an engine? Nothing else than the fact that his mental activity is, as it were, also in his hands which, as material agents, belong to the world of material things and thus are capable of acting upon other material things. If, then, the human mind is conceived as a separate entity in the body, it is really conceived as a spiritual-material entity, at least to make its action upon the body intelligible. If the human spirit or soul were to be conceived as a purely spiritual entity, which would not at all have to be material to act upon the body, then one would have to raise the question what such a spirit is doing in a body. For, as a pure spirit, he would not need the body in any way and would be capable of acting directly upon material beings. But it is precisely as an incarnated spirit that man belongs to the world of matter and is capable of acting upon this world.

This incarnation or embodiment, therefore, must refer to a genuine bi-unity. If the presence-in-a-body of the spirit is meaningful, then man must be essentially spirit and essentially also matter. For this reason the concurrence of freedom and determinism is a real problem, for the whole of man is spirit and the whole of man is matter. As matter, he is subject to determinism, he is merely an example of material specificities and therefore also subject to all their activities and passivities. As spirit, he is free, self-determining.

Material Determination and Spiritual Self-Determination. How, we must ask, is there room for man's freedom if the determinism of matter has already fixed all activity? To solve this difficulty, we must keep in mind the result reached by our analysis of the relationship between determinism and freedom in cases where there is an external interplay of free and deterministic causes. True, the present case is different, but some of the conclusions reached are useful here too. The first result attained in our analysis was: determinism means only that any action is followed by a determined reaction, regardless whether the action itself belongs to the system or acts upon it from without. The future, therefore, of the system is fixed in the material constellation only insofar as influences from without are excluded, i.e., insofar as the system is a closed system. As to the human body, it may be considered as a physico-chemical system which, as such, is determined, but it may not be called a closed system, precisely because the corporeal aspect is only one aspect of the material-spiritual unity which man is.

In all this it must be kept in mind that physical science is an abstract science, which in principle considers only certain aspects. Abstractly considered, the human body seems to be an independent subsistent structure, which, however, it is not. Something of this lack of independence may manifest itself also in physical science. In studying bodily activities, the biologist, the chemist, or the physicist constantly meets reactions which, viewed from the perspective of his abstract mode of consideration, give rise to the impression that they are produced by causes outside the body system. External causes seem to interfere in the system, but in such a way that no violence is done to physical and chemical laws.

In this respect the situation may be compared to that of a hand which manipulates a machine or plays a piano. That certain tones originate from the piano is fully explained by the structure of the instrument and by the fact that this or that key is touched. But why this or that key is touched so that a particular melody is produced wholly escapes the physicist, although he may understand or feel it as a musician. The situation, however, becomes different when the touching of the keys is automatically governed by a mechanical piano player on which the melody has been fixed. In this case the physicist understands also the sequence in which the keys are touched, he understands that the piano plays the melody. Nevertheless, even here the problem has really only been postponed, for the distribution of the holes in the player piano remained unexplainable.

Man's Body is Not Merely *a Physico-Chemical System.* This parallel may not be pushed too far, for the situation of the human body differs widely from that of the piano. What in the case of the piano or of the player piano must be attributed to an external cause occurs from within in the case of the human body. What, viewed from the onesided abstracted standpoint of physical science, seems to be an external cause interfering from without belongs in reality to one and the same man. Man's free will is an original source of activity within the very essence of man. However, free will is a principle of a different order from pure matter, and for this reason its activity gives rise to the impression, within the horizon of physical science, that an external cause constantly penetrates into the physio-chemical system of the body.

In reality, there is no question of an external cause here. The cause belongs to the living spiritual-material unity itself and thus raises the physico-chemical system to a higher order than that of the *purely* physico-chemical systems. Physical science, however, does not know this. It knows only that the physico-chemical system is not a closed system in the sense in which this term is used in physical science.   There constantly are "intrusions" which belong neither to the system itself nor to its physical surroundings.[5]   In this way it is possible for the physico-chemical system, which the human body *also* is, to seem to be wholly deterministic, although the total being, man, is not deterministic.

This absence of determination, however, must not be conceived as if in man everything is freedom and spontaneous activity. If we may use again the parallel of the piano player and the piano, we could say that man's free activities constantly impress programs on the material substratum, as is done also by cognitive impressions which are not consciously developed.   Many future activities, therefore, are determined either wholly or at least in part, by these programs.

Man is Not Pure *Freedom in his Spiritual Activities.* Because of the connection between man's spiritual and material activities, it is not difficult to find an intimate relationship between all kinds of technical, biological, and intellectual processes.   This relationship sometimes gives rise to the conclusion that man's intellectuality and freedom are nothing else than very complex material processes, somewhat in the same way as, but with a greater complexity than biological processes.   This conclusion appears to arise from the expectation that intellectual and free happenings would have to be wholly different from material events, to such an extent that any relationship between the two would contradict the distinction between matter and spirit.

Such a conclusion, however, is ultimately based on the idea of dualism.   When one carefully takes into consideration that man is a material-spiritual unity, a wholly different picture will arise. In the perspective of this unity the bond of spirit to matter means that the spirit can exercise its activities only in and through matter, so that the way in which matter works leaves its traces in all spiritual activities. We are not thinking here merely of the refined instrumental methods of perception in which the mind sees the

---

[5]It is very much open to doubt whether the physicist will ever be able to track these "intrusions" down in their physical operations. Because of the delicate nature of the micro-structures, these starting operations may be so small that they are lost in the no-man's-land in which physical science is unable to observe determinism because its models are not adequate. These operations may seem to be processes which start spontaneously. From their macro-effects, however, it is apparent that this spontaneity is not arbitrary, but arises from man's acts of will, which escape the physicist as such.

material limitation of the senses and at the same time manages to find physical possibilities to overcome this limitation. In these methods the mind makes matter subservient to itself as a real instrument. We are thinking also of the fact that, before the mind can make use of these possibilities, it has first to awake and, so to speak, find itself. Here also we encounter all these material mechanisms. The mind does not consciously make them subservient to itself but, nevertheless, it is in them and through them that the mind is awakened.

Thus it is not surprising that all kinds of analogies manifest themselves between spiritual and material processes. Likewise, it should not cause us to be astonished that much of so-called intellectual work, such as calculating and the solution of differential equations, can be done by machines, and even better than it can be done by man himself. This fact does not mean that the machines perform really intellectual labor, but only that many mechanisms are contained in man's thinking. It could hardly be otherwise if man is really a spiritual-material being and not a spirit dwelling in a body. Thus it is hardly surprising that it is possible for the human spirit to arrange material factors in such a way that they can perform the mechanical functions of thinking in a way similar to that in which man's mind itself performs these functions. All this, however, should not lead us into the temptation to equate matter and spirit unqualifiedly and thus to arrive at a kind of monism.

A Misunderstanding of the Function of Physical Science. It is hardly possible to investigate the many analogies between the spiritual and the material without entering into certain problems pertaining to the philosophy of life. The matter-spirit relationship is, as it were, foreshadowed by the relationship of the living and the non-living. Man, as spirit-in-matter, is embodied spirit, i.e., in one way or another the spiritual pertains to the sphere of life which we encounter also in non-human living beings. For this reason the problems which have drawn our attention regarding the relationship of determinism and freedom are met also, albeit on a different level, in the philosophy of life.

This, however, is not the only reason why we want to examine here some of the philosophical problems regarding life. The tendency of scientists to equate matter and spirit ultimately has its foundation in a serious misunderstanding about the nature and competency of physical science. This misunderstanding is similar to that which plays a role in the well-known struggle between mechanism and vitalism among biologists. This struggle is concerned with a problem that shows a great similarity to the question which occupies our attention here, although it is situated on a lower level. For the issue between vitalism and mechanism is the distinction between living and non-living. Thus in a certain sense it is possible to see this issue as a precursor of the distinction between matter and spirit. For this reason it is worth while to devote here a few pages to the struggle between mechanism and vitalism.

2. *Mechanism and Vitalism*

a. The History of the Problem

The term "mechanism" or "mechanicism" has a long list of diversified meanings. Without, however, doing violence to this diversity, we may summarize its views with respect to the phenomena of life by saying that all vital phenomena can ultimately be explained in full on a physico-chemical basis. This thesis is denied by vitalism, which claims that in living beings there is a principle at work that is essentially superior to the factors present in non-living matter which constitute the object of physics and chemistry.

Forms of Vitalism. Vitalism always endeavors to draw attention to phenomena of life which cannot be explained by physical science alone and in whose explanation an appeal has to be made to specific principles of life. Such phenomena are readily discernible even nowadays, but in former times they seemed to be even more obviously present. For instance, till the beginning of the nineteenth century it had not been possible to synthetize the chemical substances of living beings in the laboratory. These substances seemed to arise only under the influence of a *vis vitalis,* a vital force.

In 1828, however, Wöhler synthetized urea. This success was soon followed by a steady flow of new syntheses of organic substances. It did not take very long before the general conviction gained ground that all organic compounds could be produced in the laboratory. Thus vitalism was forced to abandon its thesis. There is no reason to appeal to other forces than ordinary chemical and physical factors to explain the origin of the chemical building blocks constituting a living organism. The breach of this rampart, however, did not discourage the vitalists, for there were many other positions from which they could defend their view.

One of the best-known is that of Hans Driesch. He held that the remarkable phenomena of regulation and regeneration in the development of an adult from an embryo could be explained only under the influence of a non-material principle, which he called an "entelechy." But here also subsequent physical research showed that there was no need to appeal to a non-material principle which would act, as it were, as a stage-manager, summoning every part to do its job at the precise moment needed for the development of the organism. For the developmental processes could be explained also on the basis of physical science alone.

Biology and Vitalism. Many other aspects of the struggle between vitalism and mechanism could be adduced to illustrate the course of the dispute. However, the result was every time the same: whatever the concrete point to which vitalism clung in its attempts to indicate that ordinary physical and chemical forces were essentially insufficient, sooner or later it had to evacuate its position before the relentless advance of its opponents. As von Bertalanffy correctly wrote, "The refutation of vitalism is the history of biology."[6] This remark is not merely a statement of the historical march of events, but also and especially indicates the program pursued by biology.

For what else inspires the development of biology than the will to explain all perceptible phenomena of life by the methods of physical science? As a physical science, biology correctly starts from the presupposition that everything which is empirically perceptible and subject to experiments belongs to the domain of its competence. For this reason the unexplained does not constitute a boundary barring biology, as vitalism would have us believe, but presents it with a task and a challenge.

There is, moreover, in this matter another important point, to which von Bertalanffy draws attention.[7] He emphasizes that when in biology there is question of physico-chemical explanations, people usually think of the explanation of complex vital phenomena by means of the physico-chemical laws which man has learned in his study of non-living material systems. But, says von Bertalanffy, precisely the study of the biological systems is likely to reveal new aspects pertain-

[6]L. von Bertalanffy, *Das biologische Weltbild,* Bern, 1949, p. 21.
[7]*Op. cit.,* Ch. IV.

ing to the general properties of matter and thus may give rise to a broadened physics and chemistry.

There is much in this view which recommends it. It harmonizes with what has been happening even within traditional physics and chemistry. For instance, the properties of the electron can be known only by studying the atom, i.e., by studying the greater whole in which the electron plays a partial role. In a similar way one may expect that atoms and molecules will be thoroughly known in their physical and chemical properties when man will have succeeded in fathoming the physico-chemical properties of living systems. When this stage will be reached, many of the qualities which at present are often cited in physical science as specific differences between living and non-living systems will disappear, or rather, they will be understood by means of the same fundamental principles.

As an example we may adduce here the difference with respect to entropy. In non-living systems we observe a tendency to a greater entropy, while living systems tend to lessen it, or expressed in somewhat more biological terms, living systems reveal a constantly increasing differentiation, while non-living systems tend all the time to less differentiation. It is quite possible that a better knowledge of the living system will make us understand why this system must reveal a decrease of entropy upon the basis of the same material laws which lead to an increase in entropy in non-living systems.[8]

b. The Abstractness of Physical Science

Does this expectation mean that with the progress of physical science the differences between the living and the non-living, which at first sight impress the ingenuous observer as strikingly essential, will be gradually reduced to structural differences of essentially the same substratum? Does it mean also that we may expect a similar fate for the differences which are regarded as typical between man's spiritual activities and his purely material activities? The fact that all kinds of "thinking" have become incorporated in calculating machines may seem to point in this direction. Must we, therefore, conclude that mechanism is one hundred percent right and vitalism entirely wrong?

Physical Reduction and the Distinction Between the Living and the Non-Living. This conclusion would, indeed, follow if physical

---

[8]Cf. E. Schrödinger, *What is Life?*, Cambridge, 1948, Ch. VII.

science were not the abstract science which it is. Within the abstract view of physical science the distinction between the living and the non-living will always have to present itself as a distinction which, in principle, is subject to description and explanation in terms of physics and chemistry. What else could be expected if we pay attention to the nature of physical science? Physical science will never accept that within a living system a material substance behaves differently than when outside the system, and if its behavior seems to be different, physical science will try to explain this difference on the basis of the other structural relationships in which the substance in question finds itself in the living system. But the mysterious claim that we are dealing here with a phenomenon of life will never be accepted by physical science. Of course, this science recognizes the distinction between a living and a non-living system, but from its viewpoint the distinction is based on a difference in complexity of structures which gives rise to all kinds of interactions in living systems that are absent from the non-living.

No matter, however, how much all this may be true, it does not at all decide the issue of whether there is an essential difference between the living and the non-living. For the reduction performed by physical science remains wholly silent with respect to a distinction of the living from the non-living which would lie outside the perspective of physics and chemistry. For instance, a physical analysis of the sound produced by human speech will reveal differences from similar analyses made of other sounds. But who would want to claim that the only difference between human speech, the singing of a nightingale, and the rolling of thunder is the difference discovered by means of physical analysis, so that these sounds do not indicate any essential difference?

To raise this question is to reply to it. As sound, human speech belongs wholly to the competence of physics, just as other sounds do. Nevertheless, this fact does not at all deny that human speech possesses something of its own which makes it differ essentially from other sounds. In a similar way the phenomena of life, as *material* phenomena, lie fully within the competence of physics and chemistry and, therefore, in principle, they are not accorded a privileged position transcending that of other material phenomena. But this equality within the physical perspective does not at all exclude the possibility of differences which do not belong to the competence of physics and chemistry.

The Basic Mistake of Vitalism and Mechanism. We are touching here the fundamental error which underlies the struggle between vitalism and mechanism. Both views start with the assumption that their differences can be decided by physical science, either because it would be possible to explain the phenomena of life fully in a physico-chemical way (mechanism) or because the definitive failure of such an explanation would establish the correctness of the vitalistic view. The very basis of this assumption, however, is wrong. If the living really differs essentially from the non-living, the essential aspect of this difference cannot reveal itself in the research performed by physical science. The reason is simply this that physical research always refers only to those aspects which in principle are common to living and non-living systems. That living bodies possess such aspects alongside possible essential differences is sufficiently certain from the fact that they are always living *matter*. Nevertheless, even this essential similarity does not preclude that there could be also essential differences.

To place the whole problem of the possible essential difference between the living and the non-living into the sharpest focus, we want to devote a few moments to a proposed solution of the issue of mechanism versus vitalism which often nowadays is looked upon with favor. Some biologists and philosophers point out that, although the phenomena of life themselves may be perhaps explained in a physico-chemical way, this explanation does not take away from the fact that life is essentially different. For all physico-chemical explanations start from the *de facto* given order of life, but they cannot explain this order itself. It is precisely in this, the existence of this order, that the mystery of life would be hidden.

We may view this idea perhaps as a last desperate effort of vitalism to maintain itself on a scientific basis. Undoubtedly, it contains much truth. On the other hand, it does not go far enough in its thinking and thus makes a distinction between the living and the non-living which is too sharp. For it suggests that the mystery begins only with life and, therefore, appears to admit implicity that the non-living can be fully and completely explained by physical science. This is a serious mistake. Surprisingly enough, both mechanism and vitalism commit here the same fundamental error.

In reality, physical science is an *abstract* science not only with respect to living bodies but also insofar as non-living matter is concerned. For this reason the non-living may not simply be identified with the physico-chemical. The non-living indicates a full reality, that of non-living matter, while the physico-chemical refers to certain aspects which belong to both the non-living and the living, to both also the non-human and the human. That physical science does have such an abstract character with respect also to the non-living, inorganic nature, appears from this that the *existence,* the *being* of this nature with the laws inherent in this being cannot be explained at all by physical science itself. Physics simply starts from the assumption that this nature does exist.

However, the fact that there is an inorganic nature and not rather none is at least just as much a mystery as the existence of life. We may even say that it is a greater mystery if we pursue the line of thought along which science proceeds nowadays. For it is quite possible that the realm of the living will at some time be explained as a necessary consequence flowing from the existence of the non-living order of nature. There are all kinds of indications pointing in this direction.[9] Perhaps we will arrive at a stage in which we will understand that, when matter finds itself in a particular constellation of factors, simple living organisms will evolve in a spontaneous fashion, i.e., by virtue of the immanent laws of nature, and that these simple organisms evolve into higher types.

The Boundary of Scientific Explanation. Simpson, who thinks that there is a very real possibility of science ever reaching this stage, is led to remark about such a process of evolution: "It need not have been miraculous, except as the existence of the physical universe may be considered a miracle."[10] The mystery, indeed, does not begin with life but is already contained in the very existence of matter itself. We do not mean to say, of course, that the mystery of life may now be simply pushed aside. But in this view the mystery of the realm of life to which many modern biologists love to appeal becomes a development of the mystery of material being.

What is implied in the proposed view means that in the scientific investigation of life we will never reach anywhere a boundary where this kind of research has to stop. Such a boundary, if this term is to be used, is present both always and never. It is never present, because one cannot indicate any particular concrete point among the phenomena of life that would not be susceptible of a scientific explana-

---

[9]Cf., e.g., A. I. Oparin, *The Origin of Life on the Earth,* London, 3rd ed., 1957.
    [10]G. G. Simpson, *The Meaning of Evolution,* New York, 1951, p. 13.

tion. There is no point where scientific research reaches an invincible barrier, whether with respect to vital functions—vitalism is a rueful witness here—or with respect to the origin of life. On the other hand, there is always a boundary, insofar as in one way or another a physical science always has to start from the *given* order of nature,[11] so that no phenomenon can ever be completely explained by physical science.

The Problem of the Essential Difference Between the Living and the Non-Living. Thus our original question imposes itself all the more urgently. Is there still any reason to speak of an essential difference between the living and the non-living? This question is given added emphasis by the fact that biologists are inclined to see certain types of viruses as gradual forms of transition between non-living complexes and living organisms.[12] Despite the fact that the problem of abiogenesis, no matter how optimistic some biologists may sound, is far from being solved, the above-mentioned transitional forms lead many contemporary biologists to doubt the reality of the essential difference between the living and the non-living. They do not mean to say that they have no reason to admit a difference in some way, for biology itself, as a special physical science, is based upon the presence of such a difference. The question, however, is whether the difference is essential.

c. The Difficulty of Defining Life

Self-Movement. Another difficulty is connected with the preceding problem. Whenever an attempt is made to define life, we note that none of the proposed definitions is quite satisfactory. Classical philosophy, for instance, speaks of life as self-movement. However, self-movement is characteristic also of a self-regulating automatic machine. Of course, the machine's self-movement differs wholly from that of a living being. Ultimately its self-movement is given to the machine from without by means of a program punched into a card. A living being, on the other hand, possesses its "program," if we may use this term, "from within." Thus we are not going to lose sight of the difference between the two types of self-movement. However, this is due not so much to a sharp conceptual distinction laid down in a

---

[11] The concept "order of nature" allows many different shades of meaning. We will come back to this point in Chapter Nine.

[12] This does not mean that virus is an evolutionary link between the living and the non-living. Cf. Frederick C. Bawden, "Evolution and Viruses," *Symposium on Evolution,* Pittsburgh, 1959, pp. 11 ff.

definition as to a kind of intuitive awareness of what is proper to life which always influences the application of the definition.

Other Characteristics. The same remarks may be made with respect to the three classical specific properties of life—namely, nutrition, growth, and reproduction. It is not difficult to discover analogous properties in non-living bodies. For instance, the astronomer Minnaert shows that stars exhibit similar qualities.[13]

Other qualities also are adduced as characteristics of vital phenomena; for instance, individuality, totality, immanence, adaptability, and finality. However, they also appear to be not at all limited to living being, although in general we will have no difficulty in distinguishing the living individual from the non-living individual, the living totality from the non-living totality, etc. For life always has something that is wholly proper to it, even though we experience great difficulty in trying to formulate its proper character in a conceptual way.

What about such concepts as consciousness, memory, perception, thinking and learning? They are not used to distinguish the living from the non-living, because they do not apply to all living beings but only to the higher types of life. However, even these concepts seem to lose their exclusive applicability to higher forms of life, now that man constructs all kinds of machines which perform calculations and other "thinking" activities. Yet even here it remains strikingly true that no one will consider the thinking, learning, and remembering of such machines as acts of real thinking and remembering, because the machine does not really *live*.

The Paradox of Life. Thus we are faced here with a strange paradox. On the one hand, man knows life intuitively in such a clear fashion that the biologist has no difficulty in distinguishing the object of his science from other objects. On the other hand, it remains extremely difficult to express this intuitive knowledge conceptually in a sharply defined fashion. This paradox reminds us of what we have seen in Chapter IV about the use of analogous concepts. Man uses such concepts with respect to realities which, despite their clear distinction, cannot be separately analyzed in a conceptual way. To emphasize the difficulty and even the actual impossibility of a satisfactory conceptual analysis, we noted that in analogous concepts the

---

[13]M. Minnaert, "The Significance of Astronomy for Biology," *Publications of the Astronomic Society of the Pacific,* vol. 63 (1951), pp. 272-282.

difference lies precisely in the similarity and the dissimilarity in the resemblance.[14]

The paradox which we encounter here in speaking of life confronts us again with a general and very fundamental philosophical problem—namely, the question whether the simple contradictory opposition of concepts, which makes us here distinguish sharply between living and non-living, is really capable of doing justice to the real state of affairs. Is conceptual thinking in terms of contradictories not too much attuned to univocity? If the reply is in the affirmative, such thinking would be deceptive as soon as there is question of thought which is not solely oriented to matter, as known through our external senses, but also to the different levels of being on which matter is present as living and as non-living matter.

Thus we are brought back again to the question whether there is an essential difference between living and non-living. The various approaches made to this question justify the expectation that the reply will have to be qualified. A simple affirmation or negation would not clarify anything.

To prepare the reply, we will return to what we have mentioned before—namely, that there is no definite, demonstrable boundary at which physical science offers no longer any possibility of finding an explanation. If, nevertheless, life reveals something inexplicable, something of a mystery, the reason is that even the non-living material being contains a mystery. Viewed in this way, the living does not essentially differ from the non-living. The living may arouse our wonder more readily, but this wonder finds its proper orientation only when even the inorganic material being succeeds in causing it. If, then, the mystery of life is fundamentally no other mystery than that of being, it follows that we must investigate the relationship between the concepts of life and of being.

d. Life as the Unfolding of Being

The Unsatisfactory Aspect of the Traditional Three Grades of Life. The first thing which strikes us is that there is something peculiar about the use made of such concepts as *life* and *being* as well as *knowing*, which are of fundamental importance in the characterization of the hierarchy ruling the material world. To the lowest step of this hierarchy, the inorganic world, we attribute merely *being*, but not life or knowledge. For inorganic things *exist*, although they

---

[14]Ch. IV, pp. 66 ff.

do not *live* and *know*. According to our usage of the terms, therefore, a thing may *exist* without living or knowing. To plants we ascribe in addition to *being* also *life,* apparently as something extra added over and above being. In the case of animals we join *sense knowledge* to *being* and *living,* and in man the pyramid is completed by the addition of *intellectual knowledge.*

Although we do not want to deny the practical value possessed by this way of representing the situation, we must remark that it is really very unsatisfactory. There is, of course, first of all, the fact that the hierarchical scale leaves no room for all kinds of intermediaries between different grades of life. But there is also another and more important reason. The unsatisfactory aspect of the scale lies especially in this that living and knowing are, as it were, located outside being and added to it from without. Nevertheless, it is precisely man's *knowing* existence in the world and his self-knowledge which constitute his being and his properly human life, just as also the being of a plant or of an animal is their being *alive.* To live and to know, therefore, are not at all situated outside being, but constitute the unfolding of being. To live is not "to be" *plus* life, but is *to be* in a higher and more developed fashion. Viewed in this way, living and knowing are being *par excellence,* they are being, arrived at a perfection of its own and not being with the addition of a few particular attributes. Purely material being in this way becomes a diminution of being, a being on an extremely primitive level.

The Analogy of Life. If we pursue this line of thought somewhat further, all kinds of interesting perspectives reveal themselves. If living matter is not matter plus life, but materiality which has attained a fuller development, it becomes possible to understand why living organisms function fully in accord with the laws of matter, despite the fact that life represents a higher level of being. We understand also why the concepts by which we endeavor to characterize life show so little exclusiveness. From the above-mentioned viewpoint the situation could not be different, and every characteristic of life must have a corresponding analogate in mere matter. For life does not add something foreign to matter, but material being itself finds its unfolding in living matter. Likewise, the discovery of intermediaries between non-living complexes and living organisms becomes less enigmatic. For there is no longer any difficulty if a being shows characteristics of life in one respect but not in another.

The interplay also of freedom and determinism, of spirituality and materiality, in man appears in a new light. For, strictly speaking, it is no longer the interplay of two components which are foreign to each other (as it appears to be in dualistic views), but it is material being itself which has reached the level of the spiritual for which it had a capacity. Thus determinism is no longer a foreign element in freedom, but constitutes a basis upon which freedom is realized. Just as spirit and matter, living and non-living, so also freedom and determinism are not contradictorily opposed. For this reason life does not have to be an addition to the non-living, or the spiritual an addition to the material, or freedom an addition to determinism.

In this way the problem of the distinction between the living and the non-living is placed in a wider frame—that of the hierarchy of being, in which man also occupies a place. We will therefore provisionally leave the dispute between mechanism and vitalism and proceed to examine the proposed solution in this broadened frame in which man himself enters into the picture. For a series of difficulties arises here which could make us hesitate to accept the proposed solution.

3. *The Hierarchy of Being*

a. The Problem of Matter-Spirit

Many of the difficulties which give rise to the dispute between vitalism and mechanism and to the differentiation between the living and the non-living are connected, as we have seen, with man's tendency to place all kinds of concepts in contradictory opposition and even to define them more or less in this way. The same is true of the difficulties arising in the problem of matter-spirit and the related issue of the interplay between freedom and determinism. Because of the above-mentioned tendency, we define free as non-deterministic, and deterministic as non-free, just as we define material as non-spiritual and spiritual as non-material. Strictly speaking, this way of defining these entities is very peculiar. For the only spiritual reality which we experience directly is the human reality in which spirit and matter are precisely given in unity.

Spirit-in-Matter and Pure Spirit. While we do know pure matter, we do not know pure spirit. Whatever spirit there is in our experience, we encounter as spirit-in-matter, as an animated material structure. For this reason there may seem to be little reason to make a big problem out of the relationship of matter to spirit. Spirit, so it seems, should not be defined in opposition to matter but in dependence upon it, as we experience the matter-spirit relationship in man. Accordingly, in speaking of the spiritual as the unfolding of being, as we have done in the preceding pages, we remain fully loyal to what we actually experience.

Nevertheless, we should beware of self-deception here, for the perspective opened here contains also great difficulties. These difficulties arise from the fact that it is not without reason that man has placed spirit and matter in contradictory opposition. Man has never been satisfied in a permanent fashion with speaking only about the *human* spirit. He has always seen that peculiar union of spirit and matter which characterizes man as a degraded form of spiritual being, precisely because the human spirit is not a pure or immaterial spirit. What is the reason which has induced man to speak of spirit also in the sense of pure spirit? This is an important question, for it is only when we have a good understanding of the ontological level of the spiritual that we may attempt to see man's being as the unfolding of material being. Without such an understanding we would easily lapse into an ill-fated and fruitless kind of monism.

Abstraction and the Origin of the Idea "Pure Spirit." Let us examine what in man's self-experience—for this experience is and remains the only possible starting point—makes us speak of spirit in such a way that it can give rise to the idea of a pure spirit and the subsequent contradictory opposition of spirit and matter. This opposition is evidently connected with the fact that we perceive material reality with our senses in an external cognitive contact, while we experience spirituality in our reflection upon man's intellectual knowledge. Considered in itself, however, this difference does not tell us very much. It could even be the source of the mistake which considers spirituality as a foreign factor added to matter.

What is more important than this difference in the origin of our knowledge is that in our reflection upon our cognitive activities we experience something very peculiar—namely, the fact that by virtue of their abstractness and universality our concepts are beyond the limitations of time and space. This is true even with respect to the concepts we form of material things. Such things are first perceived by the senses; therefore, the concepts in question remain attached to the sense image from which they have arisen. If, for instance, the concept "red" is detached from the red that is perceived or imagined, it loses its content; nevertheless, in its abstractness the concept is no longer attached to this or that concrete realization. However, the abstractness of univocal concepts, such as that of red or of other perceptible things, is merely a first step of spiritualization. One could even say that univocal concepts manifest *par excellence* the bond which ties our intellectual knowledge to sense perceptible matter, not only insofar as the origin of these concepts through abstraction from sense data is concerned, but also with respect to their subsequent use.

More important than the mere abstractness of our concepts is the fact that man is aware of their abstractness, just as he is aware also of the greater or lesser attachment to matter which our concepts retain. Thus, by reflecting upon the exercise of his intellectual act of knowing, man discovers the characteristic limitations of this act. It is this awareness of the limitation in question which provides him with an outlook on unlimited, i.e., purely spiritual, knowledge. Man experiences something similar with respect to his freedom. This freedom is limited, but man is aware of its limitation and thus in a certain sense transcends it. In this peculiar intermingling of limitation and unlimitedness man experiences his own being-spiritual as a spiritual-being-bound-up-with-matter and at the same time he acquires a distant view of a higher form of being which is without any limitation.

Accordingly, the most essential aspect of human intellectual knowledge is not the mirroring of the known in the knower, but the fact that at the same time this mirroring is evaluated as a mirroring, so that man rises to a certain extent above all the limitation, the fragmentary nature, and the deformation which are proper to mirrored knowledge. By virtue of his ability to determine his position as a cognitive being, man rises essentially above every position. It is for this reason that he is aware of the fact that he himself possesses something of the pure spirit, and in this way the problem of spirit versus matter is born. The spirit is opposed to matter as the open to the closed, as the free to the bound, as the self-present to what merely exists. How is it possible that both modes of being, both ontological levels be present in one and the same being, in man?

Man's Unity and Philosophers. It is easy to see that reflection upon what has been said above can easily lead to all kinds of dualism. On the one hand, man strongly experiences within himself the unity of matter and spirit. This experience is perhaps even stronger than ever in our time because of the development of physical science, but this point will be considered later. Meanwhile it is certain that the awareness of this unity is not solely the result of modern physical science, for even in Greek antiquity we find it explicitly emphasized by Aristotle in opposition to Plato. Aristotle, however, did not go far enough for, although he did not make the soul an addition to the body but its form, he accepted alongside the soul a more or less independent spirit or intellect.

Confronted with the views of Plato and Aristotle, St. Thomas was convinced of the unity of the body and the spiritual soul as well as of what properly pertains to the spirit. He expressed his vision in a famous formula in which the human soul, as subsistent spirit, is the form of the body. It is a formulation which delicately balances on the edge of contradiction, but it is also thanks to this delicate balance that it owes its attractiveness. On the one hand, the formulation affirms most unhesitatingly the bond of the soul, even considered as spirit, to matter. As soul, the spirit makes the material structure a human body and thus develops together with the body. On the other hand, however, the formulation of St. Thomas emphasizes that, despite this bond, the spirit has an originality of its own, it is the taker of the initiative and is not passively developed together with the body, but remains, in a sense, aloof, so much so that, when man dies, the spirit does not perish together with the body, but can continue to live independently.

Contemporary philosophers prefer to speak of man as an embodied or incarnated spirit, which comes close to the view of St. Thomas. Their formulation contains also the same kind of contradiction. For embodied spirit points both to a total bond with matter and to an act of incarnation or embodiment, i.e., the entrance into matter of something which itself is already existent.

The Paradox of Man. Let us try to penetrate somewhat more profoundly into the meaning of these philosophical expressions. Since modern physics also confronts us with complementary forms of thought, there is no reason to censure philosophy for not being afraid of apparent contradictions, at least if experience forces us to affirm two aspects which seem to be contradictory. Moreover, it is essential that the experience of our own spiritual-material being remain the basis of all such affirmations for, as we have seen, philosophical formulas are not like mathematical formulae. A mathe-

matical formula can lead a life of its own, regardless of our experience, but not so a philosophical formula. It is only in close contact
with our own existential experience that philosophical formulae can
remain alive and meaningful for us. When this contact is broken,
they die and degenerate into pure verbalism.

Concrete experience, whether it be the everyday type or strictly
scientific, teaches us that our body is at the same time the condition
and means as well as an impediment and a restriction with respect
to the exercise of our spiritual activities. Certain cerebral structures
make thinking possible but, on the other hand, they also restrict it.
We see the same happening in technology: the determinism of
matter enables us to realize an idea in matter, but at the same time
it limits the possibilities of realizing this idea. The artist experiences
the same: matter is for him a means of expression, but a recalcitrant
means. Likewise, speech serves to reveal our thoughts and feelings,
but at the same time it conceals them at least in part. Thought
demands to be embodied in words, but is never fully encompassed
by them. For instance, the necessity of using analogous concepts
shows that not everything known to us can be fully conceptualized
and embodied in words.

What has been said here about man's spiritual activities applies
also to the spirit itself. The spirit is embodied, but is not fully encompassed by the body. There always remains a distance between
matter and spirit, and this distance makes itself constantly felt. The
spirit sees possibilities which transcend matter but, nevertheless, the
spirit has to realize itself in the matter which is its body, just as in
arts and technology it has to realize its ideas in external matter.

The spirit's incapacity to realize itself fully in matter is connected with the closed character of matter, i.e., the being limited of
every material thing to what it is, to a certain form or function. This
limitation explains also why extremely complex structures are needed
when matter is made to take part in spiritual activities. The complexity of structure encountered in living bodies as well as in technological creations likewise bears witness to this essential limitation
of matter.

The "Monistic" View of Man. The question arises here whether
this line of thought does not surreptitiously lead us to a materialistic
standpoint. Does it not follow that man's spiritual functions would
have to be considered to result from complex material structures?
Biological phenomena, sensitivity, and self-consciousness, which are

indications of increasing interiority or, as we have said above, of the unfolding of being, would seem to be only the "inside" of what presents itself externally as a more complex structure.

Such a view does not immediately have to be branded as materialistic. It could just as well be called spiritualistic, for the essential distinction of matter and spirit no longer plays a role in it. Teilhard de Chardin, for example, presents a typical example of the spiritualistic interpretation that is still possible if this view is accepted.[15]

Nevertheless, with respect to this idea of a gradual unfolding of being, we have to keep in mind that in reality there exists no continuous transition between infraliving material being, vegetative, sensitive, and intellectual life. Apparently there is here every time a threshold that has to be overcome. The fact that there are no abiogenesis and macro-evolution in our world of experience points to the truth of this statement. All life in our experience arises from life, all animals from animals, all men from human beings. If, then, there is question of a gradual unfolding of being, this unfolding seems to take place in a stage-wise fashion. Both scientific experience and the data of self-reflection bear witness to this point. Viewing life as the unfolding of being, therefore, does not simplify the matter.

Nevertheless, it will be useful to pursue this monistic line of thought somewhat further, without taking a stand with respect to its materialistic or spiritualistic interpretation. The right to do so is based on the fact that our thinking has to be of a complementary nature, because we are not able to see everything at once. If any corrections need to be made, they can be conveniently made thereafter.

The Pros and Cons of the Monistic View. We may start by drawing attention to the reason why the monistic line of thought is so attractive. It seems to be the only line which pays more than a token respect to the profound conviction of physical science that everything which enters within its realm of vision is, in principle, subject to its method of explanation. This conviction, as we have seen, is the source from which the mechanistic view draws its strength and its success as well as the reason for the discomfiture and weakness of vitalism.

The difficulty, however, of the monistic view is that it wipes out the essential differences between the different levels of being. A similar difficulty can be raised against our line of thinking which

---

[15]Pierre Teilhard de Chardin, *The Phenomenon of Man,* New York, 1959.

views life and knowledge, including spiritual knowledge, as unfoldings of being. It seems that this view must necessarily lead to a standpoint which equates matter and spirit, so that man's unique character is lost. Or, if we want to hold fast to the unicity of man's being, it seems to follow inevitably that a material being in which there is no life and no knowledge is not really being at all.

As a matter of fact, there are thinkers who draw the last-named conclusion. They evaluate purely material being as a *"Vorwirkichkeit,"* a pre-reality, which becomes real only as living.[16] For many others it is only in man that there is question of real existence, so that it is only in their relationship to man that things come to be and begin to exist. From this viewpoint it is meaningless to speak of a material world in itself. There is only a human world, and in this world things are in their way, which is a being-for-man.[17] Everything, therefore, is viewed here from man's side.

The Physicist and this View. It should hardly surprise us that this line of thought does not greatly please the physicist. Physical science has become great precisely because it opened itself as rigor-ously as possible to material reality, as reality, for it is as active reality that matter reveals itself in experiments and technology.

True, the modern physicist is far more acutely aware of the human element in his theories and models than was his nineteenth century colleague. He knows that his model is not just a picture of reality. However, this does not take away from the fact that on the basis of his scientific method he will always consider material nature as a reality facing the knowing subject, a reality which is not less **real** than his hands which interfere in this nature. He is not satisfied with evaluating nature merely as a pre-reality: material nature itself is active, it has an autonomous existence, which we can investigate

---

[16]See, e.g., Th. von Uexküll, *Der Mensch und die Natur,* Bern, 1953, pp. 142 ff.

[17]Such a view should not be understood merely in an epistemological sense, for from the epistemological standpoint its content would be trivial. For man as a knower, things exist, of course, only when they have come to his knowledge, and thus their mode of being is permeated with man's mode of knowing. The crucial point, however, is whether or not this known existence contains a refer-ence to an existence which goes beyond the being-known. Moreover, one may ask whether existing-for-man itself does not in principle point to something that transcends man. For the whole problem of the material world's existence for man or for itself can arise only in a knower who as a knower is not locked up in himself but aware of his own position as a knower. Because he knows the way in which he knows, such a knower goes beyond the limitations that characterize his way of knowing.

and make our own in such a way that we are able to make nature a reality which does work for us. This investigation and utilization of nature require that its autonomy be safeguarded, for otherwise nothing whatsoever can be accomplished by research and the technological organization of matter.

Thus when the physicist is confronted with data which give rise to viewing *all* being as living and knowing being, he will be inclined to think in the opposite direction and explain life and knowledge from the viewpoint of material activities. He will see the distinction between living and non-living not as something essential but as something accidental, as a question of a more complex material organization, and he will want to explain spiritual activities also in a similar fashion.

A Dilemma. Accordingly, it seems that a view which considers life and knowledge not as additions to being, but as its unfoldings must terminate either in a denial of purely material being or in a materialization of life and knowledge. Nevertheless, this forced choice between apparently inevitable onesided views does not have to disturb us. It is fully in line with man's way of thinking. As was pointed out before, man knows in two ways which, despite their close interconnection, can be clearly distinguished. One way is that of external sense contact, which has been perfected by physical science; the other is that of self-reflection, which is based upon the internal contact man has with his own spiritual activity. For this reason man is always exposed to two dangers.

First of all, there is the danger that man will judge everything from the standpoint of the human mode of being, i.e., as it were, from above. This danger appears in all kinds of anthropomorphisms. Man ascribes to animals, plants, and things human activities, human feelings, and human motives. It may manifest itself also in another form—namely, the one which we have seen above, which denies the being-in-itself of the infrahuman, because it does not have the unfolding of being that is characteristic of man. The infrahuman has being only insofar as it exists for man, it has meaning only insofar as man has given a meaning to it. This mode of thinking from the higher to the lower is more or less characteristic of the non-physical sciences. They study man himself as spiritual being and as creative of culture and extend also to material things insofar as these things have been integrated into the cultural order.

Secondly, there is danger that man will try to think only from the lower to the higher, from the standpoint of external sense contact with things. In this case there occurs a reification. Man himself becomes an object among objects, albeit an object that is somewhat more complex than other material things. Because he is more complex, he functions in a more involved fashion and therefore is more difficult to control. This reification applies, of course, *a fortiori* to animals. They are considered as things which are somewhat less complex than man but still much more complicated than any other things. This way of thinking from the lower to the higher is typical of physical science.

The Basis of this Dilemma. Despite their onesidedness, both these ways of thinking are based upon the same truth which, however, they pursue in different directions. Both start from the view that things, living bodies, and man somehow belong to the same order. Consequently, they should show fundamentally the same characteristics, so that they can also be studied in the same way. This statement may seem to imply a surrender to the objectifying standpoint which simply observes that materiality and material processes are found everywhere in things, in living being, and in man, and therefore wants to explain everything through matter.

For, if we want to start our thinking from the other end and avoid at the same time anthropomorphism, the exceptional character of man's being strikes us immediately. Man's intellectual knowledge and man's freedom are unique and are not found anywhere outside man. Thus the way of viewing everything from above does not seem to leave the possibility of seeing anything outside man. Nevertheless, this possibility exists, as is shown by the viewpoint of the cultural sciences. They look upon the infrahuman as a kind of amorphous material which is given form and meaning through man's consideration and adaptation. Thus it is true also of this way of viewing reality that everything is placed on the same line. The difference merely is that this time the proper material being of things, their own inherent form, recedes before what man makes of them either literally or figuratively.

Is there a way out of this dilemma of onesidenesses, an escape which does full justice not only to the physical standpoint that emphasizes the reality of the material processes, even in man, but also to the wholly special dimensions of organic life, of intellectuality and freedom? Such a perspective would have to maintain, on the one hand, that only with respect to human being can there be question of being in the full sense of the term and, on the other, it may not deny ontological value to material being, so that matter sinks to the level of amorphous "pre-reality." Let us try to open such a perspective. Even if we will not fully succeed, the effort will teach us something.

b. The Non-Living as the Foundation of the Living

We will take our starting point in the thesis that life and knowledge, as experienced in man, are not additions to, but inner unfoldings of material being. As far as organic life is concerned, this thesis can readily be shown to be true. As we have mentioned before, all concepts by which we endeavor to characterize life labor under the difficulty that they are not sufficiently exclusive. The reason is that there appears to be something in the non-living which in itself is not wholly foreign to life. It would be strange if the situation were different, for the non-living as food passes over into the living; hence the non-living is potentially alive.

The inner relationship between the non-living and the living becomes manifest also from other considerations. When, for instance, we justly observe that the living manifests finality, we may not forget that there is question here of a finality which arises from the determined orientations or tendencies of non-living matter discovered by physics and chemistry. For in its own fashion determinism also is finality; it expresses that something is naturally directed in a certain way, unconsciously, of course, and unintentionally, but nevertheless directed. Sodium, for instance, always reacts with chlorine to form ordinary salt, hydrogen always reacts with oxygen to form water, heat always makes ice melt, etc. The finality which characterizes life is a further development of the directions and tendencies present in non-living nature, which it uses to its advantage. And if life reveals itself in growth, development, and reproduction, these functions take place in a way which flows fully from the existing physico-chemical order. In many respects, therefore, life continues a pattern which is already present in the non-living.

c. Cognitive Functions in Matter

The fact that in non-living matter we may find the first beginnings of life gives rise to the question whether perhaps the same may be affirmed with respect to knowing. At first, the distance separating cognitive activity from the activity of non-living matter seems too great to reply in the affirmative. Even with respect to the animal we experience great difficulty in evaluating its acts of knowing correctly. Its knowledge has something similar to that of man, yet the distance is so great that Buytendijk speaks of mere shadows of knowledge in animals.[18] How, then, could there be something like knowledge in non-living matter? Such knowledge would have to be a shadow of a shadow. Understood in this way, the question, therefore, has to receive a negative reply.

However, we may ask, is denial the only and the final answer? Does knowing lie wholly and entirely outside the sphere of matter? Put in this form, the question is embarrassing. We know, for instance, that modern technology in relation to self-regulating machines speaks of *perception*-mechanisms which regulate the operation of a machine by feed-back. The mechanism, e.g., an automatic heating unit, is constructed and programmed in such a way that it keeps a room at a constant temperature. In one way or another, therefore, the mechanism has to perceive, i.e., know, the temperature.

Not a Crude Anthropomorphism but a True Analogy. Of course, it is quite appropriate to remark here again that the machine does not really live and really know. Nevertheless, this does not mean that the use of the terms "perceiving" and "knowing" with respect to such mechanisms is nothing but a crude anthropomorphism. In support of this assertion we may point to a rather strange fact—namely, that the science of cybernetics, which studies feed-back mechanisms, has become an important auxiliary science for the biologist, the psychologist, and the physician, especially in the study of the interplay between cognitive and motor functions.[19] If there were question only of a crude, unjustifiable anthropomorphism, cybernetics could lead us only into error, because it would attribute to a lower being something which it does not have at all. In other words, there is question here of a genuine analogy, in which we find the same quality again on a lower level, but in a different way.

Something, therefore, of the cognitive function is found in the automatic machine, in a purely material thing. Or must we say perhaps that a machine is not a purely material thing, because it has been built by a thinking and planning human being who has embodied a

---

[18]F. Buytendijk, "Schaduwen van kennen," *Tijdschrift v. Philosophie,* vol. 1 (1939), pp. 5-28.

[19]Norbert Wiener, *Cybernetics,* New York, 1948; *The Human Use of Human Beings: Cybernetics and Society,* Boston, 1950.

certain idea in it? According to this view, the machine would exercise the higher functions only by virtue of the idea embodied in it. In other words, when there is question of a cognitive function of the machine, this function would be not a function of matter, but ultimately only of man. Of course, we could hardly deny that the machine knows thanks to man, but this admission does not weaken our assertion that we may speak in an analogous fashion of a cognitive function in matter. For, what is the reason that this cognitive function can be embodied in matter? No other than that matter somehow offers a possibility of embodying this function. In other words, knowing does not lie wholly and entirely outside the sphere of matter.

Moreover, placing knowledge entirely outside the sphere of matter would make unintelligible not only the possibility of a machine with a cognitive function but also the cognitive acts of man himself. As was pointed out in Chapter IV, in knowing the knower becomes the other, the object known. Somehow that which constitutes the essence of the object known determines the mind of the knower. In the act of knowing the knowable and the knower are one. This unity, however, is possible only when the knower and the object have a certain similarity. Hence nothing knowable is really foreign to knowledge. Accordingly, if material being were placed entirely outside the sphere of knowledge, it would not be knowable, and man would not know anything about matter. Or to say it differently, by being, everything is in principle knowable, so that being and knowing are intimately connected.

The objection which presents itself immediately is that being knowable is something passive, while the act of knowing is eminently active; hence a wide gap separates the two. Of course, we do not wish to deny that there is an essential difference between actively knowing and passively being known. Nevertheless, this difference is not the point at issue here. What interests us here primarily is that knowledge does not lie wholly outside the sphere of material being. Once this point has been established, we may pay attention to the difference between the active knowing of man and the passive being-known of matter, because this difference will force us to delve more deeply into the nature of knowledge. For, if it is true that knowing is not an addition to being but its unfolding, then it follows that a thing *is* only insofar as it *knows*. Forcefully expressed, as a thing knows, so it is. The level of knowing determines the level of being. If, therefore, matter is purely passive with respect to knowledge, it would have to be purely passive also with respect to being. What, however, could be the meaning of passive being?

The Function of Knowledge in Man. To delineate the vagueness of this expression somewhat more sharply, let us pay attention to the function which intellectual knowledge fulfills in man. In and through knowing, man enters into a new relationship with himself, with other men, and with things. Man becomes present to himself, the other becomes his fellow man, and things become a world for him. In and through knowledge man discovers himself, and his relationship to beings becomes his *own* relationship. This is the reason also why knowledge is accompanied by freedom. As we have seen, freedom is self-determination. Self-determination is possible only where there is self-presence and a going-out from this self-presence to things in which at the same time we discover and give a meaning.[20]

Presently we will see how both aspects, the discovery of meaning and the free giving of meaning, are characteristic of human activity. First, however, we must ask what the situation is of the above-mentioned relationships in the material being. Here too we find determination, but this determination is a having-been determined. Sodium, for example, always reacts with clorine in a determined way which is implied in the nature of these substances. There is no question of self-determination. Their activity and reactivity are specifically fixed. Strictly speaking, what reacts here is not this piece of sodium with chlorine but this instance of sodium, as we expressed it in a previous chapter when we showed the relationship of the determinism of matter with its species-individual structure.

Accordingly, the individual undergoes activity rather than exercising it. Material activity is at the same time passivity. This statement may be confirmed by the following consideration. We say that one substance acts upon another, e.g., muriatic acid on iron. Strictly speaking, however, it is just as true that the iron acts upon the acid. What is called active and what passive in such a process depends more or less on the attitude which man in his knowing and acting assumes toward the process in question. If, for instance, we put the teapot on the stove, we say that the fire heats the water and not that the water cools the fire. But we do use the last-named expression when we refer to the extinguishing of a conflagration. Accordingly, it is the human standpoint which makes one and the

---

[20]Cf. Stephan Strasser, "Het wezen van de mens," *Annalen van het Thijmgenootschap*, vol. 46 (1958), pp. 20 ff.

same process appear in a certain perspective and thus determines which substance will be called active and which passive.

These considerations lead to two conclusions. First of all, man retains his position as the original giver of meaning and the source of activity. It is his standpoint as knower which freely places things in a particular relationship. For instance, we are interested in iron and therefore say that iron is affected by muriatic acid. Man's activity, moreover, as connected with his knowledge may be what determines which reality will be considered active cause and which passive effect. For example, we want to heat water and therefore we say that fire heats water.

Secondly, as should be clear, this free giving of meaning and this free activity are only relatively free. There is a fixed relationship of activity between iron and muriatic acid, between the flame and the warming of the water. This relationship is not laid down by man, but is determined by the nature of the substances in question. In other words, the giving of meanings implies the drawing from a source of meaning. Thus there is something which may be called the proper activity of the material world, even though it remains true that this activity is also passivity, that it is more undergone than exercised. Matter is not at all master of its activity but, on the other hand, like matter itself, the activity of matter is a reality and not a mere pre-reality.

Man's freedom, therefore, in the manipulating of material activity must be based upon knowledge of this activity. Man's cognitive function gives him his freedom. In his cognitive function man does not "undergo" himself and the things he knows, but is able to place himself face to face with them. Thus his activity assumes the very special character of free activity. Let us see now what, aside from passive knowability, corresponds in matter to this cognitive function.

Passivity and Activity Coincide in Material Beings. The deterministic character of material activity could be expressed also by saying that matter "knows" exactly how it has to behave. Water "knows" exactly what to do when it is being heated. Sodium "knows" exactly how to react with chlorine and how to act upon water. Of course, the use of the term "knows" is metaphorical here. On the other hand, it is not a meaningless metaphor, for it expresses that something of the function of knowing in man, insofar as knowledge determines action, can be found also in matter. The "knowing," however, of how to act and to react in matter is nothing else than the being-determined of the activities through the immutable nature of the matter in question. The nature of sodium determines exactly how it has to behave with respect to chlorine or water. Thus in matter there is no distance between knowing and being, just as also there is no distance between activity and being, because the determination of the activity as well as its execution lie contained in the nature of matter.

Accordingly, in matter we have to do with a level of being in which activity and passivity, being and acting, being and knowing lie inside each other, so that it is not very well possible to apply these different concepts in a strict sense. In this way the above-mentioned expression "passive being" also receives a less obscure sense. The passivity of material being must be understood as a being in which activity and passivity coincide, just as also knowing and knowability fuse together because matter becomes knowable to us through its activities. To express it somewhat too emphatically, matter becomes knowable to the physicist because it knows how to behave in accord with its nature when it is placed in experimental situations.

In this way passive knowability goes together with something pertaining to activity in a cognitive function, because matter possesses real activity, even though its activity is at the same time passivity. Nevertheless, we cannot speak of self-revelation in the strict sense of the term when matter makes itself known and thus becomes knowable. Such a self-revelation occurs when a human being reveals himself, bares his soul to another. This self-revelation implies an activity which is really the subject's own activity and is based upon a real self-presence. Yet it remains meaningful to say that matter reveals its nature in the experiment, that it replies to the questions asked by the experimenter. The answer, however, is and remains a reply which is fully contained in the deterministic working of its nature. Thus the experiment is not a real dialogue between man and nature, although it is akin to it. The physicist takes part in the dialogue by placing matter in a particular situation, and nature replies by reacting to this situation in a determined way which reveals the nature of the matter in question.

Life and Knowledge as Unfolding of Being. In the light of these considerations, therefore, it appears meaningful to consider life and knowing as the unfolding of material being and not as an addition to it. For something of life and knowing is to be found also on the material level. On the ontological level of matter we find all subsequent unfoldings of being present in an incipient way. Must we conclude now that there is only a gradual and not an essential difference between living and non-living, between spiritual and material, as seems to be suggested by the term "unfolding" or "development" of being? Must we not say that man's tendency to posit essential differences seems to flow from his schematizing way of understanding and expressing himself? Man seems to cut through continuous transitions so as to arrive at sharply-defined boundaries.

Undoubtedly, it is true that man has such a tendency and undoubtedly also the sharp distinction that he makes between living and non-living, between the spiritual and the material is based upon this tendency. However, this admission does not contribute very much to the present problem. For, if we speak here of a gradual distinction instead of an essential difference, we are still schematizing, and this schematization likewise does violence to reality. Even if in the preceding pages we have managed to discover in material activity something of man's intellectual knowing and free acting, which are pre-eminently spiritual activities, it does not follow that the evident distinction between material and spiritual activity has been obliterated in any way.

On the contrary, this distinction has been rendered even sharper. We may have found something of the cognitive function in matter, but what we have found has so little to do with intellectual knowledge that we are less than ever inclined to speak here of knowledge.

A question which arises here spontaneously is whether we are disinclined to speak of knowledge here because we have compared the two extremes—man and non-living matter. Must we not take into account that the gap between these two extremes is somewhat bridged by a whole scale of living beings? And is it not precisely this scale which makes us speak of gradual distinctions? We must reply in the affirmative. If there were only human beings and material things and no infrahuman life, it would not make much sense to speak of gradual distinctions. Let us consider this matter somewhat more in detail.

d. Infrahuman Life as the Link Between Matter and Spirit

When from non-living matter we ascend through vegetative and sensitive life to man, we are confronted by an ever-increasing complexity and centralization of the externally perceptible material structures. This situation is accompanied by an emergence of interiority, which apparently is connected with this greater differentiation and centralization. What is peculiar here is that the two ways in which we experience, respectively, the externally perceptible structures and the emergent interiority remain always separate.

The Biological Level. With respect to the study of the phenomena of life, Nicolai Hartmann points out that we are always exposed to the danger of using categories which are either too low or too high. Too low, insofar as organic life is studied by means of concepts borrowed from physics and chemistry, so that the specific element of life is not reached; too high, insofar as categories borrowed from man's self-consciousness are applied to organic life, so that the ontological level of the infra-human is never properly reached.[21]

Although this remark is true to a certain extent, we cannot agree fully with it. It cannot be said that the physical and chemical categories are not applicable to living matter. They do apply, although they do not reach the core of the living. The same, however, is true also with respect to the non-living.

As we have pointed out in a preceding chapter, it is wrong simply to identify the abstract physico-chemical object with the non-living. The abstract physico-chemical object is the organization of matter insofar as this organization enters into the perspective of the method used by physics and chemistry. Whether this material organization is alive or not, human or not human, is irrelevant to this object. The physicist simply observes that his object shows an ever-increasing organization but limits himself to this external aspect. This situation is the result of his working method and of the consequent methodic abstraction of physical science.

On the other hand, we have a different way of knowing, self-reflection, which gives us internal contact with our spiritual activities. However, even in this internal contact we do not see—and this is an essential point—how our spiritual activities are connected with the complex organic structure. Our self-knowledge also has an abstract character. From numerous experiences, both pre-scientific and experimental, we know that all kinds of spiritual functions are dependent upon our material organization, but the "how" of this dependence simply escapes us. We have, as it were, internal contact only with the summit of spiritual activity and not with its basis. For this reason we can observe only a certain external connection between particular cerebral organizations and particular spiritual activities, but we do not internally

[21]Nicolai Hartmann, *Philosophie der Natur*, Berlin, 1950, p. 688.

penetrate into their relationship. This situation is the basis of Hartmann's remark about the study of the phenomena of life.

The Animal Level. When we study an animal, we find, on the one hand, a similar material organization as in man but, on the other, we see also all kinds of behavior and expressions which impress us as human. We find something of ourselves in animals. What we find, however, is precisely the level which lies below the intellectual and which, therefore, we understand so poorly even in ourselves. The animal level is transparent to us neither in its own nature nor in its relationships either to the lower, purely material level, or to the higher, the intellectual level. For this reason we easily fail to give the animal its due: either it is considered merely as a complex material organization or it is viewed as a lower and primitive kind of human being. The animal is no more the latter than the former, for it displays none of the specific unfoldings proper to man. True, the animal shows much of what is found in man, but not the self-presence which can express itself to others in self-revelation.

Only a Partial Link with Man. Considering all this, we see that the scale of vegetative and sensitive life bridges the distance between man and material things only in a very restricted sense. There is a bridge, insofar as the externally perceptible material structures are gradually interconnected, but there is none precisely insofar as man is spiritual. With man something entirely new makes its appearance. It is therefore not without reason that one may speak about the *reception* of spirit in matter rather than the *unfolding* of matter toward the spiritual. Both expressions, however, are meaningful. The former to underscore that with man something entirely new makes its appearance, the latter to stress that this new element, the spiritual life of man, is not entirely foreign to matter, for otherwise we would have to deny the material-spiritual unity of man. Knowledge, as we encounter it in man, is both entirely new and not entirely new. It is not entirely new, because there is something of knowledge in matter, yet it is entirely new, insofar as what in matter is only passivity becomes in man active self-possession and, therefore, knowledge in the proper sense.

Accordingly, although life and knowing are unfoldings and developments of material being, there is no question of denying the essential difference on the ontological level between man and material being. The concepts that have been used may sometimes suggest the opposite, but this is inevitable. For all our concepts are rather defective, because they remain bound up with sense representations. We always see more in our experience than our concept can express, and we constantly have to appeal to what is beyond our concepts. Of course, this situation does not absolve us from the duty to express ourselves as clearly and as sharply as possible in concepts, even in analogous concepts, because without concepts no insight at all is possible. Nevertheless, we will have to resign ourselves to the fact that much will remain obscure to us and that the proper character of many things will never become transparent to us.

The Hazardous Nature of Philosophy. The term "unfolding of being" may be deceptive for anyone who takes it too literally, because in this way there is no escape from the conclusion of gradual transition. Nevertheless, it has its usefulness, because the mind reaches beyond what is explicit laid down in concepts. It is, moreover, precisely this transcendence, this going beyond the concept and beyond the bond of human knowledge with matter which opens for us the possibility of seeing the limitation of conceptualization. If our view did not reach beyond the concept, how could we even know about the limitation of our concepts?

All this shows what a hazardous undertaking philosophy is, which wants to seize what lies beyond the conceptual but, in doing so, has to have recourse to concepts. However, we may ask, does this hazardous situation apply only to philosophy? Even in physical science, the ultimate aim is always man's self-knowledge, albeit not in a direct way. For, let us not forget, in his desire to understand the happenings of nature man is involved in two ways. First of all, he is involved in it as *object*. He knows that he belongs also to nature, that what happens here before him happens also *in* him. Man is also a chemical, morphological, and physiological structure, with all the consequences flowing from this fact. Secondly, man is involved in physical science as *subject*. In pursuing physical science, in the way in which he enriches his knowledge in this pursuit, in its possibilities and its limitations, he experiences also his own being. Nevertheless, it remains true that physical science is not *directly* concerned with these problems. For this reason the physicist does not immediately experience the hazardous character of philosophical thinking.

e. The Presuppositions of Science and the Hierarchy of Being

In the preceding chapters we have seen repeatedly that physical science is based upon presuppositions and that it has to be so of necessity. These presuppositions mean that philosophy is present also in physical science. Physical science, however, merely makes use of its philosophical presuppositions but does not explicitate them. For this reason in the pursuit of physical science itself one does not easily notice the hazardous character of philosophy, or more generally speaking, the hazardous nature of human knowledge which expresses itself in philosophy.

Physics and Chemistry. Physical concepts remain as close as possible to what is empirically verifiable. It is here that they find their general convincing force and their exactness. Within the realm of physical science convincing power and exactness are greatest in physics and chemistry, because they study matter in its externally perceptible aspects. These two sciences apply wherever there is something material. For this reason they can be satisfied with presuppositions which refer exclusively to what is common to all material beings, such as the species-individual structure and its consequences, the qualitative-quantitative structure, and the determinism of matter. The ontological level of its object does not need to be considered in these sciences, because it is sufficiently fixed by their methodological presuppositions.

Biology. As soon, however, as biology is reached, the situation changes. Of course, the general presuppositions of physical science remain in force. They are what gives strength to the mechanistic viewpoint which claims that all phenomena of life, as material phenomena, belong to the realm that has to be explained by the methods of physical science. Alongside these presuppositions, however, the higher unfolding of being which is life imposes its demands. Man knows intuitively that he is dealing here with a higher level of being, even though he is not able to conceptualize the matter clearly. Man knows about life, as he knows also about his own human being. He evaluates life as the inner development of the material level of being in the direction of man.

The enduring attractiveness of vitalism lies precisely in the realization that life has a level of its own. Its weakness lies in its failure to see that this proper level of being is an unfolding of the level pertaining to non-living matter. Vitalism tacitly accepts that what physics and chemistry say about matter is everything that can be said about non-living matter. We must repeat here what we have said before— as abstract sciences, physics and chemistry do not exhaust the knowledge of matter: they do not exhaust it in the case of "human matter," as should be evident, they do not exhaust it in the case of "living matter," and they do not exhaust it with respect to non-living matter. The mystery of man, like that of life, begins with matter.

The physicist or the chemist may permit himself to leave this mystery alone, because in the pursuit of his science he has to deal only with those aspects of matter which enter explicitly into his science. The biologist, however, can do so only to a lesser extent, for he is constantly confronted with the opposition between living and non-living matter. As biologist, he has to take this difference into consideration, regardless of whether he reflects philosophically on it or not. In one way or another he has to evaluate this difference. For this reason the original experience of life remains normative in his whole science, if only insofar as he sees to it that all phenomena which he studies are really phenomena of *life*, because otherwise they would not be object of his science. The biologist is not unqualifiedly interested in the physical and chemical study of matter. The use of physical and chemical methods remains subordinated to the study of the proper object of his science, which he knows to be life.

Even if the biologist would succeed in finding the proper laws governing a living system and in seeing these laws as consequences of the general laws of matter, the above-mentioned intuitive knowledge of life would remain his natural reference point to determine whether something really lives. The factor which ultimately determines the direction of his research is the knowledge that in living beings he is dealing with an unfolding of being not possessed by non-living beings. Biology, then, as distinguished from the other physical sciences, subsists on the presupposition that there is a difference between the living and the non-living. The explicit philosophical evaluation of this presupposition, however, lies beyond the horizon of the biologist as biologist, just as also the philosophical evaluation of the general presuppositions regarding matter lies beyond the perspective of the physicist or the chemist.

Philosophical Presuppositions and Positive Science. Broadly speaking, we may say that positive science is not concerned with the ultimate philosophical evaluation of being as unfolding itself in constantly higher ways, which are indicated by the traditional grades of being: non-living matter, infrahuman life, and human life. On the other hand, it remains true that all positive sciences through their presuppositions take this hierarchy of being into account and thus attune their method essentially to the level of being proper to their object. In this way every positive science is accompanied and guided by an intuitive knowledge and evaluation of its own object. Thus it is possible also to explain why man, before there was question of physical and non-physical sciences in the modern sense of the terms, knew about the proper value and level of being of material things, plants, animals, and men. The various sciences which arose later have sharpened and refined this prescientific experience, but they have not modified it in an essential way.

The Distinction Between Physical and Cultural Science. It may not be amiss to return here briefly to the distinction between physical and cultural sciences. Previously, in Chapter IV, this distinction was approached especially from the viewpoint of the concepts and methods used in these sciences. We duly noted there that cultural or non-physical sciences always have a somewhat meta-exact character. A few remarks may now be added about this question.

Cultural sciences will never manifest the strictly positive or aphilosophical nature which characterizes the physical sciences. Because physical sciences are exclusively concerned with the positive, i.e., what is directly registrable, and the interrelationships between positive things, they can dispense with the philosophical evaluations of their results. Of course, the scientist will not limit himself in his reflections about the material world to the abstract level proper to physical science. For, as we have mentioned above, physical science serves also to make man know himself. For this reason the physicist or the chemist will either consciously or unwittingly see the abstract whole of his science in a certain philosophical perspective. However, this philosophical thinking is not an explicit part of his physical science.

With respect to the cultural sciences, on the other hand, no matter how much they tend, as empirical sciences, to arrive at the positivity that characterizes physical science, they will never be wholly successful in their efforts. It seems to us that the reason for this situation is as follows. The object of physical science has a univocal status of being—namely, the material as material. Thus the physicist or the chemist does not have to worry about the philosophical evaluation of the status of being in question. He accepts this status as it presents itself to him and does not have to place himself philosophically at a distance from this status, because he has to deal only with one status. For what kind of a status this is, is sufficiently laid down in the presuppositions of his method. One who pursues a cultural science, on the other hand, encounters not only the material but also man in his spiritual aspects, man as spirit-in-matter. He, therefore, has to evaluate in some way what is proper to the human element as distinct from the non-human.

True, within his science the historian, the jurist, or the psychologist will not explicitly propose a philosophical treatise of what man is or what freedom is. However, the philosophical replies to such questions as, what is man? or, what is the proper level of being of man?, play a role in the theoretical structure of his science. This role flows from the fact that anyone who undertakes a scientific study of man has to take into account not only the presuppositions regarding matter in general, which apply also to man, but also others which are concerned with the proper ontological level of man. These special presuppositions speak about being-a-person, freedom, intellectual knowledge, and love. By virtue of being a person, man is more than a mere instance of a species; hence there is no mere repeatability in what is human, so that we cannot be satisfied with simple registration as in physical science.

It seems to us, therefore, that the more or less philosophical overtone of the non-physical sciences is not the result of the immature status in which these sciences still are, but is inherent in their object. This feature, which makes its first shy appearance in biology, presents itself boldly in the cultural sciences.

How Does Man Know About the Grades of Being? If we ask ourselves whence man has this prescientific knowledge of the various grades of being and their interconnection, there appears to be only one answer. Man has this knowledge because he knows about himself, in whom the material, the living, and the spiritual are fused into one and the same *being* which he is. In himself he knows about the mysterious interplay of freedom and determinism. He has this knowledge prior to any question of science.

To clarify the interplay of freedom and determinism, we have pointed to the way in which this interplay occurs in the pursuit of physical science as an experimental science. The experiment is based both on the determinism of matter and on the free interference of man. What happens in the experiment, however, is nothing else than a methodic refinement of what occurs constantly in daily life when man thoughtfully handles things. To understand a science, therefore, man must place it in the totality of human self-experience. He has to see its method in the light of the totality of human being and to philosophize from this standpoint about the science and its object. It is not possible to philosophize fruitfully on a narrow basis.

f. Determinism in Freedom

The starting point of the considerations presented in this chapter was the opposition between freedom and determinism. Our initial definitions described them as each other's negation and we endeavored to arrive at understanding them by means of this mutual opposition. Viewed merely as each other's opposite, freedom and determinism seem to be mutually exclusive. For this reason it is very difficult to grasp the possibility of their interplay within the one being that man is. Many see no other alternative than to deny either the determinism of matter or man's freedom. However, the study we have devoted to the grades of being supply us with a few insights which throw a new light also upon the problem of freedom and determinism.

Cognitive Function of Determinism. As we have seen, man's spirituality, expressing itself in his intellectual knowledge, may be viewed as an unfolding of being. In the light of this perspective we endeavored to discover some element of knowledge also in material being. We found there, of course, the passive knowability of matter, but also a kind of "knowing" how to react, which is determined by the nature of the matter in question and which may be called the self-expression of matter. Determinism, therefore, plays a role that is similar to the cognitive function of man.

Freedom as the Unfolding of Determinism. As was pointed out previously, freedom does not at all mean arbitrariness. A clear example illustrating this assertion is the pursuit of science. This pursuit is a free activity, but at the same time this activity is strikingly *pre*scribed by the nature of the matter that is investigated and by the nature of human knowledge. When the experimenter interferes in nature and freely introduces a certain arrangement for the sake of increasing his knowledge, his activity is very definitely guided by the situation of his science which demands that this experiment and no other be performed. Above, we have considered this fact as a difficulty against man's freedom, and given a provisional reply to it. We are now in a position to go beyond this first reply.

Basing ourselves upon the insight that knowing is not an addition to being, we have previously argued from the higher to the lower and discovered something of knowledge even on the purely material level. The same insight, however, entitles us to think also in the opposite direction. On the basis of the same reasons which were put forward above with respect to knowledge, we may say that freedom is not an addition to being, but its inner unfolding and more specifically the inner unfolding of the determinism of matter. If this is true, then it must be possible to find something of determinism in freedom, it must be possible to see determinism even in freedom itself. As determinism makes matter act and react according to its nature, so does freedom on the level of man's being. Freedom is not without orientation, but in his freedom man is oriented to the fullness of being proper to his own level of being. In the free activity, for instance, which is the pursuit of science man is oriented to the fullness of science, and this orientation drives him on. Nevertheless, he remains free.

Freedom is self-determination, but for the sake of self-unfolding, i.e., the unfolding of being. This view of freedom as an extension of determinism does not at all mean that there is only a difference of degree between determinism and freedom. All it implies is that the two are viewed not only as opposites but also as analogous, with all the hazards attached to such a view. Nevertheless, we must not hesitate to take such a view, because otherwise we cannot understand anything about the interplay of determinism and freedom, which permeates man's entire activity as the prolongation of his material-spiritual nature on the dynamic level.

Evolution and Determinism. If the theory of evolution is right,[22] the determinism of matter drives non-living matter on toward life, and life toward man. Many have been repelled by this idea as containing a degradation of man. However, the process may also be looked upon from the opposite direction—namely, as an elevation of matter. Whatever viewpoint is taken, it is certain that with the appearance of man and his freedom in the material world an entirely new and original element enters into the process of evolution. For, through his pursuit of science, his culture, and technology, man consciously begins to guide this process, even though it remains true that, as we have seen, a kind of natural urge continues to influence this conscious guidance. These points will occupy our attention in the second part of this book.

---

[22]Cf. Andrew G. van Melsen, "Philosophical Aspects of Evolution," *Symposium on Evolution,* Pittsburgh, 1959, pp. 59 ff.

PART TWO

THE INFLUENCE OF PHYSICAL SCIENCE
UPON CULTURE

CHAPTER EIGHT

INFLUENCES UPON THE DEVELOPMENT OF PHYSICAL SCIENCE

1. *Introductory Considerations*

When we reflect upon the influence which physical science has exercised in the past and continues to exercise in an ever-increasing way upon man's life in all its aspects, our thoughts turn spontaneously to the influence which this science has upon culture by way of technology. We think immediately of the broad possibilities which physical science has created for putting the data of nature to work for man. It is here that lies the beginning of all civilization, for man, as a spiritual-*material* being, is dependent upon nature because he himself also is *nature*. However, he is not a part of nature in a purely passive way, he does not simply "undergo" his nature, but places himself actively before it and in a sense "at a distance" from it.

Man Places Himself "at a Distance" from Nature. The expression "placing himself at a distance" is one of those analogous terms which should not be taken literally, especially when there is question of intellectual knowledge. When in his thinking man places himself at a distance from himself so as to be able to consider himself and his situation in a more suitable way, he does not literally go a certain distance away as he does when he wants to experience the whole of a building or of a painting. Nevertheless, even as applied to intellectual self-knowledge, the expression is not merely a metaphor, for what takes place in this case cannot be described better than by saying that man places himself "at a distance."

The profound meaning of this expression becomes evident when we pursue a line of thought which was mentioned in the preceding chapter where we spoke of the relationship between non-living matter, plants, animals, and man. As we noted there, in the ascending hierarchy of being, on each new level there is not so much question of adding something to being than of the unfolding of being. Reflecting upon animal being with its characteristic sense knowledge, we note that in the evaluation of this knowledge the concept of distance in its literal or spatial sense plays a very special role. By virtue of its sensitivity, the animal is present in its entire vital space in a strikingly special fashion. It perceives from a distance what is useful or harmful for itself, so that it is able to move actively toward or away from what it perceives. For this reason also the animal occupies a special position among other things of nature. Thus, through the acts of knowing and the motor reactions flowing from them, the concept of distance acquires a new meaning, which transcends the being-distant from each other of two physical objects deprived of sense knowledge.

Such objects also act upon one another. The gravitational influence flowing from mass allows us to say that a physical body is present wherever its gravitational action makes itself felt. In knowledge, however, there is also another element. All the physical processes which are connected with the acts of sense perception become subservient to the living individual in a new way when there is question of knowing. They make the individual be present in the surrounding world in a special fashion. The world of the animal is full of meanings that are attuned to the needs and interests of its nature. The animal occupies a place of its own in the midst of the things of nature. It belongs to them; nevertheless, it is not just like any of them, but has a kind of aloofness. Because of this aloofness, there is a certain distance from all other things, a distance which at the same time is a presence. In its knowledge the whole surrounding world is present precisely because there is a certain distance.

For the reasons pointed out in the preceding chapter, it is difficult for us to discover exactly how an animal internally experiences all this. True, in man's own knowledge we may make a distinction between sensitive and intellectual knowledge. Thus we are inclined to evaluate the animal's knowledge as purely sensitive knowledge. However, we do not really know what purely sensitive knowledge is. For our own sense knowledge is always permeated with intellectuality, which is the reason why we know this kind of sense knowledge to some extent from within. It is, however, dangerous to evaluate the animal's sense knowledge from the standpoint of this internal experience of sensitive knowing. On the other hand, it may be the only way in which we can evaluate it at all.

Meanwhile, what interests us here is not the sense knowledge of the animal but that of man. With respect to this knowledge, precisely because it is permeated with intellectuality, it is eminently true that we place ourselves at a distance from things to make them present in a new way in our acts of knowing. A stone is no longer merely a peculiarly shaped piece of rock, but becomes something to strike a light, something that can be used as, or fashioned into an axe or hammer. A thing, therefore, is not merely seen as it actually is, but also as a realm of possibilities for human usage. It is given a plurality of meanings, whose number increases constantly as our knowledge makes more progress. In the Stone Age the stone suddenly acquired an entirely new meaning for man and became something different.

Accordingly, at the root of all culture, insofar as it is a refashioning and reshaping of nature, we find the distance-from-things created by knowledge. Thus distance makes everything appear susceptive of new meaning. The same applies to all culture. It holds for immanent culture of the mind as much as for external civilization. Culture is always first seeing in the data of nature possibilities which can serve the development of man.

Interconnection Between Knowing and Making. Thus from their very beginning making and knowing are very intimately connected and make each other fruitful. In speaking about the nature of physical science, we saw a particularly striking example of this interconnection. For the birth of physical science depended upon the experience acquired in the prescientific handling of things, and its development remains dependent upon the scientific experiment. On the other hand, the technical possibilities which man has at his disposal thanks to physical science cover a range which is enormously more varied than would have been the case without physical science.

Nevertheless, this intimate connection between knowing and making in physical science does not justify the conclusion that all scientific knowledge is as much connected with making and doing as is suggested by the relationship of physical science and technology. For, first of all, not all science is physical science and, secondly, the very history of physical science shows several aspects which indicate that certain qualifications apply even to the interconnection between physical science and technology.

What history shows us is not at all a rectilinear evolution of physical science and technology as a bi-unity. On the contrary, in Greek thought the scientific consideration of nature detached itself from the sphere of experiential knowledge which was immediately connected with making and doing. The scientific consideration was seen as a goal in itself, and this situation remained unchanged even long after the era of modern physical science had started. In his reflection upon nature the Greek sought to attain a clear understanding of nature and of his own position in nature, but this search had no direct consequences for man's control over nature.

Accordingly, the influence which physical science has exercised upon the history of culture must not be sought exclusively in the technical applications of this science. Historically speaking, there is no justification for such a limitation, and this fact does not at all seem to be a mere coincidence. For there is every reason to claim that for the rise of physical science in the modern sense of the term decisive importance must be attached precisely to the fact that in its philosophical speculation and in the pursuit of pure mathematics the Greek mind remained aloof from immediate applicability.

It may be true that "thinking with the hands," as the unity of thinking and doing is sometimes very strikingly described, was what gave the first impetus to the pursuit of science. On the other hand, it appears to be true also that, in order to expand his practical science, man had first to arrive at a concept of himself in the pursuit of pure science.

Two Types of Influence: Theoretical and Practical. For this reason it is necessary to make a distinction between two influences of physical science: the one which it exercised as a part of theoretical knowledge upon man's vision of nature and of himself, and the other which passed through technology. Of course, the two are not independent of each other. As we have pointed out, the original withdrawal of physical science to a purely theoretical basis was of the greatest importance for its subsequent practical application. Likewise, the technical applicability of physical science, which was discovered later, induced man to reflect again upon himself.

This interdependence should not surprise us. If in man spirituality and materiality are united, then this unity must reveal itself also in the relationship between material and spiritual culture. On the other hand, the emphasis placed upon this unity does not mean that all distinction between the two must be erased. Just as it is meaningful to speak of spirit and matter with respect to man, so also it makes sense to distinguish between material and spiritual culture.

For this reason we will examine in the following chapters, first, the influence of physical science upon the culture of the spirit and, second, its influence upon material culture. In doing so, we will keep in mind that the two are most intimately connected.

The Autonomy of Physical Science Enables it to Influence the Culture of the Spirit. In speaking about the influence of physical science upon the culture of the mind, we should pay attention to a peculiar fact which reveals itself immediately. This fact is that physical science itself is a culture of the spirit, for it is an enrichment of the mind. As such, it does not merely exercise influence upon this culture, but makes a contribution to it. Speaking about the *influence* of physical science upon spiritual culture seems to suggest that this science itself is not yet a culture of the spirit.

Nevertheless, it is meaningful to speak of such an influence. For through its object physical science is directed to matter, and this orientation has the peculiar consequence, mentioned in the first chapter, of making physical science non-reflective. More than the other sciences physical science has an element of spontaneity. It is a certain way of doing things, based upon a view of nature and of man which, however, is not explicitly formulated. In a certain sense, therefore, it is true that physical science is a product of an intellectual culture rather than a constituent of this culture. For it was on the basis of the explicit insights into what nature is and what man's cognitive powers are, acquired by Greek thinking, that physical science was able to arise in the culture of the West and to go there through a period of development. This development, however, took at least in part an autonomous course of spontaneous development.

It is precisely this autonomous aspect in the development of physical science which makes it possible to speak of an *influence* of physical science on the general culture of the mind, in addition to the proper contribution which this science makes within the whole of man's spiritual culture. The crucial question here is to what extent physical science is really autonomous in its development and to what extent its evolution, especially insofar as it has repercussions in the general life of the spirit, is itself under the influence of factors that are extraneous to physical science. One has only to pay attention to the diversity of character and attitude of Greek, medieval, classical, and modern physical science, to be faced with the question of what causes these mutual differences. Are they to be attributed to factors that are foreign to physical science? Or should they be explained by the logic of its internal development? Or perhaps by both?

Before examining this question, which is crucial for the entire second part of this book, we must make certain that the above-mentioned differences are clear in our mind. For the very character of these differences will contain the first indications of their possible causes. We will limit ourselves, however, to a few major characteristics. Some of the differences between ancient, medieval, classical, and modern physical science will receive a more extensive treatment in the following chapters. At present we will have to be satisfied with a provisional confrontation of the most obvious differences.

2. *The Historical Forms of Physical Science*

Ancient Physical Science. Let us begin by briefly characterizing the physical science of antiquity, several aspects of which have already been mentioned in the preceding chapters. This ancient science was of a speculative nature. Its predominant characteristic was the intellectual consideration of the general nature possessed by the cosmos. Although observation, even accurate observation, was not neglected, the experiment in the modern sense of the term remained unknown. There was great confidence in the powers of the intellect, acting in conjunction with the senses, to understand nature, but no awareness that such an understanding would require man's active interference in nature.

Moreover, the Greeks did not primarily aim at the understanding of the detailed experiential datum in its particularity. They were more interested in the general character revealed by this datum, because of the perspective it opened upon the general nature of the cosmos. Concretely experienced changes were studied as instances of change in general and not as this or that particular kind of change. The aim was not so much to understand why this kind of change takes this course and that one goes a different path, why iron becomes rusty and gold does not, as to attain an insight into what change itself is. The purpose was to understand material nature as changeable and as unchangeable. Briefly put, the Greeks wanted to see nature as the immutable support of human existence and as to a certain extent susceptible to human manipulation.

Thus the study of nature was undertaken without any motive of self-interest. It was not guided by usefulness, by the desire to make nature more subservient to man. It was knowledge for the sake of knowledge, without any immediate practical consequences for man's relationship to nature. Nature remained what it was. What is changed by science is not *nature* but *man* who in considering nature learns to know himself. For the Greeks the highest manifestation of human activity was the purely spiritual activity of contemplation, the consideration of what is. By its very nature, science was *theory,* the knowing why things are as they are. Science, therefore, was primarily a formation of the *mind,* an enrichment of the spirit, and not a means to enrich the entire life of man in body as well as in soul.

Medieval Physical Science. Medieval thought saw that this Greek vision offered a gratefully accepted possibility of being christianized. It did not change the original Greek ideal, but gave it a new orientation and put it in the perspective of Revelation. The order of nature was seen as the order of creation, the given order was a gift of God, the existing laws of the cosmos were laws imposed by God upon nature. The philosophical analyses of the Greeks, especially of Plato and Aristotle, stood in the center of interest in the Middle Ages, because they gave an understanding of reality. Thus they led man to the kind of self-reflection which is the condition on which man can freely accept in faith the truth revealed by God.

To give an example, the study of the changeable character proper to the things of nature would naturally confirm the awareness of nature's contingency and consequently would increase man's openness to a correct understanding of creation. Since the order of nature could not explain itself because of its contingent character, its origin had to lie in God, who was also the source of man's rationality. Accordingly, great as it was, the interest which the medieval thinker had in the theory of nature remained subordinate to the contemplation of God and things divine. It was here that he saw the meaning of all theory, because here also was the meaning of human existence.

The self-evaluation of man in the study of nature made him aware of his own position in this nature as being placed in it by God with a task to be done. This idea gave strength to the consideration of nature as something man could work with. For man is not only a likeness of God insofar as his intellectual knowledge participates in God's knowledge, but he is also God's image in his creative activities. Provisionally, however, this creative activity was viewed in a general cultural sense rather than in a technical perspective. There was not yet a direct connection between scientific knowledge of nature and technical creativity.

Classical Physical Science. Such a connection was still lacking even in the seventeenth century. True, a new type of knowledge arose in this era and this knowledge contained the germ of a connection with technique. Nevertheless, the purpose remained preponderantly that of theoretical science, although the accent had been shifted from a general insight into the natural order to an understanding of even the smallest details of nature in the light of mathematically expressed general laws of nature. The aim was to understand every concrete datum in its specific nature. The natural order was no longer primarily an order pointing to God, but had become the foundation of our knowledge regarding the phenomena occurring around us.

It would be wrong to conclude that the thinkers of the seventeenth century were not deeply-convinced Christians and that the order of nature was not for them God's order. Nevertheless, their physical science received its own status, attuned to the explanation of phenomena in their empirical details. In the seventeenth century, moreover, not only theology and profane science went their own ways, but the distinction also between physical science and philosophy began to assume a more sharply defined character. This distinction manifested itself in the revival of Democritus' atomism. For this Greek philosopher himself the focal point was the desire to make change intelligible. By means of his atomic theory he wanted to reply to the question how change is possible, despite the fact that Parmenides, relying on rational grounds, had declared all change mere appearance. Thus Democritus was primarily concerned with making the order of nature intelligible, with explaining how mutability and immutability could go together.

The center of interest, however, of the seventeenth century atomists did not lie in the same area. They were less concerned with rethinking the atomistic theory than with using it to explain concrete changes in their specific details. Robert Boyle, for example, did not hesitate to base his theory on Democritus and Descartes, although there were enormous differences between these two thinkers from a philosophical point of view. Because classical mechanics had provided the seventeenth century with a universal means of physical explanation which they thought applicable to all phenomena in all their specific details, the philosophical perspective of change could gradually withdraw into the background. The focus of interest was no longer the question of how mutability in general could be made intelligible, but the way in which a particular concrete change had to be understood.

Expressing the matter in the terminology used in the first chapter, we could say: there was no longer interest in a general view of nature but in its concrete phenomena. For this reason this general view did not remain an explicit object of investigation but persisted merely as a presupposition of the method used by physical science. All attention was concentrated upon the use of this method, which had shown itself so successful.

Despite this predominantly positive character, seventeenth century science remained provisionally strongly theoretical. True, some thinkers, such as Descartes and Francis Bacon, foresaw in principle the applicability of science to life. However, even for them it was true that their imagination remained far below what later would become reality. Meanwhile there is no reason to be surprised by the fact that the seventeenth century had but little awareness of the intimate connection between physical science and technology. For the great successes of this century were in the realm of astronomy, and in this realm the practical consequences of theoretical deductions did not exactly strike the eye.

As a typical example we may refer here to the attitude of eighteenth century authors writing about space travel.[1] The sole purpose of their work was to show that, if man were to travel through cosmic space, he would really find everything exactly as contemporary astronomy described it. There was, however, no one who believed that man could make such travels, because imagination failed to show as yet what technology guided by physical science would be able to do. Thus the entire attitude of mind in which these space novels were written was more a manifestation of delight with man's knowledge of the universe than of the desire to take possession of this universe. Physical science remained oriented to knowledge for the sake of knowledge, although this orientation assumed a new form by aiming at understanding the natural order in its concrete manifestations by means of the general principles of mechanics. In this way the seventeenth century gave a new program to science.

Modern Physical Science. In the centuries that followed this program began to be implemented with ever-increasing success.

---

[1] M. Schwonke, *Vom Staatsroman zur Science Fiction,* Stuttgart, 1957, pp. 22 ff.

More and more phenomena came within the grasp of the mathe-matical-experimental method. At the same time, however, something else happened. Once a certain level of intellectual control had been reached, technical control followed. Man's technical control gradu-ally began to occupy a more prominent place and science began to adapt itself to technique. In this way physical science became a means and a condition of technology. The entire purpose of physical science thus seemed to have changed. Hitherto its aim had been knowledge for the sake of knowledge, knowledge for the sake of man's intellectual self-development. As soon, however, as physical science revealed its applicability, its meaning appeared in a new perspective and threw a new light also upon man himself in his pursuit of science.

Physical science became the means through which man under-takes to control nature, i.e., it was made subservient in a hitherto unknown way to the aspiration and desires of man. Nature is thus, as it were, humanized, permeated with human creations in which certain ideas are materialized. By virtue of man's technological control, together with his intellectual control, science is no longer merely an intellectual or internal self-development of man but also a corporeal, externally effective development. This new development of human potentialities breaks down the fixed relationship of man and world. Nature is no longer a reality that is given and taken *as it is,* but becomes a realm of possibilities. Man is seen as the discoverer of nature's possibilities, and in these possibilities he discovers also entirely new perspectives for himself. With a force greater than that of any political power whatsoever physical science transforms human society and the world.

Inevitably, these few remarks do no more than present a bare sketch of the various stages through which science has passed. Nevertheless the major lines of this sketch are correct. For this reason it may be used as a background for the question about the causes of this evolution of science. The different forms and ideals of science in the above-mentioned eras contain a first indication of the influences which have acted upon the course of physical science. For science is a human undertaking and, if in different periods different ideals guide this undertaking, the nature of these ideals suggests a first reply to the question of which causes determined the choice of a particular ideal and the corresponding type of knowledge.

3. *The Causes of the Difference in the Ideal of Science*

When the question is raised which causes determined the differences in the successive ideals of science, we find that the replies are far from unanimous. A great variety of factors are named to explain the evolution of physical science. Let us present a few.[2]

The Socio-Economic Structure. Sometimes an appeal is made to the social and economic structure of ancient society to explain the Greek ideal of science. This ideal was that of the upper classes, which did not have to work and could devote themselves without worry to contemplation. Any labor required to secure the necessities of life was done by slaves. There was no need of technology in the modern sense of the term, because the existing supply of labor was cheap and quite sufficient. In later societies, however, slavery was no longer tolerated because man had become aware of the value any human person has. As a result, technology and technologically oriented science became a vital necessity, and this situation led to its flourishing condition.

Hardly anyone will claim that this line of thinking is wholly devoid of truth. Even nowadays we observe that when there is a scarcity of cheap labor there is also an increasing urge to rationalize and automatize industry. This urge means that technology is presented with a new problem and has to search for new technical means. The resulting search stimulates physical research, as is exemplified by the huge research laboratories of large industries.

Nevertheless, this explanation can hardly be put forward as the fundamental reason for the development of physical science. In the past physical science, which is what has made technology possible, used to go its own ways. These ways were not determined by social necessities but by the urge to understand the phenomena of nature. We may refer here also to the fact, pointed out in preceding chapters, that ancient knowledge of technique, which was based only upon experience, rendered more service to physical science than it received in return.

Ideals of Life. The break between the medieval and the modern ideal of science is sometimes explained by appealing to the different ideals of life prevalent in these periods. The ideal of the Middle Ages

---

[2]For a brief survey, cf. Robert S. Cohen, "Alternative Interpretations of the History of Science," *The Scientific Monthly,* 1955, pp. 111 ff.

is supposed to have been more spiritualistic, and that of modern times more materialistic. Or also, since the Renaissance, man in his earthly existence has been placed more in the center of attention.

Let us abstract provisionally from the problem to what extent these characterizations of the periods in question are correct and limit ourselves to their explanatory value with respect to the different attitudes toward physical science. In this sense they appear to fall short of what is required. The shift after 1600 from religious contemplative knowledge to physical science which is so fruitful for man's earthly life may certainly not be ascribed to a sickening of the religious spirit or to a secularization of the Christian idea of redemption.

As we have pointed out previously, it was very difficult for positive physical science to make a start. The conditions enabling it to rise looked somewhat like a vicious circle, because theory had to be based upon experiment, and vice versa. For this reason it was *inevitable* that the Greek and medieval study of nature would be philosophical and religious. Medieval man simply did not have any possibility to dedicate himself fully to the intellectual delight of a positive physical science.

If the pursuit of physical science is a result of sinful materialism, one can hardly claim that medieval man was like the person, spoken of in the book of Wisdom, who did not sin, although he could have done it. Moreover, when in the thirteenth century Greek and Arabian sciences and skills became known in the West, it were precisely the medieval theologians Albert the Great and Thomas Aquinas, revered as Saints and Doctors by the Catholic Church, who created room for profane science in the Christian West. Thus it seems far from obvious that profane science would owe its origin to an attitude of mind which is centered exclusively upon man's earthly existence.

Later we will have to devote more attention to the problem of the cultural shift in intellectual attention which accompanied the rise of physical science. We will have to investigate also how this shift has to be evaluated with respect to man's integral existence and what causal connection it has with the rise of modern physical science. For the present, however, we may restrict ourselves to pointing out that we cannot be satisfied with excessive praise of the Middle Ages and their religious attitude of mind or with disparaging the subsequent centuries for orienting their science to the earth. At any rate, these two attitudes do not suffice to explain the evolution of physical science.

Other Explanations. Still other explanations of this evolution are sometimes given. Occasionally it is pointed out that the dominant role attributed to the concept of law in the physical science of later times is connected with certain political and legalistic evolutions and with the rise of a legalistic idea of God as the supreme Lawgiver. It is indeed a fact that the Greeks did not speak about the laws of *nature* but about ethical laws.[3]

However, we may ask, is this fact as important here as it is supposed to be? The idea of an order, of a necessary connection between the phenomena of nature was well-known to Greek thought. The presence of this idea is essentially far more important for the rise of physical science than the way in which the Greeks formulated the idea.

In this way the tendency of physical science to express its data in laws must have been the result of its own internal evolution through the increasing universality of its mathematico-experimental method rather than the effect of an external influence. Of course, external factors may have exercised influence, but this influence was not directed to the proper content of physical science and its evolution, save in an accidental fashion. For instance, military or industrial needs may stimulate the development of certain parts of physical science; the end-result of this development, however, is not determined by the need but by the problems which arise in the research of science. Likewise, the fact that scientists began to speak of *laws* and not of functions may have been the result of external influences, but this does not mean that this fact determined the content of the laws in question. Evidently, this content is far more important than the name given to it.

Philosophy. Accordingly, to understand the evolution of physical science, attention has to be paid first of all to internal influences. In principle, philosophy may be counted among these internal influences. For, as we have seen, for the Greeks as well as the Middle Ages, there was a very intimate connection between the study of nature and general philosophy. Moreover, it was Greek philosophy that presented the view of man and of nature from which physical science

---

[3]Cf. J. Clay, *Schets ener critische geschiedenis van het begrip natuurwet in de nieuwere wijsbegeerte,* Leiden, 1915, Ch. I.

in the modern sense could gradually develop. Finally, the first beginnings of physical science in the form of astronomy likewise occurred among the Greeks.

The question, then, which will demand our attention here in particular is to what extent the evolution of philosophy with its succession of different views of nature and of man must be held responsible for the divergent shapes and purposes of physical science in the various periods of its history. Or should we perhaps have to reverse this question? Is it perhaps the status of physical science in a given period which codetermines the philosophical views of that time?

4. *Philosophy as the Possible Cause*

A Complex Problem. Both of these views can be supported by an impressive array of arguments. With respect to the first view, we have already mentioned the unmistakable connection between the Greek attitude of mind and the origin of physical science in the realm of Greek civilization, which extended also to medieval western Europe. Secondly, one could point to the revival of Democritus in the seventeenth century, in which physical science assumed its definitive form. A plethora of seventeenth century scholars could be named who acknowledge that their thinking was rendered fruitful by Democritus' ideas. Classical physics, moreover, was indebted also to Descartes, the *philosopher*. Even in our time physicists, such as Heisenberg, Bohr, and de Broglie, continue to speak of the Cartesian ideal of science. True, they are of the opinion that the time has come to revise this ideal, but this opinion is less important than the acknowledgment that Descartes' ideas have continued to guide science even in the nineteenth century. Thus there is every reason to attribute a central position to philosophy in reply to the question about the causes which gave rise to the evolution of physical science.

Meanwhile, however, we should beware of being too quick in presenting a ready-made answer. For it is evident also that the influence of philosophy upon physical science has a counterpart in the influence of physical science upon philosophical thought. Let us quote an unequivocal example. It is impossible to understand the philosophy of Kant, which has exercised such a decisive influence upon modern thought, without the physical science of Newton. And as far as Descartes himself is concerned, we may legitimately ask whether his philosophy has really influenced his physical science or whether his philosophy is to be understood as a reflection upon the rise of mechanics.

The problem, therefore, is rather complex. We may add that the climate of our time is more suitable for thinking of the influence of physical science upon philosophy than for the reverse. About the first kind of influence there is an abundance of literature, while the second is hardly mentioned. This situation, of course, is not surprising, for the influences of physical science upon philosophy are more readily discernible than those of philosophy upon physical science. We are thinking here not only of the above-mentioned case of Kant but also of positivism and especially of the important place which nowadays is assigned to so-called "philosophy of the exact sciences" in the whole of philosophy. In this philosophy of the exact sciences the influence of physical science is present in the very starting point itself. This philosophy usually does not consider its task limited to reflection upon exact science, but endeavors also to arrive in this way at an exact philosophy.

It would be wrong, however, to refer only to these palpable examples. Certain contemporary philosophical trends, such as phenomenology and existentialism, are far removed from "scientific" philosophy. Nevertheless, even of them it is true that many philosophical themes which are in the center of their interest, e.g., that of historicity, would never have drawn so much attention if through the influence of physical science there had not been such a startling and continuing development in man's existence in the world.

An Irrefutable Fact. The question, therefore, of the influence exercised by philosophy upon physical science is very complex. There is, however, at least one irrefutable fact which can serve as a starting point for the reply—the fact that modern physical science drew its origin from the philosophical thinking of the Greeks. This fact is not subject to any doubt. The Greeks, and the Greeks alone, through their philosophy created the intellectual climate in which physical science could germinate and prosper.

As was pointed out in the first chapter, the Greeks possessed the principles of everything which now constitutes the permanent basis of physical science—namely, the knowledge that a science of nature is possible, the conviction that this science should have a mathematical structure, and the demand that it be founded upon empirical research. In the same chapter we raised the question why it had to take two thousand years—till after 1600—before physical science in the modern sense of the term did arise. The question remained largely unanswered but now we are in a position to supply a more complete reply, because the analysis of the character proper to physical science has supplied us with additional data. This reply will be useful also to summarize various casual remarks that have been made about the same question and thus throw light upon the problem from all sides.

The Delayed Rise of Physical Science. Let us begin with the following remark. The long delay in the rise of physical science, one could say, was due perhaps to a negative influence of philosophy upon this science. For the philosophical critique of Plato and Aristotle upon Democritus pushed his atomistic ideas, which were so fruitful for physical science, into the background. This critique concentrated attention upon a philosophical study of nature and of man which, despite its broad scope, could not lead to physical science because it was too contemplative.[4] If this view is true, if Greek philosophy after Democritus did exercise such a negative influence, one can understand why it had to take till long after the Middle Ages before physical science in the modern sense could flourish, for even during the Middle Ages in some respects at least science continued to breathe the same spirit as in ancient Greece.

Nevertheless, we do not think that the contemplative attitude of Greek and medieval thought is the true reason why it took two thousand years before the classical physical science of Galileo, Newton, and Descartes could execute the program of Democritus, Pythagoras, and Plato's *Timaeus*. For the execution of this program, which consisted in a mathematical description and explanation of cosmic phenomena, was undertaken by the Greeks themselves and continued from their time on practically without any real interruption.

The possibilities, however, of implementing the program were originally rather limited because of the empirical character of physical science, of which we have spoken extensively in Chapter II. Apart from a few minor areas, such as statics, only astronomy offered immediate possibilities. For with respect to astronomical phenomena the aspect that can be treated mathematically imposes itself so strikingly that it can be treated in isolation from other aspects. The perceivable magnitudes, i.e., the orbits described by stars and planets,

---

[4]This does not take away from the fact that Plato and Aristotle also made, as we have seen, important contributions to physical science. Nevertheless, the contemplative element predominated in their thinking.

can readily be connected with mathematical magnitudes.[5] For this reason Greek astronomy was immediately able to reach a high standard of perfection which later generations had merely to develop further. Copernicus' famous revolution, therefore, was far less important for astronomy itself than for philosophy and theology.

In the description of terrestrial motions, however, the Greeks experienced far more difficulties, because here the phenomena were rendered more complex by the friction of the air and other media. Thus Aristotle took the wrong track, as he had done also in chemistry with his theory of elements. Of course, it was not at all easy to find the correct approach in these realms. As we have pointed out repeatedly, the conditions on which empirical sciences, such as physics and chemistry, could arise contained something akin to a vicious circle. The correct view of the empirical data and—which is even more important—the fruitful experimental question depend upon solid theoretical insights. These insights, however, can be acquired only by means of empirical data. Thus the Greeks were unable to build an empirical science, because the necessary time was lacking. The required empirical data had to be known first and, through lack of theoretical guidance, these data could be acquired only in an extremely slow fashion.

Greek and Medieval Achievements in Exact Science. For this reason it is not surprising that all permanent achievements of the Greeks in the realm of exact science—we exclude here philosophy— lie in areas in which the rational structure of phenomena could be discovered without recourse to extensive empirical and experimental research. These phenomena extended to areas in which the relevant could be separated from the irrelevant by means of purely intellectual abstraction. This separation was possible in mathematics, logic, and astronomy.

It is easy to see, therefore, that the intellectual attention of the Greeks and of their scientific heirs, the Arabs and the medievals, had to be concentrated upon general philosophy and theology and, in addition, mathematics and astronomy, but could not extend to physical science. From a scientific viewpoint the object of physical science did not offer them anything, because nothing was visible there as yet, except philosophy of nature and a few fairly obvious but faulty and

---

[5]This explained also why the Greeks and the medievals considered astronomy a form of mathematics rather than a physical science. Cf. p. 56.

fruitless attempts to formulate some general physical theories. Detailed empirical knowledge of matter remained for centuries a question of techniques and practical experiential knowledge. Apart from the few privileged areas mentioned above, nothing else offered an opportunity to execute the program of physical science which was implicitly contained in Greek philosophy and for which the human mind was, in principle, sufficiently prepared. Moreover, the real foundation which gave rise to the privileged position of the few areas in question had a relatively narrow scope, because no science can go very far without the support of other sciences. Astronomy and statics had to do without the stimulus which in later centuries would be provided by other branches of physical science. We have to recall here only how, e.g., in the seventeenth century dynamics stimulated astronomy, and astronomy in its turn mathematics, how in our time chemistry stimulates biology. An isolated science is always exposed to impoverishment and degeneration. This rule applies also to philosophy. In the thirteenth century, for example, philosophy experienced a period of bloom, partly at least because of its confrontation with theological thought, then it gradually degenerated, to revive again in the seventeenth century under the stimulus of the new emancipated physical science.

The Importance of Philosophy for the Development of Physical Science. The new physical science itself was the result of an encounter between the Greek scientific attitude of mind and practical experiential knowledge. From the origin of pure science in Greece these two had walked on different paths, but in the seventeeth century they came together. Since the Middle Ages all kinds of technical skills, such as alchemy, medicine, architecture, and instrument making, had slowly gathered data about materials and processes until they had a sufficient quantity and variety of them to make it possible to attempt the formulation of theories based upon this experience. Thus it was the growth of technical knowledge which enabled man to break the vicious circle about which we have spoken above. Nevertheless, the break-through was a slow process, for the necessary experience could not accumulate in any quick fashion so long as it could not be guided by a theory that was attuned to this experience.

One has to think here only of the difference in growth of chemical knowledge before and after the beginning of the nineteenth century, i.e., before and after Lavoisier, Dalton and others had discovered the theoretical foundations of classical chemistry.   In Greek and medieval thought the only existing theory was of a philosophical nature.   Although this theory had an unsurpassed value with respect to a view of nature that makes science of nature possible, it itself could not be of any service in the work of research proper to physical science.   For a general philosophical theory of change has to abstract from the particular nature characterizing the various concrete changes. It does not say anything specific about the boiling of water, the rusting of iron, the rotting of wood, or the blackening of silver.   The understanding of these widely different changes demands specific theories or, if a general theory applies to them, it requires that this theory can be differentiated with respect to the various kinds of phenomena.

Accordingly, the philosophical theory has no *direct* importance for the development of physical science.   On the other hand, however, it would not be correct to minimize the influence of the philosophical theory.   For this theory makes man realize and keep in mind that it is possible to find a theoretical solution of the specialized problems which philosophy itself cannot solve.   The ideas that there is a fixed order of nature, that phenomena are interconnected, and that this order and this connection can be known by man are insights possessing an enormous general stimulating power in relation to the pursuit of science and skills.   The truth of this assertion manifests itself very clearly if we pay attention to what happened in the West when Greco-Arabian science and skills became known there around the year 1200.

According to Dijksterhuis,[6] this science was then a literary tradition rather than a really living science, but it found a favorable soil in the western world.   The most spectacular aspect of the medieval reaction to the "new" Greek and Arab science was at first the theological and philosophical reflection which it provoked.   This reflection led to the theological and philosophical *Summae* of Thomas Aquinas, in which the emphasis was placed, of course, upon the further development of the Greeks' fundamental ideas and upon placing them in the light of the Christian view of creation.

Although this kind of labor was not immediately of importance for physical science, it was directly connected with St. Thomas' view that alongside theology and metaphysics there was room for a physical

[6]"Renaissance en natuurwetenschap," *Mededelingen der Kon. Ned. Akademie* v. *Wetenschappen, afd. Letterkunde, Nieuwe Reeks,* Deel 19, no. 5, Amsterdam, 1956, p. 28.

science based upon sense experience[7] which had to be largely autonomous. This view was, of course, of the utmost importance for physical
science. Historically speaking, therefore, it is justified to say that the
revival of physical science began in the thirteenth century. The large
place which the theologians left open for profane science on the basis
of their theological and philosophical vision is not irrelevant to the
beginning of this revival, for it vigorously stimulated physical research.
Hand in hand with the theoretical assignment of a place to physical
science there was a lively pursuit of practical physical skills and an
intensive study of the new physical and technical works, as is proved
by the scientific heritage of St. Albert the Great, the Master of
Thomas Aquinas.

This intense attention to physical knowledge and technical skill
made the Middle Ages soon aware of the many obvious faults in
Aristotle' views of all kinds of physical and chemical questions. As
a result, many theories were formulated to explain a multitude of
physical details. Although these theories remained provisionally
within the framework of general philosophy and were expressed in
the current philosophical terminology, they are easily recognizable
as camouflaged physical theories. It is well-known, for instance, to
what extent the mechanical insights of the fourteenth century Parisian
nominalists prepared the classical mechanics of the sixteenth and
seventeenth centuries.[8] Likewise, the seventeenth century corpuscular
theories did not suddenly appear from nowhere, but had been prepared in the Middle Ages.

Sometimes the situation is presented as if the revival of Democritus' ideas in the seventeenth century constitutes the starting point
of the modern scientific atomic theory and, consequenly, also of
chemistry. If this presentation were true, it would offer a splendid
proof that a philosophical system can directly influence the development of physical science. As in the Middle Ages, one could say, the
predominance of Aristotle prevented the rise of physical science, so
the revival of Democritus' atomism made the emergence of science
possible. The two cases would graphically illustrate a negative and a
positive influence of philosophy upon physical science.

Historical truth, however, differs from this picture. During the
Middle Ages corpuscular theories—the *minima naturalia*—were de-

---

[7]*In Boethium de Trinitate,* q.6, a.2. See also the author's commentary on
this article in *The Philosophy of Nature,* 3rd impr., Pittsburgh, 1959, Ch. III.
    [8]Cf. E. J. Dijksterhuis, *Die Mechanisierung des Weltbildes,* Berlin 1954,
Ch. II, nos. 105 ff.

veloped within the various Aristotelian trends of thought. Even before there was any revival of atomism, these theories fulfilled with respect to the growing experiential knowledge of nature theoretical functions similar to those which atomism was to fulfill in the seventeenth century.[9] The existence, moreover, of these corpuscular theories in the preceding centuries explains also the astonishing fact that seventeenth century atomism was immediately considered to be of direct value for physical science. For this appreciation had been prepared during the preceding centuries.

Thus it is not surprising that the principal exponents of seventeenth century corpuscular thinking made use of a philosophical opportunism. Although they appealed to Democritus, either directly or through Gassendi, his contemporary exponent, they did not propose the purely philosophical theory of Democritus, but an atomism that could render services to their time. This kind of atomism admitted, it is true, atoms without qualities, but conceived them fused into "concretions" in such a way that qualitatively different smallest particles resulted. These particles were useful for the chemist who had to work with qualitatively different substances and saw no advantage in atoms without qualities. Thus Dalton's atoms were qualitatively different and specifically distinct for each element.

Philosophical Reflection and the Limited Applicability of the Physical Method. These few historical data suffice to make clear how complex the situation is which is touched by the question regarding the influence of philosophy upon physical science. There is an unmistakable general influence, exercised by Greek philosophy and its continuation in the West, upon the rise and the pursuit of physical science insofar as this philosophy produced the mental attitude which could lead to physical science. This attitude contained a certain view of nature and of man's cognitive possibilities which made physical science a meaningful undertaking and determined in principle what its method would be. However, this method could not immediately be applied in a successful way to all areas, but only to those in which mathematical insights could readily be connected with experientially acquired magnitudes, i.e., the area in which empirical knowledge did not have to be obtained through experimental preparation. This area, as has been mentioned before, was that of astronomy.

---

[9] Cf. the author's *From Atomos to Atom*, Pittsburgh, 1952, Chs. II and III.

The limited possibility of using the method of physical science which prevailed in Antiquity and the Middle Ages did not fail to have repercussions in philosophy itself and especially in the philosophy of science. If attention is paid to the forms of science that existed and were pursued in those times, one can understand the essential requirements which the Greeks and medievals demanded of science—namely, absolute certainty and insight into the "why" of things. These demands themselves in their turn exercised influence upon the actual pursuit of science. A single example may be given here to illustrate the points.

In the fourteenth century some thinkers were profoundly convinced that the measurements of physical phenomena could not have any immediate scientific value, because mathematical exactness and strictness are inevitably lost as soon as measurements are made.[10] Thus actual measurements could not contribute anything to science in the strict sense. For this reason scientific thinkers confined themselves to the sphere of theoretical geometry and mathematics, in which there was no need to perform measurements in the physical sense of the term. Thus we have here a clear case demonstrating, firstly, the influence which the general status of science during a particular period exercises upon philosophical reflection and, secondly, the repercussion of this reflection upon the pursuit of science. It would, indeed, have been surprising if the philosophical view of the value to be attached to the process of physical measurement had not influenced the slow start of a physical science which makes constant use of measuring and experimenting.

On the other hand, it would be wrong to attribute too much importance to this obstructing influence. Something else must have been much more important than this theoretical view of physical measurements which, moreover, was not as wrong as may seem, for it formulates the difference between mathematics and physical science. This second adverse factor was the fact that at first it proved very difficult to find a suitable starting point of measurements in the complexity of phenomena except, as has been mentioned before, in a few privileged areas, such as astronomy, statics and, of course, the various realms in which arithmetic and geometry could be immediately applied, e.g., surveying. This application, however, lay outside

---

[10]Cf. Anneliese Maier, "Die Anfänge des physikalischen Denkens im 14 Jahrhundert," *Philosophia Naturalis,* vol. I (1950), pp. 1-35.

the realm of science. All the philosophical theory did was subsequently justify the failure of measurements for scientific purposes by appealing to a principle which was correct in itself but ineptly applied. The history of the philosophy of nature is full of similar inept applications of true principles. (The same could be said about other realms of learning and science!)

The Most Important Event of the Seventeenth Century. In the light of these considerations we must conclude, therefore, that the most important event of the seventeenth century was *not* the fact that an entirely new kind of science arose under the influence of a different philosophy. What really happened was that the expansion of experience gathered in the preceding centuries reached a point at which it became possible to assign a universal scope to a kind of science which on a limited scale had existed since ancient times—namely, mathematico-physical science. In the seventeenth century the empirical data had gradually reached a status of great variety and abundance, thanks to the pursuit of many practical skills and thanks also to the rise of numerous more or less successful partial theories applicable to a multitude of particular phenomena. Thus the time had become ripe for a general theory of mechanics, embracing *all* phenomena of motion, whether celestial or terrestrial. Mechanics became a kind of general science and took the place of philosophy as the general framework in which all cosmic phenomena were viewed. In this sense it may be said that a new type of science came into existence.

In this way one can understand also why Democritus' atomism experienced a revival: it resulted from the success of mechanics and at the same time stimulated the new attitude. The success of mechanics seemed to confirm the views of Democritus and, reversely, these views provided the new science with the necessary desired support. For hitherto every scientific theory had always sought support in a general philosophical vision, to such an extent that this support was considered indispensable. The general conviction, inherited from the Greeks, continued to prevail that, in order to pursue science, one had to know what science is, not only implicitly but explicitly. Hitherto Aristotle had been the leading philosopher as well as the teacher *par excellence* in the concrete knowledge of nature. In the seventeenth century his place was taken by Democritus and Descartes, not in a few limited realms but in everything.

The contemporaries, however, of Descartes and Newton failed to notice that the new physical science was really a new type of general science. In their eyes it seemed that a faulty all-embracing system had merely been replaced by a new and better system. The old philosophy had been succeeded by a new one. The term "philosophy of nature," which for many years continued to indicate physical science, clearly bears witness to this situation.[11]

The idea that physical theories were of necessity intimately connected with a general system of philosophy explains also why the Middle Ages had not dropped Aristotle despite the fact that he was known to be wrong in many questions.[12] The various partial theories that existed could not be integrated into any other general framework. Such a frame was provided only by seventeenth century mechanics. It resulted quickly in a break with Aristotle. He was radically abandoned, and subsequently Democritus was appealed to as if the revival of his thinking had been the cause of the new science.[13]

Evidently, the substitution of Democritus and Descartes for Aristotle found its weightiest support in the *de facto* success of mechanics. This success was not limited to providing a better explanation of *known* phenomena. The initial success made guided experimentation possible, which led to an enormous increase in the data of experience, and this increase in its turn gave rise to the refinement of the theoretical views. In this way physical knowledge increased at a rapid rate, just as in the nineteenth century the discovery of the theoretical foundations of classical chemistry led to guided chemical experimentation and, consequently, to an almost unimaginable expansion of chemical knowledge.

The Interplay of Philosophy and Physical Science. Although the actual success of the scientific theories is the main motive force in the evolution of physical science, it is certainly not the only factor to which attention must be paid. Just as the initial lack of success of the mathematico-empirical method had its repercussions in the philo-

---

[11]The titles given to trail-blazing works of physical science provide some interesting examples: Newton's *Philosophiae naturalis principia mathematica;* Dalton's *A New System of Chemical Philosophy.* Even nowadays it is customary in the United States to indicate a doctorate in physical science as a Ph.D., a doctorate in philosophy.

[12]For a few interesting examples, see E. J. Dijksterhuis, *Die Mechanisierung des Weltbildes,* Ch. II, nos. 124, 127; Ch. III, no. 55; Ch. IV, no. 81.

[13]For a more detailed study of the seventeenth century, see the author's *The Philosophy of Nature,* Ch. II, sect. 5, pp. 70 ff.

sophical theory of the sciences, so also the success of the seventeenth century did not fail to influence this theory. It gave strength to the view that there is a universal mathematical order, as we pointed out in passing when we considered the causes leading to the revival of Democritus' atomism.

The rise of such a general conviction was not without importance. As Koyré points out correctly, the fact that the obtained results of mathematical measurements agreed with the mathematical formula only in a relatively imperfect fashion did not dismay Galileo's contemporaries, because they were *a priori* convinced that there had to be such a formula.[14] Anyone who is at home in philosophy and science will readily discern here the influence of Plato's *Timaeus*. It would be possible even to trace this influence historically. However, the fact that in the sixteenth century Plato's thought was given a new chance in the midst of a predominating Aristotelianism resulted from the new successes of mathematics. In this way there is a subtle interplay between general philosophical convictions and the progress of physical science. The widely divergent ways in which the fourteenth and the seventeenth centuries evaluated the inaccuracies of physical measurements provides a splendid example of this assertion.

It will not be devoid of interest to note here that the above-mentioned views about accurate measurability still retain all their actual importance. One has only to read Bohr and Einstein to become convinced of this point.[15] Einstein's confidence that quantum mechanics will ultimately be perfected in such a way that the outcome of individual measurement can again be accurately predicted reminds us very strongly of the optimism prevalent in seventeenth century thought; on the other hand, Bohr's denial of this possibility makes us think of the scepticism current in the fourteenth century, which likewise was based upon the inevitable inaccuracy of measurements.

Of course, the twentieth century discussion does not move on the same level as that of former ages, but, we may ask, are the basic leading thoughts behind it really very different? Does not the modern discussion ultimately imply the same age-old problem—a prob-

[14]A. Koyré, "Influence of Philosophic Trends on the Formulation of Scientific Theories," *Scientific Monthly*, 1955, pp. 107 ff.

[15]Niels Bohr, "On the Notions of Causality and Complementarity," and Albert Einstein, "Quanten-Mechanik und Wirklichkeit," *Dialectica*, vol. 2 (1948), pp. 312-325. More extensively the discussion is carried on in *Albert Einstein, Philosopher-Scientist*, New York, 2nd ed., 1951.

lem which even in Greek antiquity made Plato and Aristotle both go their separate ways and which is an inseparable companion of the entire history of science? We mean the fact that man experiences, on the one hand, a possibility of obtaining a rational insight into the realm of phenomena and, on the other, realizes that these phenomena escape his grasp, because he is ultimately dependent on mere sensitively experienced facts.

The Greater Independence of Modern Physical Science. An additional remark must be made with respect to the parallel between the modern discussion in physical science and that of former times. In the fourteenth century a philosophical view was still capable of delaying the evolution of physical science, and in the sixteenth century another view could still accelerate this evolution, but it is much less probable that in our days philosophy could exercise a delaying or accelerating influence. For at present physical science has found its methodic equilibrium so accurately that its independence from the philosophical principles connected with this method is now much more firmly established than it was in former times.

For instance, the nineteenth century positivistic critique upon the use of the concept "atom" as being a kind of metaphysical intrusion hardly exercised any influence upon physical science. Likewise, the mechanistic background of classical physical science, which was inherited from the seventeenth century revival of Greek atomism, did not constitute a road block preventing the progress of physical science when this mechanism had to be abandoned in the beginning of the present century. For this reason there appears to be no ground for Einstein's concern that the definitive acceptance of the statistical interpretation of quantum mechanics contains a danger for the future development of physical science. No matter how valuable philosophical reflection upon physical science may be in itself, this science is now urged on far more by the problems arising in its own bosom than by philosophy.

Similar remarks could be made with respect to the various philosophical controversies in biological matters as, for instance, the dispute between mechanism and vitalism about which we spoke in Chapter VIII. In biology also physical research runs its course as dictated by the actual state of affairs, without being disturbed by the passing and temporary predominance of more vitalistic or more mechanistic trends of thought.

The Continuing Role of Philosophy. Must we conclude, therefore, that the role of philosophy has come to an end and that, since physical science has been fully established as a science, there can no longer be any question of an influence of philosophy upon physics? If this conclusion were correct, philosophy could be evaluated only as the incipient stage of science, as a first vague attempt to arrive at an all-embracing science which has gradually to give way for solid and genuine science. If any value could still be attributed to philosophy in our time, it would be in a new realm of learning where it could perform some exploratory and pioneering services, but ultimately it would be doomed to disappear entirely.

Or again, philosophy could be appreciated as a synthesis of the results acquired by the various sciences. Whatever view be taken, there could be no question of any decisive influence of philosophy upon the course of physical science. At most, one could speak of a stimulating influence, and even then philosophy would be able to exercise its exploratory or synthetizing function in a meaningful way only if it remained dependent upon physical science.

Anyone who would limit himself to drawing such conclusions from the preceding considerations would be badly mistaken. True, once established, science progresses more under its own impulse than through being stimulated by philosophy. Such stimulations are and remain of secondary importance. This, however, does not mean that there is no longer any philosophical influence, for, we must ask, what exactly is meant by this impulse of physical science itself? The reply can only be that the inner impulse is the original vision of the nature proper to man's being, of the cognitive and creative powers which characterize man, and the view of material nature that is implied in this vision. It is to Greek and medieval philosophy that we owe the explicitation of these views. They have been integrated into the scientific methods which gradually were developed, and it is on this original investment that physical science lives. Here, then, we find the unique and essential contribution which philosophy has made to physical science.

This contribution manifested itself most clearly in the initial phase of physical science, because then it had to work explicitly. It remained, however, implicitly present in the whole subsequent development of this science, because this development was determined by the perspectives which gradually were opened through the consistent application of the scientific method. The influence, therefore, of philosophy upon physical science is an intrinsic influence. Nevertheless, when we consider how this influence works we must conclude that the evolution of physical science reveals a certain autonomy. It is guided not from without but from within. This conclusion has a very important bearing upon the problems which occupy our attention in this book.

5. *Physical Science as an Autonomous Factor in Culture*

Keeping in mind the results obtained by our investigation of the driving forces controlling the evolution of physical science, we may now return to the question whether physical science is capable of exercising influence upon culture. Is not this science itself simply a part of this culture? Without having to give a negative reply to the last question, we must observe that physical science, once it had begun to run its course, revealed such inner dynamism that it could autonomously influence subsequent culture, not only material culture but also the culture of the mind. These two, of course, also exercised influence upon physical science, but with respect to the speed of its development rather than its character and scope.

The different scientific ideals of ancient, medieval, modern, and contemporary physical science, then, are determined not so much from without as by the internal possibilities revealing themselves within the perspective of physical science itself. It is from this perspective that these possibilities have exercised great influence upon the thinking, life, and society of man.

These influences need to be examined more in detail. We may begin with the influence which the evolution of science has exercised upon the way man considers nature, upon the picture he forms of the world around him and of his own place in this world. For it should be obvious that, if physical science has exercised any influence at all upon the thinking of man, this influence must have been directed in a very special way to man's concept of nature and to his world view.

CHAPTER NINE

CHANGES IN THE CONCEPTION OF NATURE AND IN THE WORLD VIEW

1. *The Concepts "Nature" and "World View"*

Various Meanings of the Term "Nature." "Nature" and "world" are concepts which are so immediately attached to our primary experience that it is difficult to define them clearly. They have, moreover, a strongly analogous character. The term "nature" has a complete spectrum of meanings, which manifest themselves most clearly when we pay attention to the various opposite concepts with which it can be connected. Nature, for instance, is opposed to culture, and in this way it expresses what things are before man has done something with them or to them. Although nature here is conceptually defined and set aside from culture in a very clear fashion, nevertheless it remains possible to speak of a "natural culture" in opposition to an "unnatural culture." The former is a culture which, as it were, flows from nature or fuses with it, while the latter does violence to original nature. The fact that we may meaningfully speak of natural and unnatural culture indicates how flexible the meaning of "nature" is. The expression "natural culture" points to another contrast than that between nature and culture—namely, the contrast which distinguishes between "in harmony with nature" and "not in harmony with it."

Sometimes also nature is opposed to mind or spirit; for instance, when we distinguish the sciences of nature from the sciences of man's spiritual activities. However, even this distinction does not prevent us from speaking of the nature of the mind. The term "nature," moreover, is used to indicate the contrast between the natural and the supernatural, but here also there are, as we will see, interesting shifts of meaning.

In subsequent chapters, in which we will reflect upon the character of technology, we will have an opportunity to delve deeper into the concept of nature and to analyze the different meanings attached to this term. At present we will restrict ourselves to indicating the common root of these meanings. Briefly put, in all its meanings "nature" refers to that which in one way or another is independent of

201

man's activity. The various meanings, moreover, depend not only upon the many contrasts in which the term occurs. There are also clear historical shifts of meaning. This is not surprising, because the concept is intimately connected with man's spontaneous view and experience of nature, which in their turn depend on the cultural situation of man. As van Peursen expresses it, nature is really a product of culture.[1]

The Concept "World View." The purpose of this chapter is to throw some light upon these historical shifts of meaning and more especially to examine whether physical science has exercised any influence upon these modifications. While examining the shifts of meanings attached to the terms "nature" and the changing ways in which man views and experiences nature, we will devote our attention also to the meaning of "world view." This term likewise reveals a spectrum of meanings. They arise not so much from external contrasts—for "world" indicates a totality—as from internal oppositions, i.e., from the ways in which man views the world. For the concept "world view" refers, on the one hand, to the world as the totality of everything which man somehow encounters around himself and, on the other, to man himself who makes this world his own by forming a picture of it. Thus the concept indicates the dialectic tension between passively registering all that is encountered in the world and actively unifying all these things. Accordingly, many different world views are possible depending on the attitude of mind with which man considers his world. On the elementary level of everyday life we are familiar with the simultaneous existence of many world views, for different people experience "the same reality" in wholly different fashions. A forest ranger, for instance, does not view a reservation in the same way as an automobilist, and a fire watcher does not look at it in the same way as a hiker.

The question which will occupy us here especially is whether or not it may be said that the world view of physical science is not a world view alongside many other such views but *the* world view *par excellence,* the only critically justified and eminently objective view of the world and consequently also the only justifiable way of viewing nature. We say the "only justifiable view of nature," for any world view necessarily contains some kind of a view of

---

[1]C. A. van Peursen, "Natuur en mens wijsgerig bezien," *Natuur en Mens,* Groningen, 1957, p. 9.

nature, because nature as the component part of the world which is independent of man constitutes, as it were, the foundation of man's world view.

The modifications in the view of nature and in the world picture will be illustrated by an investigation of the same periods which we distinguished in the preceding chapter—namely, antiquity, the Middle Ages, the modern period, and the contemporary period, which Guardini very appropriately calls *"das Ende der Neuzeit,"* "the end of the modern period." Evidently, such an investigation has to make use of rather schematic characterizations and therefore runs the risk of arbitrarily imposing certain patterns upon these periods. Nevertheless, the investigation has to be made, although we should keep in mind that the value to be attributed to its results may not be made absolute in any way but should remain relative.

2. *The Ancient View of Nature*

The Egyptian World View. In nearly all ancient civilizations the concept of nature, of cosmos, was much broader than ours. It meant the totality of everything and included man, because man and everything human was viewed more or less as a passive part of the cosmos. There was hardly question as yet of any clear opposition between man and nature. These assertions find their confirmation, e.g., in the fragments of the Isis religion, which originated in Egypt and spread from there to many parts of the ancient world.[2] It is interesting to see how in the preserved texts the ordering influence of the divinity is described in practically the same way with respect to the order of nature and with regard to human affairs.

A first text says: "I have separated the earth from heaven. . . . I have assigned paths to the stars. . . . I have prescribed the road of the sun and the moon." All this refers to what we would call the order of nature. Alongside these, however, we find also other texts: "I have given power to right. . . . I have ordered that parents be loved by their children. . . . I have brought man and woman together. . . . I have made women accept the love of men." Although these texts refer to the ethical order and not to that of the cosmos, they could still be included in the ordering of nature because they regulate something about human nature as it is.

---

[2]Cf. Th.P. van Baaren, "Wereldschepping en wereldbeeld in het oude Oosten," *Veranderend Wereldbeeld,* Groningen, 1959.

There are, however, also statements concerning the cultural order. For instance, "I have instituted wedding contracts for women. . . . I have invented navigation. . . . I am the one who first discovered the use of grain for human nutrition." As van Baaren summarizes the matter, "In the ancient East the cosmic and the ethical order were not yet or hardly distinguished, and culture itself remained an organic part of the one great ordered totality."[3] In the oriental view the realm of nature, the moral realm of interhuman relationships, and the realm of culture with everything implied by it were inseparably united; an infringement of the order in any of these realms led inevitably to disasters in the other realms.[4]

Accordingly, the whole of society and the whole of nature were seen as a single fixed order within which human life runs its course. It was an order in which even the smallest details were naturally determined. "Naturally determined" contained the connotation of "determined by the divinity." The natural order possessed at the same time a religious sacredness. It contained not only man's possibilities and limitations, but also his duties and his rights.

The Greek World View. The ancient Greek world view closely followed that of the Near East. True, in Greek philosophy man became conscious of his ability to penetrate into the world order through his reflection and thus to discover its principles and laws. On the other hand, however, in the Greek view, man could not make interference in the order of nature result from his thinking. As we have seen in the preceding chapter, strictly speaking, the Greeks were right in this respect, for their scientific achievements had still to remain limited to the realm of typically theoretical sciences. Nevertheless, there was a beginning of physical science, which later would show its true character, i.e., its intimate relationship with technology. For nature was no longer viewed as a cosmos governed by the whims of gods, as was the case in Greek mythology, but as a cosmos ruled by rational principles.

The substitution of a rational order for a mythological rule, however, did not mean at all that all religious ideas were eliminated. Belief in myths was, of course, undermined, but the same may not be said of religious ideas in general. Rather the opposite was the case. The clear realization that the cosmos constituted a single order to

[3] *Op. cit.,* p. 16.
[4] *Op. cit.,* p. 17.

which man himself also belonged strengthened the awareness of a bond with something transcending individual man as well as human society. The divine, as the primordial element of the world, manifested itself in the beautiful order of the cosmos. In this way the natural and the supernatural were practically the same as far as the Greeks were concerned.

The fact that the Greeks viewed the natural order as an orderly cosmos did not supply any answer to the question of how exactly this order was arranged. There was not even any agreement about the question whether this cosmos was changeable or immutable, as appears from the views taken by Parmenides and Heraclitus. It is interesting also to see that several Greek thinkers manifested the first rudiments of evolutionistic thought.[5] This evolution, however, was always one in which man did not play a role. For man, nature was an order which he could theoretically contemplate and study, but not influence. As Guardini expresses it, "There existed a desire, which was deeply rooted in the character of antiquity, to dwell in what had been established."[6] Man had to remain within the order assigned to him.

To finish this brief sketch of the ancient view of nature, we may add a few words about the Greek world view in the stricter sense of the term—the idea which Greek science and especially astronomy had formed of the cosmos. Properly speaking, there is even less justification for using the term "world view" in the singular than there exists for the singular use of "view of nature." What a difference there is, for instance, between the world view of Aristotle and that of Democritus. Interesting, for example, is the fact that for Aristotle every thing had its own nature, while for Democritus the concept "nature" referred rather to something common to all things because apparently different natures, such as water and gold, were based merely upon a different configuration of essentially the same component atoms.

In other respects we may limit ourselves here to briefly recalling Aristotle's world view, because it was this view which made the most profound impression upon subsequent thought.[7] Aristotle conceived the earth as consisting of the element earth and as placed in the center

---

[5]Cf. W. J. W. Koster, "Het wereldbeeld in de Grieks Romeinse oudheid," *Veranderend Wereldbeeld,* Groningen, 1959, p. 26.

[6]R. Guardini, *Das Ende der Neuzeit,* Würzburg, 1950, p. 13.

[7]For other Greek world views, cf. Koster, *op. cit.*

of the cosmos. The earth was supposed to be surrounded by the sphere of the element water, about which were the spheres of air and fire. Things consisting mostly of earth, i.e., solids, tended to move toward the center of the earth, because this center was their "natural place." They were "heavy." Fire and air, however, were "light," because their "natural place" lay above the earth; hence they moved upward. The sphere of celestial bodies lay beyond the spheres of terrestrial elements. These bodies were supposed to be of an entirely different nature from terrestrial bodies. Their matter was incorruptible, immutable, and subject only to endless perfect local movement, i.e., to circular motion.

3. *The Medieval View of Nature*

Because in the Middle Ages physical science scarcely rose above that of the Greeks, it should not surprise us that the medieval world view and conception of nature were in many respects little different from those of the Greeks. There was, however, one very important difference. The world was seen as a creation of the transcendent and sovereign God upon whom this world was wholly dependent, while He Himself was not in any way dependent upon the world. He had placed this world at the disposal of man, whom He had created to His image and likeness. Thus man was assigned a position with respect to nature which implied much more freedom than was allotted to him in previous world views. Man's greatness, however, was seen primarily in his capacity to know his Creator and to serve Him freely, to serve Him especially in spirit and truth. For this reason medieval man paid attention to the world only insofar as this world spoke to him of God. It is typical, for instance, that the year's cycle of seasons was integrated into the liturgical cycle: thus earthly reality was made a symbol of supernatural reality without, however, being identified with it, as had happened usually in ancient world views.

Culture also, as produced by man, expressed in its own way the orientation of life proper to medieval man. Culture was above all the service of God. It concentrated upon divine worship. A sign of this attitude is the place which the church edifice occupied. It was not only the center of the medieval city, but also the focal point of all artistic expression. Art was religious art. The lofty steeples of the church towers gave an external expression to the inner orientation of medieval man: they pointed to God's dwelling place in Heaven, which was also the future abode of man for whom the earth did not

constitute a permanent home. Thus the way in which medieval man
built his world reflected his world view. With respect to science also,
as we have seen in the preceding chapter, it was true that it primarily
pointed to God. The science *par excellence* was theology, in which
man reflected upon his place before His Creator and Redeemer in the
light of the truth revealed by God Himself. Philosophy was the
handmaid of theology.

Although in this way the light in which the world and the order
of nature were viewed was different, the world itself and the natural
order remained the same as that of the Greeks. This statement is true
not only of the world view in the narrow sense, as a geocentric universe, but also and especially of the givenness of the natural order:
man had to accept it, precisely because the Creator had placed it at
his disposal. It must be added, however, that the Christian idea of
charity, which urged medieval man to care really for his neighbor,
contained a powerful appeal to him to work given nature in such a
way that this care would really be effective. For this reason the
predominantly spiritual orientation of life in the Middle Ages did
not at all prevent the extensive pursuit of all kinds of sciences and
skills. As we have seen in the preceding chapter, this factor was
extremely important for the rise of seventeenth century science.

4. *The World View of More Modern Times*

The rise of physical science in the sixteenth and seventeenth
centuries caused the collapse of the familiar Greek and medieval world
view. At first, this collapse extended only to the world view in the
narrow sense, but through a combination of causes the world view
in the broad sense also shared the same fate.

The Collapse of the World View in the Strict Sense. From a
general scientific viewpoint the most important factor was that the
mechanics of celestial bodies revealed itself applicable also to earthly
bodies. Thus there were not two material natures—one "sublunary"
and the other "celestial"—but only one. Next, it became evident that
the sun did not revolve around the earth but just the opposite. This
was a terrible blow, for it caused the collapse of the trusted old
world view. The apparently stable cosmos, built protectively around
the earth, the abode of man, was exposed as fiction. The famous
Galileo dispute was certainly not only concerned with the question
whether the earth or the sun was the center of the solar system—a

question which is not so very important after all from the viewpoint of pure physical science. Likewise, its primary importance did not lie in a conflict between the new science and the expressions used in Scripture. The crucial issue overriding everything else was the place of man in the cosmos.

From being the king of the earth, in the heart of a universe created for his sake, man became the inhabitant of just another planet, somewhere in cosmic space, which through an accidental combination of cosmic forces had been rendered suitable as the abode of living beings. Man lost his trusted "natural place," just as the elements of the old world picture had lost theirs. The shock was rendered worse by the fact that, as we will see more in detail later, the theologians of the seventeenth century were unable to cope with the situation. They fell short of the stature of their thirteenth century predecessors who had successfully faced the crisis caused by the spread of Greco-Arab science.

The World View in the Broader Sense. In this way the new era saw a break arise between faith and science. This breach had far-reaching effects for the entire world view, for it gave the world view of physics an opportunity to become *the* world view, the only critically justified and eminently objective view of the world, as classical physical science fondly believed.

To the naive earthly spectator it seemed that the sun rose every morning and set every night. But the seventeenth century astronomer knew better: the sun did not orbit, but the earth itself turned round its axis. A chunk of gold seemed perfectly homogeneous, but in reality it consisted of innumerable small particles. The world view of physics presented objective reality as it was in itself. All other world views were subjective considerations, dependent upon a limited standpoint, in the literal as well as the figurative sense of the term. Of course, classical physics realized that its standpoint was still incomplete, but this incompleteness was merely a matter of details. The broad lines had been firmly established.[8] Thus the

----

[8]As far as the nineteenth century is concerned, this self-assuredness reveals itself very strikingly in a story told by Max Planck during an address delivered in 1924 at the University of Munich, where fifty years before he had embarked upon his scientific career. "When I began to study physics, I went for advice about the conditions and prospects of my studies to my esteemed teacher Philip von Jolly. He portrayed physics to me as a highly developed, almost wholly mature science, which in a sense had been crowned by the discovery of the principle of the conservation of energy and therefore should soon assume its final stable form. Of course, here and there in a corner there could perhaps still

scientific world view did not tolerate any other world view, whether religious or philosophical. All other world views were supposed to have risen from earlier primitive phases of human thought and to belong to the same category as the primitive world picture of daily life in which the sun rises and sets every day.

Kantian Critique. For the sake of completeness it should be mentioned that eighteenth century philosophical reflection, as it took shape in Kant's thought, placed great emphasis upon the subjective character proper even to the world view of physical science, because not even this view could portray reality as it was in itself. However, Kant's critique did not greatly impress his contemporary scientists. First of all, this critique did not throw any doubt upon the uniqueness of the world view presented by physical science. For this view was and remained the only objective world picture, because it had to be valid for *all* human beings by virtue of the cognitive structure of man. Kant's critique did not prevent objectivity but made objectivity possible. Secondly, physical science had already learned to go its own way and no longer worried about philosophical considerations. In the seventeenth century it had still sought support in Descartes and Democritus, but it had soon discovered the power inherent in its own method and was determined not to seek nourishment anywhere else.

Consequences for the Concept of Nature. It was inevitable that these radical changes in the scientific world view would have equally radical consequences for the concept of nature and man's view of nature. The degradation of the "natural" world view was bound to make a profound impression. Nature no longer was what revealed itself immediately but something which manifested itself only in and through science. To express it differently, nature began to lose its

---

be a speck of dust or a bubble that remained to be explored and assigned its proper place. The system as a whole, however, was rather firmly established, and theoretical physics clearly approached the same degree of perfection which geometry had possessed for several centuries already." *Wege der physikalischen Erkenntnis,* Leipzig, 1934, p. 128: "Als ich meine physikalischen Studien begann und bei meinen ehrwürdigen Lehrer Philipp v. Jolly wegen der Bedingungen und Aussichten meines Studium mir Rat erholte, schilderte mir dieser die Physik als eine hochentwickelte, nahezu voll ausgereifte Wissenschaft, die nunmehr, nachdem ihr durch die Entdeckung des Prinzips der Erhaltung der Energie gewissermassen die Krone aufgesetzt sei, wohl bald ihre endgültige stabile form angenommen haben würde. Wohl gäbe es vielleicht in einen oder dem anderen Winkel noch ein Stäubchen oder ein Bläschen zu prüfen und einzuordnen, aber das System als Ganzes stehe ziemlich gesichert da, und die theoretische Physik nähere sich merklich demjenigen Grade der Vollendung, wie ihn etwa die Geometry schon seit Jahrhunderten besitze."

formed character and stature to become something elementary which is subject to laws and capable of being given form in a multitude of ways. It became the sum-total of elementary forces and materials. True, nature remained something primordially given, but no longer something that was originally formed: it was now that which can be formed and reorganized in many fashions by virtue of elementary laws. On the other hand, as the primordially given, nature retained its normative meaning.

It was perhaps precisely the conflict of faith and science which strengthened the meaning of nature as the divinely mysterious, so that in this respect we find again a return to Greek thought. True, nature became predictable in its concrete forms of appearance but, at first it did not yet manifest itself as subject to control. Provisionally physical science remained still speculative, a fact which was connected also with its origin from astronomy. Despite man's familiarity with nature because of its knowability, nature continued at first to impose itself in its totality as something which man was capable of considering and investigating but unable to change. If these points are kept in mind, one can readily agree with Guardini when he says that the concept of nature proper to the new era was at the same time a concept of value. Nature constituted the norm applying to all of man's knowledge and creativity. The natural was the right, the healthy and the perfect. Nature expressed "therefore something ultimate, beyond which one could not possibly go."[9] Whatever could be deduced from nature was fully explained, whatever could be based upon nature had found its justification. Nature had become the God-nature.

Human Subjectivity. While it was true that man continued to see nature as his norm—for many it constituted perhaps the only norm—on the other hand, man was also more than ever convinced of the value of his reason, of his power to penetrate into the secrets of nature. The era considered here was the time also in which the meaning of subjectivity was realized more clearly than ever before. According as nature revealed itself more as determined and predictable, the distinction between man and nature manifested itself more clearly and in a new fashion. Man realized that he belonged to nature but at the same time it was man who knew nature. The result was a peculiar divorce in the philosophy of the modern era. On the one hand, it terminated in absolute determinism, in which man is simply reduced to being a

---

[9]". . . etwas Letztes aus, hinter das zurückgreifen nicht möglich ist." *Das Ende der Neuzeit,* Würzburg, 1950, p. 46.

part of nature. On the other, however, we find a very strong emphasis upon the subjectivity and irreducibility of the human mind. The awareness of man's dual character was very sharp in Descartes. As is so often the case in history, a single thinker here not only gave expression to the direction which the evolution of thought would take but also contributed mightily to this evolution. According to Descartes, man is both autonomous spirit and matter, two orders of being which, in his view, were contradictorily opposed. The whole history of the new era was destined to remain in the grip of Descartes conception of man.

The Struggle of Faith and Science. It would not be correct, of course, to attribute the dualistic view of man which prevailed in the seventeenth century solely to the evolution of physical science, even though it is true that physical science had something to do with this view because of the influence it exercised upon the conception of nature. As a general rule, in speaking about the influence of physical science it is always necessary to distinguish between its direct and indirect influence. The evolution of physical science in the seventeenth century was bound to administer a direct shock to the old world view as well as to the conception of nature as the fixed order of things. But it is a totally different question whether, for instance, the struggle between faith and science, as it *de facto* did prevail in the new era, had to be a direct consequence of the rising new physical science. It is certain that a host of other factors were at work and that the failure of seventeenth century theology to view the new situation in the proper perspective was one of the most important of these factors. Another important role was played by the grim religious wars of the century and by the way in which these wars were conducted. For they discredited the Christian Church in its concrete appearance. Thus many were led to the conclusion that only a natural religion, based upon the rational investigation of nature, could solve the conflict.

All this was bound to contribute to the fact that God's sovereignty as an explanation of the phenomena of nature was pushed more and more into the background. For many every new explanation of a natural phenomenon meant that this phenomenon was now withdrawn from God's omnipotence. Lightning was no longer the punishing arm of God, but an electric discharge, against which a lightning rod offered a much more efficacious protection than did holy water. It was especially in the eighteenth century that rationalism began to present itself deliberately as a counter-religion and to display an enormous activity of propaganda, appealing all the time to the success of reason in physical science. Reason was considered to be autonomous, it was no longer a gift of God, but a property of man. Culture, as a product of man, likewise received a new character. It was no longer, as in the Middle Ages, service of God, but became service of man. It is here that we find foreshadowed the meaning which technology was to assume later. This meaning was implicitly present in the rationalism of the seventeenth century.[10]

There was no lack, of course, of counter-currents which were aware of the fact that reason had only limited possibilities. Empiricism especially keenly realized the empirical content of physical science and set out to undermine the unlimited trust in reason. However, what Hume offered as a substitute was merely a kind of scepticism, which affected Christian faith just as adversely as rationalism itself. In the eighteenth century struggle between faith and reason rationalism and empiricism were allies rather than enemies.

The Struggle of Empiricism and Rationalism and the Influence of Physical Science on Culture. Viewed in its entirety, this struggle throws a clear light upon the question of the influence which physical science exercised upon the events of the seventeenth and eighteenth centuries. The new physical science owed its origin to an interplay of mathematical rationality and refined experience. Hence both rationalism and empiricism could appeal to physical science, albeit only through a one-sided interpretation of this science. Surprisingly enough, it was precisely the rationalism of Descartes, which was not exactly fortunate in its scientific explanations,[11] that made the greatest impression and began to dominate the field. This fact cannot be explained solely by the influence of physical science. Therefore, other factors must have contributed to it. Apparently the seventeenth century climate of juvenile enthusiasm was far less open to empiricistic scepticism than to rationalistic optimism. A striking phenomenon, moreover, is the difference between the development of affairs in

---

[10]"A rationalistic trend began to make it its task to consider human reason no longer in its divine origin but in its effective activity." Emile Bréhier, *Histoire de la philosophie*, vol. 2, Paris, 1947, p. 19: "Un rationalisme commence qui prend pour tâche de considérer la raison humaine non pas dans son origine divine, mais dans son activité effective."

[11]Comparing Descartes with Galileo, W. Whewell says: "Of the mechanical truths which were easily attainable in the beginning of the seventeenth century, Galileo took hold of as many and Descartes of as few, as was well possible for a man of genius." *History of the Inductive Sciences*, vol. 2, London, 2nd ed., 1847, p. 52.

England and on the continent. In England the empiricistic tradition managed to retain the upperhand. Accordingly, although the development of physical science undoubtedly exercised influence upon the rise of rationalism and empiricism, it did not necessarily have to lead to either of these two trends. The same may be said with respect to the struggle between faith and reason.

Although it is not easy to determine which influence exercised by the evolution of physical science upon the cultural life of the seventeenth and eighteenth centuries was direct and which merely indirect, it is certain that its influence was *de facto* enormous. It reveals itself clearly also in the way in which Kant sought to solve the opposition between empiricism and rationalism. He limited the power of reason to the realm of physical science where it brings order into the data of experience and imposes itself in spite of its subjectivity. But he eliminated reason as the source of a natural religion and thus appeared to deprive physical science of the universal importance which it seemed to acquire in the seventeenth and eighteenth centuries. However, there is more appearance here than reality, for physical science remained the only way in which reason, according to Kant, could fruitfully operate. For this reason the world view of physics remained the world view *par excellence*. Before any change could take place in this situation, physical science itself had to undergo important developments. In this way we are brought back to a consideration of the direct influences exercised by physical science upon the world view.

5. *The Contemporary World View*

The Difference Between the Contemporary World View and that of Classical Physical Science. The world view and the conception of nature of our present time differ in two important points from those of classical physics. Both of these differences clearly flow from internal developments of this science. One of the developments has a theoretical nature, and the other is practical. Let us begin with the theoretical development.

Classical physics lived in the belief that its theoretical structure was definitive and therefore put absolute confidence in its world view. This trust, however, was severely tempted in the twentieth century when it became clear that the traditional models—the particle model and the wave model—were inadequate for the understanding of certain phenomena. Perhaps even worse was the fact that it remained necessary to make use of these models.

For instance, the wave model had hitherto been satisfactory to explain light, but now the discovery of new properties forced science to make an appeal also to the particle model. The particle model alone, however, was not able to explain all phenomena of light. Thus both models had to be retained. Yet they exclude each other. For the particle model implies an entity which is concentrated in a particular place and nowhere else, while the wave model implies that the entity in question is spread out in space, without being localized in the proper sense. True, the mathematical description offered a possibility of reconciling the contradictory models, but its abstract formulation lacks the visualizing power of the classical description. For this reason the mathematical description cannot replace the classical world view. Because of its evident abstractness it does not result in an explicit world picture.

Thus a peculiar situation has arisen. On the one hand, contemporary physical science continues to work with the world view of classical physics, for it did not change its models but, on the other, a radical change has taken place in the evaluation of this world picture. Because of the above-mentioned facts, physical science has become aware of the relativity of its models[12] and consequently also of the relativity proper to the world view based upon these models. To say it differently, physical science has become aware of the human character of its models. As Heisenberg expresses it, "Even in physical science the object of research is no longer nature in itself, but nature as exposed to man's questioning, and in this sense man here also encounters again himself."[13] A little later he adds: "Thus the world view of physical science has, strictly speaking, ceased to be a world view of physical science."[14]

These words go to the heart of the question. For what we have to ask ourselves is precisely whether there is such a thing as a world view of physical science. This question applies not only to physical

[12]This relativity affects *all* models, even those which did not immediately give rise to difficulties. Cf. A. M. G. Kuipers, *Model en inzicht*, Assen, 1959, Ch. VI.

[13]Auch in der Naturwissenschaft ist also der Gegenstand der Forschung nicht mehr die Natur an sich, sondern die der menschlichen Fragestellung ausgesetzte Natur, und insofern begegnet der Mensch auch hier wieder sich selbst." *Das Naturbild der heutigen Physik*, Hamburg, 1955, p. 18.

[14]"Das naturwissenschaftliche Weltbild hört damit auf, ein eigentlich Naturwissenschaftliches zu sein." *Op. cit.*, p. 21.

science in its contemporary stage but also to its classical stage. True, we have spoken of the conception which classical physics had of itself when we mentioned that this physics held its world view to be the world view *par excellence* but, strictly speaking, this expression was not correct. Not physical science itself evaluated its world view in this fashion, but man as reflecting upon his physical science. There is a great difference between these two expressions. This difference, of course, does not lie in this that in one case *man* makes a judgment and in the other *science,* for in science it is always man who makes a judgment. There is a great difference, however, between a judgment which man makes *in* a science and a judgment which he makes when he reflects *upon* a science.

For, as we have seen, every science is abstract. It approaches reality in a particular fashion which causes certain aspects to manifest themselves and others to remain hidden. For instance, within the perspective of biochemistry man appears only as a whole of chemical structures, because by virtue of the methodic abstraction proper to biochemistry only biochemical aspects can manifest themselves. Does this mean, therefore, that man is nothing else than a whole of chemical structures? An affirmative reply to this question is no longer a biochemical judgment but a judgment *about* biochemistry. For it implies that the biochemist considers his method as the only valid one, as the only scientifically justified and meaningful approach to reality.

The Fallacy of Misplaced Concreteness. The situation of the so-called world view of physics is exactly the same. Of course, within the perspective of physical science the world appears in a certain way, and in this sense one may correctly speak of a physical world view. The idea, however, that this world view is *the* world view is based upon a certain evaluation of physical science and upon a judgment concerning this science as a road to knowledge. This evaluation and this judgment are by no means an internal affair of physical science but belong to philosophy.

To consider a world view of physical science, which is abstract, as the world view *par excellence* amounts to falling into the typical fallacy of the modern period which Whitehead very appropriately characterizes as "the fallacy of misplaced concreteness."[15] This sophism deserves just as much attention as ancient well-known fallacies, such as the vicious circle. The reader will recall, we trust, that the

---

[15]*Science and the Modern World,* Cambridge, 1926, Ch. IV.

ancient logicians used the collective term "sophism" or "fallacy" to indicate serious logical faults which are very deceptive because they easily impress us as being entirely correct. This description applies quite accurately to the "fallacy of misplaced concreteness," in which we have to do with a subtle, almost imperceptible shift of meaning from the world view of physical science to the world view *par excellence*.

What causes the shift in question to be a sophism? For one would be inclined to say that the transition is quite clear and not at all imperceptible. We must keep in mind that a sophism, once it has been laid bare, always shows a shameful lack of logic and therefore takes care not to reveal its nakedness. The same applies to the fallacy we are considering here. The world view of classical physics owed its origin to the fact that this science endeavored to grasp reality by means of mechanical models and conceived all events as mechanical processes. Because these models and processes were intuitively perceptible, classical physics seemed to reveal reality as it was. It was a reality which suited man as a sensitive-spiritual being. Man's sensitivity found satisfaction in the intuitive models, and his intellect was delighted by the mathematical rationality proper to these models.

Of course, the thoughtful physicist was aware of the fact that his model represented reality only in an incomplete fashion. However, he held this incompleteness to be not the result of a fundamental and essential abstraction but a natural consequence of the fact that his models were simplified representations and therefore imperfect. In his view, the deficiency did not lie in the mechanical model but in his concrete knowledge, and especially in his inability to find the correct models or to handle his models in the correct mathematical fashion. The great success which models enjoyed at first in many areas of physical science, combined with their intuitive perceptibleness, make it easy to understand why classical physical science was hardly aware of its own fundamental limitations.

The Failure of Philosophy. We may add that in the seventeenth century theology and traditional philosophy were wholly unable to cope with the situation and often succumbed to the temptation to use quasi-scientific arguments against the new science. Their failure makes the mistake of classical physics even more understandable. Its method seemed to be *the* method, its world view *the* world view, and thus there arose the sophism which Whitehead baptized so appropriately as the "fallacy of misplaced concreteness."

On the other hand, it becomes easy to see also why, when the evolution of physics revealed the relative value of models, attention began to be paid to the limited problematic perspective contained in the method of physical science. The awareness of this relativity is highly satisfying and bears witness to the fact that the philosophical status of physical science, even in its classical era, was essentially sound. Its one-sidedness could appear to be "all-sidedness" only because of the failure of other sciences, such as philosophy and theology, which by virtue of their nature and function should have guided the reflection upon physical science into the right direction.[16] Their failure, however, did not prevent the internal evolution of physics itself to supply the necessary data for correcting the situation.

The most striking aspect of the evolution which physics has undergone in most recent years undoubtedly is that, although physics had to drop its theoretical claim of knowing the world as it is, this loss has been richly compensated by an increase in effectiveness. The resulting gain brings us to a second point in which the world view has been modified in a fairly revolutionary way.

6. *Technology and World View*

The Characteristic Feature of the Old World Views. Despite their many differences, the various world views of the preceding periods had a common feature in their contemplative character: these views were primarily *cognitive* pictures. They belonged to the realm of theoretical knowledge. In the planning of such a world view man aimed at arriving at an understanding of nature as nature essentially was.

This contemplative character of the world view was, of course, connected with the classical and ancient conception of science. The meaning of science was not sought in its possible application, but science was pursued for its own sake, for the sake of the enrichment and spiritual satisfaction it offered man in his search for understanding. As has been pointed out in the preceding chapter, the situation was still the same in the seventeenth and eighteenth centuries. Only gradually did the new physical science reveal its proper nature. The manifestation of this nature showed at the same time a new world

---

[16]We may add that the philosophical systems which arose in the new era, such as rationalism and empiricism, merely served to strengthen the claims of physical science. This assertion applies, as we have seen, in part even to Kant.

picture—new, not in the sense that it was a different picture, but in the sense that man looked at it in a different way. What impresses contemporary man most is not the theoretical modification which to-day's astronomy introduces in the astronomical picture of the world. The most striking and new element is that the cosmos appears no longer to us as an object to be studied but just as much as something which man actually takes possession of. Our science-fiction springs from a different attitude of mind than that which gave rise to its fore-runner in the eighteenth century.

The Typical Feature of the New World View: Control of Nature. In technology man appropriates the world in a new fashion. This aspect of the changing world view is at least just as important as that of the changes that occurred in the theoretical concepts which we have discussed above. Or rather, the two aspects complement each other in a very striking way. What the world has lost in intuitive perceptibleness it has gained in controllability. Man has become more aware of the relativity proper to his theoretical knowledge, of the fact that his models are bound up with sensitivity. On the other hand, he realizes also that his knowledge is more effective and is endowed with creative power. In this way the contemporary evolution of physical science, combined with that of scientific technique or technology, has managed to build a bridge from both sides, connecting the potentialities of intellectual knowing with the possibilities of bodily power, which former times had considered to be widely distant.

As an inevitable consequence, contemporary physical science had to become more strongly aware of its bond with technology than had been the case with classical physics. Nevertheless, even in classical times this bond existed in principle, because physical science, as was mentioned in Chapter Five, had an operational aspect. However, in the classical era it was still possible to think that the ultimate aim was pure science, so that techniques played only a secondary role. This situation changed when, as Remy C. Kwant expresses it, the "scien-tification" of technical knowledge took place[17] and technique became technology. After the birth of technology science is no longer only the contemplation of what *is* but also that of what can *come to be*. Science is given the function of foreseeing and understanding the possibilities of change. The former world view had provided man only with an extremely limited range of possibilities of material development, for

---

[17]*Philosophy of Labor,* Pittsburgh, 1960, pp. 49 ff.

these possibilities did not extend beyond that which *formed* nature placed at his disposal.

The Difference Between the Old and the New Technical Use of Nature. Of course, man has always viewed nature as workable, but this workability did not apply to nature as a whole but only to those aspects of it which, one could rightly say, invited man, as it were, to utilize them. The soil, for instance, invited him to till it and to make use of its natural fertility. Cleavable rock indicated the obvious way of using it for making tools. Spontaneous fires showed man how to utilize fire to satisfy his need for light and heat. Soft bluff invited him to construct a cave-dwelling. The experience of strong river currents pointed the way to the building of water-wheels. The same applied to windmills, as well as to the use of the muscular power of animal and man. Briefly put, in the most ancient techniques, which were not yet based upon science, man made use of the materials that nature invitingly placed at his disposal, such as stone, skins, wood, iron ore, and many others; in working them he made use again of the forces indicated by nature itself, such as muscular power, water power, and wind power.

What has been said here about the most ancient forms of technique applies also to some extent to the older forms of scientific technique or technology, i.e., those forms which remained limited to the utilization of certain specific substances as raw materials and certain specific materials as sources of energy. True, one could no longer say that man was restricted to the materials and sources of energy which nature invited him to use. Thanks to the progress of physical science, man had already penetrated into the secrets of nature to such an extent that he knew how to use materials and energy whose availability was not readily discernible in nature. Nevertheless, there remained a number of essential restrictions, as appears from the fear in the none too distant past that the traditional sources of energy of the new era— oil and coal—would some day fall short of man's needs. With the discovery, however, of nuclear energy man has at his disposal a source of energy which is, in principle, inexhaustible and, thanks to the possibility of transforming elements into one another, he likewise has an inexhaustible supply of raw materials. In principle, every kind of matter is now usable either as raw material or as a source of energy.

In this way nature has become more than ever before a source of available materials which can be changed into everything. It has ceased to be a fixed order of natural formations. Through the apparently fixed order of nature man sees an unlimited field of possibilities, based upon the fundamental forces of nature. Man has begun to realize that his specific task is to unveil the potentialities of nature. Nature is no longer for him the Mother Nature or the deified Nature which produces him and provides him with the necessary conditions of life, but has become a kind of warehouse filled with the neutral raw materials needed for the creations of man. Nature has ceased to be a naturally formed world in which man finds his dwelling. It has become available matter which man can transform at will. In this way nature has lost also the sacred character which characterized it in all preceding periods, from antiquity through the Middle Ages and deep into more modern times.

It goes without saying that this sketch of our world view and of our conception of nature is exaggerated. Even contemporary man realizes that, no matter how much he surpasses the achievements of former ages, *de facto* his power to transform the world remains severely limited. Strictly speaking, he does not do much more than his ancestors of the Stone Age, who by cleaving and grinding adapted the natural shape of stones to their purposes. Even on earth itself the entire technological transformation of nature remains provisionally picayune, compared with the given formed status of nature. What man has achieved on a cosmic scale in launching satellites and space missiles sinks, of course, wholly into nothingness, compared with natural cosmic events. Thus we should not be too confident that historians of future ages will not simply place what we complacently call our "technological era" in the same category as the Stone Age—perhaps as the "Noisy Period" of that Age, because of its extremely primitive and fearfully noisy technological contraptions.

At any rate, it is certain that the modification of the world view described above has been presented in a somewhat exaggerated fashion, at least insofar as the actual situation is concerned. However, in certain respects world views always are somewhat visionary, in the sense that they are ahead of the actual situation. If we keep this in mind, the character of the contemporary world view is not too patently exaggerated, for the sketch presented above very definitely expresses what really constitutes the basis of present-day physical science.

The New World View and the Method of Physics. In its rigorously pursued analytic method contemporary physical science views every concrete form of nature as an instance representing many magnitudes. Concrete things and forms simply give way for abstract magnitudes. So far as physical science is concerned, a concrete stone is not primarily a reality apart, but an instance in which a certain shape, chemical composition, hardness, color, etc. meet. The concrete dog is not so much an individual as an instance in which certain physical and chemical structures are present; the earth is not so much man's natural abode as a concentration of matter having a certain mass, size, form, and composition, situated at a certain distance from other concentrations of matter in the universe, and in which the conditions "happen" to be just right for making life possible. It is for this reason that the new world view of seventeenth century astronomy encountered such a strong reaction: the world lost its natural formed status and assumed in its stead a random form resulting from the chance meeting of natural forces.

As we have pointed out previously, the last-named consequence of the modification which classical physics introduced into the world picture did not reveal itself immediately in all its clarity, because the intrinsic connection between physical science and technology did not yet sufficiently express itself. At first it seemed that the random constellations composing nature could merely be seen by man as the result of chance but that he could not replace them by others which he judged to be more appropriate to himself. In principle, however, the essential modification of the world view had already taken place. What the technical applications of physical science in the nineteenth and twentieth centuries revealed with all possible clarity was merely the logical consequence of the vision reached in the seventeenth century. The relegation of the earth from the center of this world view was only a point of subordinate importance. Much more essential and full of consequences was the fact that the reality of nature began to be considered analytically, for in this way the actual formed status of nature lost its "natural" character, it was seen to be a random status, and consequently a status which, in principle, was subject to modification.

7. *Explicit and Implicit World View*

The preceding confrontation of the contemporary world view with that of the seventeenth century teaches us that the striking difference in their evaluation of nature is fundamentally not at all a matter of different principles but rather the result of the logical consequences which our era managed to draw from the achievements of the former period. Thus this confrontation leads to an important conclusion with respect to what should be understood by the expression "the world view of physical science." In this world view the relevant part is not merely the intuitive picture which man forms of the world in its totality and which may be appropriately called the *explicit* or expressed world view. Just as important as this explicit view is the *implicit* world picture, i.e., the vision of material reality which is embodied in the analytic and experimenting method of physical science.

The Contemporary Implicit World View is the Same as That of the Seventeenth Century. So far as the implicit world view is concerned, it is much less modified by the transition from classical to contemporary physical science than is the explicit view. For the mutual approach of technical knowledge and physical science was the logical consequence of the design assumed by classical physics in the seventeenth century. Thus the rather far-reaching modification of the concept of nature since the seventeenth century becomes less radical when it is viewed in this light. This modification is radical only in its explicit development, it *manifests* itself as radical and as such exercises great influence, but it does not arise from an entirely new vision of nature. On the contrary, it is the explicit consequence of what was already present implicitly.

The world pictures of the seventeenth and the twenties centuries, which explicitly are so strikingly different, are based upon the same implicit world view. This implicit world view, strictly speaking, is nothing else than the vision of reality which is contained in the method of physical science and which we have extensively analyzed in the first part of this work. It is this implicit world view, embodied in the method of physical science, which continues to drive this science forward along the path it has taken since the very discovery of this path. For this reason the transition from classical to contemporary physical science had to follow of necessity as soon as research had progressed sufficiently. For this transition was not the result of a change of method but merely of newly discovered facts and connections.

Thus the modifications of the explicit world view which flowed from this transition and which have been mentioned above are the direct result of the internal evolution undergone by physical science. It is not because of a new vision of nature that man's attention is so concentrated upon contemporary technology. This technology arose as a result of the possibilities which manifested themselves in physical science, and as a consequence the explicit view of nature also became modified.

The conclusion presented here had been prepared in the preceding chapter when we investigated whether the modifications in the ideal of science and in the form of physical science which occurred in the course of ages had to be ascribed to external influences or to the internal logic inherent in the evolution of the scientific undertaking. Our preparation of the conclusion, however, went much farther, for it referred not only to the transition from classical to contemporary physical science, but also to that from ancient to classical physics. As was pointed out, the Greek design of science really contained the germ of later physics, although a long incubation period was necessary before this germ could develop.

The Greek and the Contemporary View of Nature. Does it follow, therefore, that the contemporary view of nature was implicitly contained in that of the Greeks? This would be a far-reaching conclusion, which we do not dare to draw before we have first investigated the nature of technology in a more profound fashion. In a certain respect classical physics undoubtedly was indebted to that of the ancients, but this does not immediately allow us to conclude that all the explicit world views and conceptions of nature which have succeeded one another simply flowed from the status reached by physical science. Although this status was an important factor, it certainly was not the only one. The medieval concept of nature, for instance, certainly had a different origin insofar as it conceived nature as the creation of a transcendent God. Of course, we do not mean that in the medieval concept of nature the Greek concept did not continue to show its influence, but mean that the explicit concept of nature existing in a given period can be understood in all its aspects solely by paying attention to the status of physical science in that period.

As was pointed out when we spoke of the world view proper to the seventeenth century, the exclusive character which this century's science attributed to its world view, thus making it *the* world view, arose also from the failure of the then-living philosophers and theologians. Accordingly, although the explicit world views of the various cultural eras cannot be understood without taking into consideration the development reached by physics in these eras, this assertion does not mean that these views can be understood solely in the light of this development.

To conclude this chapter, we must devote some attention to another aspect of the contemporary world view. Although this aspect is only indirectly connected with physical science, it is no less essential.

8. *The Changed Picture of Society*

The Break with the Old Relationship Between Man and Nature. Technology manifests man's power to interfere radically in what is given by nature. For this reason man has acquired also a different view of human society. Man's life and his living together with others are placed within the scope provided by nature. This situation was true in former ages, and it continues to be true now. However, with the growth of physical science and technology this scope has not only increased considerably, but has also manifested hitherto unknown dimensions. Nature, as we have said, is no longer *formed* nature but a whole of elements and forces whose arrangement is subject to man's decision.

The idea of a natural order, which was fixed and independent of man, has been dropped, and as a consequence the natural forms of human society that were connected with this order have also been transcended. This situation, however, was not brought about by technological thinking alone. The biological theory of evolution which evolved in the second half of the nineteenth century also made an important contribution. This theory introduced an "historical" element into the origin of the order of nature: this order had not always been what it is and would not always remain so. True, the idea of evolution present in this theory could not yet be considered as a strictly historical element, because evolution took place independently of man's will and man's activities. Nevertheless, it offered a real possibility to man's influence. Man could deliberately take control of nature's evolution which hitherto had run its course unconsciously and guide it into a chosen direction. As a result, the theory of evolution had also great repercussions on the view taken of history. The beginning of the nineteenth century saw the rise of several great philosophical systems (Hegel, Schelling, Fichte) which viewed man as a being developing itself in history and thus placed him in the sharpest possible opposition to stable nature. In and through man as spirit this development took place within the order of

nature. Now that this order appeared no longer to be sta
respect to either living nature or non-living nature, because
evolutionary theory and because of technology, the views taken
man and of nature began to fuse. The development of mankind was
placed in the perspective of the development of nature and this acquired the overtone of being a natural process. This new concept can
be very clearly discerned in the way in which Marx and especially
Engels gave a materialistic orientation to Hegel's philosophy.

Modification of Society. Once the idea of an immutable natural
order had been dropped, the various bonds of social life also assumed
the character of being in principle subject to modification. Just as
many of man's desires to dominate nature expressed in fairy tales
have become reality in and through technology, so also many social
structures which formerly were purely utopian are now worthy of
being pursued because they have become possible. How fast and
radically man's ideas about a natural order of society have changed
may be proved also by the fact that Auguste Comte (1798-1857), the
spiritual father of sociology as a positive science, did not yet see any
possibility that society would become radically modified. Now, however, through the rise of technology the situation is no longer the same.

Thinking in categories of reform and development, of planning and
execution on a world-wide scale has become commonplace in political
economy. Man is aware now that no material obstacles prevent the
realization of a society in which not only the privileged few but all
men can lead an existence worthy of man. And in their concept of
what is worthy of man, contemporaries have long since abandoned
the norms prevalent in former ages. There is no longer question
merely of securing the prime necessities of life and of enabling man
to live in good health to the age which biologically leads him to the
end, but the aim is also to fill this life spiritually. While in former
times the large majority of mankind had to work to supply their
primary necessities, now many work for man's needs in his leisure
hours.

While the prime necessities of life remain limited in scope, at least
within the boundaries of what is provisionally taught by biology and
medical science, man's spirit offers unlimited possibilities of development. Formerly only a few were dispensed from the necessity of
working constantly to secure their necessities of life and thus only a
few could achieve spiritual self-realization. Now, however, it seems

im. Thus labor has assumed an
ugh the perspective of unlimited
task, the indispensable condition
ver-increasing possibilities. These
iny limit imposed by nature.

in the Broad Sense. A sign of
ct to society is that such sciences
gy have gone beyond the stage of
hey all possess their techniques.
ie purpose of what can be made
and conclude that much remains
s of man and of society have not
physical science in their development. Because of this
backwardness, this cultural lagging, the technical possibilities of the
material world threaten to engulf us. Man is fairly well able to control
natural disasters, but as far as disasters which are caused by man
himself and arise from his human nature are concerned, he still is
rather powerless. Two world wars and the threat of a third with all
its technical horrors are an all too evident proof of this assertion.

Thus the evolution of physical science forces us to develop the
other sciences. In this way the technological world picture in the
narrow sense, which flows from the evolution of physical science and
views material reality as predictable and controllable by man, has
become the prototype of a technical world view in the broader sense.
This broader technological world view aims not only at the material
cosmos but at the whole world of man. This observation leads us
to a last aspect of the contemporary world view—namely, its paradoxical nature.

9. *The Paradox of the Technological World View*

The Fear of the Future. A very striking phenomenon of our time
is that the optimistic belief in progress so prevalent in the nineteenth
century has almost ceased to exist. Futuristic novels, unless they are
technical science fiction, usually paint the future in the darkest colors.
Man, who is hardly afraid any longer of natural disasters, has become
scared by his own world and by his power to interfere in nature.
A very peculiar aspect of this fear is that it arises not only from the

---

[18]Cf. Remy C. Kwant, *Philosophy of Labor,* Pittsburgh, 1960.

above-mentioned backwardness of the social sciences and their techniques. Man is almost even more afraid that the social science will catch up with physics than he is of their present deficiency.

Contemporary man fears the perfectly guided social order, because he is afraid that he will lose his human character in a world that is perfectly controlled from the viewpoint of physical and socio-technical sciences. It appears to him that ultimately there is more room for the development of himself and of a human world in the original condition of nature than in the man-made order, in which the possibilities are theoretically unlimited but strict rules govern all pathways he may intend to take. He prefers the human adventurous exploration of uncharted natural regions to being whisked along carefully laid-out highways, for in the former he feels that he is living but in the latter he is, as it were, being lived. He has the impression that in the new world view man, just as nature, is being considered as a whole composed of modifiable parts.

Humanization of Nature or Dehumanization of Man? Thus we are faced with a paradoxical situation. The technological world view becomes a sign of contradiction. On the one hand, the technological order is an effect of the development which physical science has undergone and of the possibilities this development offers for man's interference in nature. Started as a form of spiritual self-realization, in which man became familiar with matter and penetrated into its nature, physical science has gradually bridged the gap between man's intellectual knowledge and his bodily power. The possibilities of the spirit have communicated themselves to his bodily powers. Through the arrangement of material factors, for instance in a radio, spatial distances have shrunk for the human ear. Thanks to technology, transformed nature begins to give reality to man's dreams. Nature becomes humanized, it loses its obstructional character and becomes subservient to man. This subservience offers man an opportunity to become more human, i.e., a material reality which in a higher degree is dominated by the spirit.

On the other hand, however, the actual effect produced by technology seems to be exactly the opposite. Man fears that technology makes him lose his human character. Is man doomed to initiate a technological order and subsequently to be submersed by it? Is this the consequence flowing from the technological world view? Guardini asks himself whether perhaps the future will bring us a non-human

human being in a non-natural nature—a pregnant question which evokes, of course, at once the problem of what exactly nature and man are.[19]

Does the Technological World View Deviate from What it Ought to Be? Are the vistas upon nature and man which appear to us in the technological world view aberrations from what man's world view ought to be? Before a reply can be given to this question, it is first necessary to reflect more profoundly upon the nature of technology. Only after such a reflection will it be possible to present an evaluation of the technological world view depicted above. Meanwhile, however, this much is certain—the technological world view is not disconnected from the world picture of former ages, but is an explicitation of the implicit foundation upon which even the physical science of the Greeks was built. However, this concession does not mean that, if the technological world view contains a falsification of man's authentic being, we necessarily have to hold Greek thought responsible for this deviation. Just as the world view of classical physical science was not the correct explicitation of what was implicitly contained in physical science, so also the technological world view does not necessarily have to be a correct explicitation of technology. In many respects the world view of classical physics incorrectly expressed the nature of physical science, and the same may be true of the technological world view with respect to technology. This line of thought will guide us in our subsequent investigation.

---

[19]Cf. Guardini, *Das Ende der Neuzeit,* Würzburg, 1950, p. 81.

CHAPTER TEN

THE EVOLUTION OF TECHNOLOGY

1. *Technique in the Narrow and in the Broad Sense of the Term*

Before attempting to discover the essential characteristics of technology in its manifold manifestations, we must first make a few distinctions. One of the most important of these is that between technique in the strict sense and in a more general sense.

Technique in the Strict Sense. In its narrow sense the term "technique" refers to the making and use of implements: tools, instruments. and machines.[1] The order of this enumeration itself indicates a certain evolution. Tools immediately complement the hand, making it capable of functions which the bare hand cannot or can hardly fulfill. Hammer and axe, for example, increase the striking power of the hand and tongs its grasping ability. By means of a knife the hand is capable of cutting. All these tools have in common that they demand to be moved, guided and powered by the hand. They are, as it were, extensions of the hand itself. With instruments the situation is different. The instrument is more complex than a mere tool and, therefore, capable of fulfilling its function more or less independently when it is put into motion. A plow, for example, demands only to be drawn and does not require as much human assistance as a spade. A machine is even more independent and needs merely to be serviced and controlled. The latest types of machine require only a very limited amount of human service and control. They function automatically.

Technique in the Broad Sense. The interesting point here is that, since physical science has begun to guide technical evolution, the concept of technique has received a much broader sense than that of making and using instruments. Technical aspects have been discovered in all of man's activities. Thus we speak of the technique of football, of art, of propaganda and advertising. In psychology we speak about the technique of conversation and of delivering an address. Of special interest here is the twofold meaning which the term "technique" has with respect to public speaking. It refers first of all to suitable and

---

[1]Cf. F. Tellegen, *Aard en zin van de technische bedrijvigheid*, Delft, 1953, pp. 3 f.

intelligible delivery, to the technically correct use of the breathing and speaking apparatus and, secondly, also to the correct division of the content of the address. One can clearly see here how the meaning of the term "technique" has been broadened.

This broadening of meaning, from the manipulation of material objects to more intellectual activities, finds its first justification in the fact that all human activities have also a material aspect and therefore have to be performed in a technically correct way if they are to be done properly. There is more, however. Just as technical skills, in the narrow sense, which originally were wholly based upon practical experience and the ready availability of natural means, have gradually fallen more and more under the influence of science, so also the techniques which are naturally present in man. All human activities are now scientifically analyzed and, as it were, reconstructed. Technique in the broad sense also nowadays is based upon scientific analysis. From his physiological knowledge of the human body man deduces the way in which all kinds of achievements can be increased. Thus the human body is considered as an instrument whose possible uses are analyzed as accurately as possible in order to increase its potentialities.

There are, however, also other techniques in which the idea of an instrument withdraws entirely into the background; for instance, the techniques of sales, advertising, and propaganda. In such techniques the attention seems to be concentrated upon the "material" to be worked with or the mechanisms that have to be operated. From the analysis of the mechanisms present in man's psyche, modern man deduces how their operation can be best influenced in the desired direction. The idea of "material to work with" has become accepted in current terminologies. In sports, for instance, the participants are referred to as good or bad "material" with which the coach or the trainer has to work. Movie actors do not fare better, for they also are material in the hand of the screen director, who analyzes their character, acting, appearance, etc., to determine how they can be used to advantage.

Man as Workable Material. All kinds of degrees are possible in the consideration of man as workable material. The most extreme view is likely to be the one which fully equates man with a technical instrument. In this view human beings are nothing more than manipulatable mechanisms which can be used to advantage for purposes foreign to their personal existence. Of course, not every consideration of man as workable material has to lead to such consequences. One may also view man as a real person, but a person in whom many mechanisms operate, so that the correct actuation of these mechanisms can be to the good of his personal being. In this case the method inspired by technical thinking takes man's personal being fully into account. Its purpose is to let his personality assert itself in the best possible way.

A gross example of the first-mentioned view would be the utilization of so-called "subliminal perception," in which brief "invisible" light flashes on the television or movie screen are used to impress the viewer in such a way that the impressions do not penetrate into his consciousness. This technique offers possibilities for inconspicuous but effective campaigns of propaganda and advertising. An example of the second view may be found in the technique of psycho-analysis.

The Aversion to Technology. It is because of its penetration into the entire realm of life that technical systematization provokes such great resistance. As much as we admire the technically perfect product of the engineer, so much also are we repelled when we see through the technically perfect mechanics of a conversation. When I discover that the other's conversation with me is purely a matter of mechanics, that it is artificial and unnatural, I am no longer interested in it. I thought that there was human contact, but there was only a clever handling of me as a mechanism which reacts in a particular fashion. There was apparently never any intention of speaking with me as a human being. I experience that the technique in question degrades me and deprives me of my human existence.

The ambivalent attitude, therefore, with respect to technology flows from the fear lest, despite the possibilities which it offers in its own realm, it dominate the whole of human life so much that man will be deprived of his human existence and reduced to a thing. For this reason, as we have mentioned in the preceding chapter, man fears perhaps even more that the social sciences will catch up with the progress of physics than that they remain in their supposedly backward condition. For it seems that this backwardness can be cured only by the development of more perfect techniques. In other words, the presupposition is that man is something like a material mechanism, somewhat more complicated, of course, than ordinary mechanisms, but in principle capable of being handled in the same way. Or, to say it differently, there would have to be no essential difference between the view which considers the laborer as a piece of machinery and the conception which takes his special human structure into account. It would merely be a matter of approaching him somewhat differently, somewhat more psychologically. Such an approach, of course, is much more efficient, but at the same time also much more dangerous for man's human existence. Although this approach may seem to save the human character of man, in reality it murders this character, precisely because of the refined way in which it handles man.

Or must we admit that there can be psychological techniques which recognize and respect man as a person? Do not being-a-person and being subject to technical handling exclude each other? These questions raise the problem of how far the possibilities of technique extend and where their boundaries lie. We will approach this problem by first devoting our attention to technique in the narrow sense and then reverting to the influence of this technique upon the entire realm of human life. For without an insight into the nature of technical activity as human activity it is impossible to arrive at a good understanding of the possibilities and limits of technical knowledge. The first step of our investigation will consist in a brief sketch of the evolution which technical knowledge has undergone. As is correctly stressed by contemporary philosophy, man unfolds and manifests his nature only in the course of history. We may affirm the same of his activities, including the one that is called "technical." For this reason we must present a brief sketch of the evolution of this activity.

2. *The Various Lines of Technical Development in the Narrow Sense*[2]

Man is not purely a being of nature, for in his intellectual knowledge he distances himself from himself and from nature around him. He is not fully circumscribed by his natural activities, as animals are. The fact that he distances himself is also an unmistakable characteristic of the way in which man makes use of the natural means placed at his disposal for the maintenance of his life. Unlike animals, which naturally are in possession of certain techniques, especially in the use they make of certain materials, e.g., in building a nest, man *develops* his techniques. Certain lines can be discerned in this development and, although these lines constantly intermingle, it is worth while to trace them separately.

---

[2]For a good introduction into the history of technology, see R. J. Forbes, *Man, the Maker,* New York, 1950, or F. Klemm, *Technik, eine Geschichte ihrer Probleme,* Freiburg, 1954.

Use of Materials. First of all, there is a development in the use of materials. Originally man resorted to stones, splitting and grinding them, to make the tools he needed for hunting or agriculture. Next, he began to use more suitable materials, such as bronze and iron, when he had learned the possibilities implied in fire. The control of fire provided him not only with light and heat and new ways of preparing and preserving food, but also disclosed new types of materials, bronze and iron, which could be used only after being treated with fire. It was a discovery which greatly impressed primitive man, as is manifested by the fact that in ancient cultures the smith was always somewhat of a sorcerer and that mythology paid special attention to him. Intuitively primitive man realized that through the use of fire he broke the shackles of nature in a special way and thus affirmed his human character. The many sagas which speak about the use of fire show also that man had an inner foreboding of how hazardous an undertaking technical development was, because it would lead him so far away from his familiar natural setting.

The line of development based upon the use of new materials was so important that it has become the basis upon which we divide the oldest cultural periods, calling them, e.g., the Stone Age, the Bronze Age, or the Iron Age.

The Shaping of Materials. Another line of technical development becomes visible when we pay attention to the increasing refinement and complexity of shapes given to materials. The oldest types of shapes, such as those of the spear and the club, were copied from nature and were in part easily understood imitations of forms which existed in the animal world as bodily means serving particular purposes. The invention of the wheel, however, has a different basis, although perhaps its experiential origin may have lain in noticing the little resistance encountered by a rolling tree trunk. The construction of a wheel is something in which the experiential datum is utilized in a very simple way, omitting everything that is irrelevant. (One could speak here of a technical abstraction.) The wheel and its many derivatives made many new complex tools possible, such as vehicles and irrigation contraptions, which were more independent in their operation than were simple tools.

Sources of Energy. Another line of technical development shows itself in the utilization of sources of energy. At first this energy was obtained from the natural muscular power of man and animals. Later man began to make use of wind and water. Even in this stage he managed to construct impressive energy producers. The Park of Versailles, for instance, contained a machine driven by water power which produced no less than seventy horsepower.

How important the development of energy sources was becomes clear when we keep in mind that it was especially the development of new sources which gave rise to the modern period of technology. The first herald of this new period was the discovery that man could use the chemical energy released by the burning of coal. Its first phase was dominated by the steam engine, later succeeded by gasoline and diesel engines. At least of equal importance was the discovery of electricity as a transmitter of energy, for it offered the opportunity of having energy available in a very simple way at any desired place or time. It is indeed not only the increase in energy potential but also the form in which this energy becomes available that make the development of sources of energy so important. "In terms of energy," says Tellegen, "we may say that a man in a Chevrolet has the power of about two thousand slaves at his disposal. The invention of the motor-car becomes clear only when we ask ourselves in what way these slaves would empower a man to move around as compared with the way his Chevrolet enables him to move."[3]

The various lines of development intermingle, of course. At first the most important factor was the control over materials, because progress in this line (e.g., from stone to metal) allowed more flexibility in shaping tools and this progress in its turn permitted man to work the existing materials more easily (e.g., wood in constructing implements). In a later stage the development of energy sources became the primary pace setter of technical evolution, but this stage demanded the search for new materials and forms capable of utilizing the newly discovered energies. In this way man deliberately developed one line because of the other. The close connection between knowing and doing which manifests itself here will be investigated presently. First, however, we must consider for what purpose man utilized the old forms of technique and what he had in mind in doing so. Here we are immediately struck by a remarkable fact.

The Twofold Function of Technique. Man did not make things only which could serve as tools and implements to satisfy his immediate physical necessities, but produced also the wherewithals to

[3]*Samenleven in een technische tijd,* Utrecht, 1957, p. 27.

express his thoughts, feelings, and desires. When we speak of technical means we should include the style as well as the hammer. It is not without reason that the Greek term *technē* and the Latin *ars* indicate both technical skill and art. From the very beginning both went together. Even in the use and especially in the development of implements and tools a certain distance began to manifest itself between laboring man and the products or means of his labor, but this distance became even greater in his artistic expressions. Primitive man did not only engage in hunting, but he also depicted the hunt. In these paintings he created a distance between himself and his immediate experience in an entirely new fashion. He did the same in the written word, which provided him with a very sensitive and particularly efficient means to give permanence to his thoughts and experiences and to let them live, as it were, a life of their own. We will revert to this point later, after devoting more attention to man's efforts to provide for the immediate necessities of life. For it is in these efforts that the meaning of technical evolution manifests itself most clearly.

3. *Cultivation and Construction*

When we speak of man's technical activity, we think, of course, first of all of making things, of constructing implements and tools. These things, however, which themselves were products of man's working of nature, served originally not for constructive work but for cultivation. Cultivation refers to living nature, while construction is concerned with non-living nature. There is a great difference between these two, which makes itself felt even in our time. According to pre-historians, man originally lived on what nature spontaneously produced: he gathered fruit and hunted animals. First he followed wild herds, and then he settled down, began to raise cattle, to clear the soil, to irrigate, and to plant. This change from a nomadic status to farming was perhaps the first great turning point in the history of culture. Man no longer continued to live in nature as he had found it, but began to build from nature a world of his own. At first, this world remained, of course, very close to nature.

Cultivation. The typical element of all agriculture and cattle raising is, as has been pointed out, the idea of cultivation. Although man performs all kinds of preparatory tasks, such as clearing, plowing, and sowing, nature itself has to do the rest. Once his preparatory task is done, man can only sit down and wait. It is the inner growing power of living nature which performs the proper work. No matter how much increase modern biological knowledge has given to man's power of intervention in the natural process of growth, it still is this process itself which determines the course of events. Man may be capable of accelerating or retarding the process, of leading it in a certain direction, but he is not able to do much more than this. For this reason the farmer, who spends his time in cultivating nature, has a feeling for nature which differs from that of the city dweller. The modern concept of nature, spoken of in the preceding chapter, is foreign to the farmer: he continues to see nature as Mother Nature, to whose care he is entrusted.

Construction. The work of the craftsman, the making of tools, implements, utensils, ornaments, and works of art, differs from that of the farmer. For the craftsman gives natural materials forms which would not naturally arise in them. The technical object is something which is not cultivated but constructed, i.e., its component parts are arranged in an artificial pattern. The fashioning of these parts forces them into forms and functions which are not naturally present in them. The natural form of iron, for instance, is not that of a plow, a cog-wheel, or a pot. Accordingly, in the work of construction there is a far more direct intervention in the natural order than there is in the work of cultivation. It is no longer a helping or guiding of natural processes in producing their natural results, but the production of forms which nature does not know or at least does not produce in this fashion.

It remains true, of course, that this production is a calling forth from nature, an actualization of potentialities present in nature. For this reason a careful choice of the material is important in any technical product, for the material must be suitable for the form and function to be assigned to it. Likewise, the process of production must be in harmony with the capacities of nature as they are known from the natural laws. In this respect the technical product also is bound by nature. Although it is not a natural product, it is a realization of nature's possibilities. The modern complicated technical product does not differ at all from the ancient primitive productions so far as this aspect is concerned, for both are artifacts produced from nature's potentialities.

At the same time, however, it remains true that we are intuitively inclined to consider a windmill or a water wheel a more natural source of power than a dynamo, a speaking-trumpet or sounding-board a more natural amplifier of the human voice than a loud-speaker, a candle more natural than an electric bulb. As Heidegger expresses it, modern technology is *"herausförderend,"*[4] i.e., it has a demanding and challenging character. Or, to use the terminology adopted in the preceding chapter, in ancient technique man, as it were, accepted nature's invitations in a way which remained fairly close to cultivating it, whereas in modern technology he wrests invitations from nature. The former way leads to a natural culture, but the latter to an unnatural kind. What is the basis for this feeling that ancient technique was more natural? It is a problem which will still have to occupy our attention quite frequently and which we will approach from different angles.

Provisionally we may say that this evaluation of ancient technique will probably be connected with the fact that it is closely connected with the knowledge of nature which man "naturally" possesses. Contrary to the construction of contemporary technical products, which is based upon scientific knowledge of the phenomena of nature, ancient technical products required only a knowledge of nature which did not go much beyond the properties of things that could be discovered by ordinary sense experience. This experience was limited to externals, to the externally observable properties of matter, but scientific knowledge penetrates into the internal structure in order to devise possible new structures from within.

All making is based upon knowing. However, as was pointed out previously, these two went their own ways. From antiquity to modern times there was no gradual and integral development of science and technique together. In the forms of philosophy and mathematics science withdraws from the original intermingling of knowing and making, and for this reason the development of technique was not continuous. For many centuries it developed only very gradually, without being supported by a competent knowledge of matter on the level of physical science. As soon, however, as physical science had developed sufficiently to be of service, technique developed at a prodigious rate in a very short time. In this way there arose a rather sharp distinction between the old and the new technique. If we want to obtain a clear understanding of this distinction, it will therefore be necessary to devote our attention to the relationship between knowing and making in both old and new technique.

---

[4]"Die Frage nach der Technik," *Die Künste im technischen Zeitalter,* München, 1956, pp. 55 ff.

4. *Knowing and Making*

Knowing. The intellectual act of knowledge is characterized by the fact that it remains within the knowing subject. As Aristotle expressed it, to know is to become the other. For, if there is to be question of real knowledge, that which typifies the cognitive object, that which makes this object what it is, somehow has to come to be in the knowing subject. The subject must make the object of knowledge his own, has to assimilate it. All these expressions throw some light on the meaning of knowing. Knowledge is *par excellence* an immanent event. True, we may speak of it as assimilating and appropriating the object, but the essential element of knowledge is that it does not modify the object known but the knowing subject. Knowledge changes the knower, because it enriches him, and does not change the object known, for this object remains what it is.

At the same time, however, it is true that the knowing subject does not lose his identity through the change which takes place in him. He does not cease to be himself but, on the contrary, becomes even more himself, for in and through knowledge knowing man properly becomes himself. It is in this point that lies the character which distinguishes knowledge as change from other changes. Material things also are subject to change. Water, for instance, can become ice, an animal can die, iron may rust, and a cold piece of rock can become hot. In all these changes, however, the changing object ceases to be what it was prior to the change. Ice is no longer a liquid, a dead dog is no longer a dog, rust has ceased to be iron, and the hot rock is no longer cold. The same cannot be affirmed with respect to the change which occurs in the act of knowing, for by "becoming the other" the knowing subject does not cease to be himself but becomes even more himself.

It is for this reason that, when in the preceding chapters there was question of matter and its mode of being, we spoke of the "closed" character of matter. The term indicates that matter is exactly and no more than it is. It can never be two things at the same time. True, a single material thing, because of its manifold aspects and the complexity of its structure, may be able to serve several purposes, but these different uses are always based upon a mode of being which is fixed. If we want to go beyond these uses, we have to actualize the potentialities that are contained in this same mode of being by introducing the concrete changes which lead to this actualization. The realization of these potentialities, however, results in the loss of other properties which first were actual. In intellectual knowledge, on the other hand, the knower becomes the other without losing his own identity. For this reason we speak of the openness of the spirit in opposition to the closedness of matter. These terms are evidently to be understood in an analogous sense. Literally understood, they would hardly have any meaning, but in the concrete context of a reflection upon what happens in the act of knowing they are significant.

Making. An entirely different situation faces us when we speak of making. To make something means that the maker changes something outside himself. To make, therefore, is not an immanent but a transient action. It passes over into the other, and the result of the action lies not in the maker but in the thing made. Knowledge plays, of course, an important role in making, for the maker has an idea of what he wants to make and intends to realize this idea in matter. The essential element of making, however, is that the idea is really realized in matter and not in the knower or the maker.

Language very appropriately knows, therefore, a twofold use of the term "to realize." This term may refer to the cognitive process, and then the realization takes place in the knower. We say, for example, that someone realized his situation, by which we want to express that he understood the existing situation, so that this situation is real no longer only outside him but also in him. Secondly, the term may refer to a transient activity—namely, when someone effectively brings about a certain situation. In such a case he is, of course, the one who has created the situation, but he is not necessarily the one *in* whom the situation has been realized. Perhaps he does not even realize (first sense) what he has realized (second sense).

This second form of realization demands active bodily intervention in the situation. When there is question of making in the strict sense of the term, we think first of all of seizing and working an object with the hand, because the hand is the part of the body in which man's grasp of the physical world realizes itself in the most natural way. *De facto,* however, the whole body can and, strictly speaking, always does take part in making things. For it is the whole body, as the corporeal presence of the spirit, which operates in the hand.

5. *The Relationship of Knowing and Making in Ancient Technique and Science*

Epistēmē and Technē. As we have seen several times, the situation of ancient technique and science was characterized by a rather radical difference between the realizations attainable to the mind and those attainable to the body, between the possibilities of knowing and those of making. This difference continues to exist somehow, for we may realize many truths without having, provisionally at least, any possibility of making them real outside us. Moreover, there are quite a few things over which we have a reasonable practical control without, however, being able to arrive at a satisfactory understanding. Nevertheless, the gap separating these two poles is no longer seen as unbridgeable, as it was prior to the latest developments of science and technology.

Formerly this gap was judged to be unbridgeable from both ends. There were, so they thought, things of which man could have a practical knowledge but which in principle were not open to a scientific theoretical understanding. Man knew, for instance, how to make iron from iron ore or how to make glass from certain raw materials, but this knowledge could not become really scientific. For it was not general, but differed from case to case. Iron had to be prepared differently from glass, but this difference was not understood as a consequence flowing from the same fundamental laws governing matter. On the other hand, there were things which man understood scientifically, but which he could not execute in reality; for instance, space travel.[5] His bodily powers of realization fell essentially short of what was required for travel in cosmic space.

Accordingly, in ancient thought there was a sharp distinction between *epistēmē,* science based upon insight, and *technē,* practical knowledge or the knowing which is needed for, and connected with making. Of course, the ancients realized that making was to some extent connected with theoretical knowledge, but this making had a function which was clearly subordinate and extrinsic to knowledge. It did not enter intrinsically into knowledge itself. For instance, the mathematician needed writing materials to calculate, compass and ruler to make his drawings. The astronomer needed instruments to

---

[5]Cf. above, p. 181.

determine the position and course of the stars, but these instruments were purely auxiliary means which served science only externally.[6]

All this goes to show that for the Greeks genuine science was, so to speak, a one way street. Making and constructing existed for the sake of the pursuit of science, but not vice versa. Science was for its own sake, for the purpose of the intellectual appropriation of the world as the enrichment of man. Science was the formation of the mind leading man to his spiritual self-realization.

The Practical Sciences.[7] The relationship of making and knowing was different, of course, with respect to the practical sciences. In these knowing served making. Although making and its implied technical skill in experimenting led to new knowledge of materials and new methods of working them, this newly acquired knowledge itself remained subservient to making. What the executing hand taught the head was used again for the better guidance of the hand. Thinking followed the action and was at the same time a pre-thinking of the next action.[8]

This knowledge of nature, which was indispensable and fruitful for ancient technique, did not rise above the level of a generalized empirical knowing, because it remained limited to the externally observable properties of materials and the possibilities of being-worked which they offered to external perception. It remained deprived of a theoretical foundation. For this reason this knowledge was so unchanging and could advance only at a snail's pace. For the same reason also ancient technique remained always very greatly dependent upon routine, i.e., the individual's personal learning of the necessary skill through constant repetition.

Speaking about Socrates' idea of technique, Dessauer remarks that the ancient sage, in using the term, thinks above all of technique which is personally acquired by, and inherent in the craftsman.[9] Such a technique may be transmitted to others, of course, insofar as they can

---

[6]There is, however, the interesting text in Aristotle, mentioned on p. 86, in which he speaks about mathematical constructions and draws constructing into knowledge itself. But this text, which throws some light upon the operational aspect of even pure science, remained an isolated remark.

[7]We limit ourselves here to the practical sciences concerned with making things and do not speak of that form of practical science which was connected with ethical doing.

[8]Cf. the excellent description of Remy C. Kwant, *Philosophy of Labor,* Pittsburgh, 1960, Ch. II.

[9]F. Dessauer, *Streit um die Technik,* Frankfurt, 1956, p. 148.

learn it. However, it lacks the character of a universal procedure which is, as it were, realized in matter. This character is precisely what is typical of contemporary techniques. Relatively little *personal* routine-like training is required to operate a machine. The experience which has been embodied in the machine itself does most of the work. The element of routine is incorporated into the way the machine functions, and the machine itself indicates the little personal routine which the operator still needs. In ancient technique, on the other hand, the routine-like experience was embodied in man, it was passed on from father to son, from mother to daughter, and from master to apprentice. Thus the old technique remained limited to the natural possibilities of man, in the sense that man's bodily powers and forces were the immediate limits of its scope. It stayed within the reach of the senses and the hand. It was this situation which gave the old techniques their character of being "natural": they dwelled in the latitude which had been "naturally" allotted to the human body.

The Greek Distinction Between Theoretical and Practical Sciences. As has been pointed out previously, the sharp distinction which the Greeks made between theoretical science and practical knowledge harmonized with the possibilities that *de facto* existed in their time to pursue science. They did not know and could not know anything about physical science in the contemporary sense of the term, because this science needed a long time before it could begin to develop. The rise of positive physical science, however, meant the appearance of a science in which the relationship between knowing and making differed essentially from that existing in the old forms of science. On the one hand, physical science exhibits the characteristics of a genuine theoretical science which gives us an understanding of nature but, on the other, it also reveals features of what was formerly proper to practical knowledge. For physical science depends upon making and, reversely, making is directly guided by this science.

In physical science there is an intrinsic connection between a philosophical view of nature, mathematical rationality, sense knowledge, and technical skills, in such a way that they aid and support one another. In physical science it becomes evident how much the intellect, the senses, and the hand constitute a fundamental cognitive and operative unity, and how this unity is characteristic of man because of his being a "spirit-in-matter." Of course, the intellect, the senses, and the hand work together in all human activities and consequently in the pursuit of any science, but the extent to which each of them participates in this pursuit may vary considerably.

Philosophy and mathematics, as typically intellectual activities, require only a minimum of sense knowledge and technical skill. The senses are needed, because in one way or another all human knowledge is gained from sense experience. In mathematics, however, there is no need to perform a detailed sensitive investigation in order to determine which data are relevant. To establish, for instance, that the sum of the angles of a triangle is 180°, it is not necessary to make measurements. Likewise, there is no need for a detailed sense investigation in philosophy to discover that concepts are characterized by universality and abstraction, even though it is true that the senses play a role in the formation of concepts. While this relative independence from the senses made an early development of philosophy and mathematics possible, it meant at the same time that these sciences did not possess any direct value with respect to detailed knowledge of matter. Or, to express it differently, the pursuit of philosophy and mathematics was a necessary but not a sufficient condition for the rise of physical science. As long as this state of affairs lasted, technical skill was destined to remain deprived of an intellectual penetration into the differentiated structures of matter. It had to rely wholly upon what was directly perceptible by the senses and therefore could make progress only in a more or less fortuitous fashion. Intellectual knowledge which is directly connected with technical skill likewise had to rely on this primitive sense knowledge and therefore remained largely limited to the confession that understanding of the reasons for the technical procedures was lacking.

Sense experience, on the other hand, was unable to penetrate deeply into the structure of matter, because it lacked the aid of the necessary experimental techniques as well as theoretical guidance by the intellect. Both of these were lacking, because more advanced sense knowledge was needed before they could be reached.

Of course, the dividing lines drawn here are somewhat too sharp for, as we have seen in Chapter Eight, certain forms of physical science were realized by the Greeks. However, these forms remained provisionally of relatively small importance and did not dominate the general picture. An exception must be made for astronomy, which was well developed. Precisely in astronomy, however, the mathematical element dominated so strongly that this discipline was considered to be a branch of mathematics rather than of physical science.[10] For this reason it did not change much the general picture outlined above.

6. *The Relationship Between Knowing and Making in Contemporary Science and Technology*

With the rise of physical science in the seventeenth century the various elements mentioned above encountered and compenetrated one another for the first time. The scientific attitude embodied in the old philosophy received a powerful support for its conviction that reality can be understood in a rational fashion, because at that time the effort became successful in several areas which hitherto had been recalcitrant to understanding. Mathematical rationality began to understand the earthly phenomena of motion, and in the process mathematics itself was greatly expanded through the discovery of analytic geometry, differential and integral calculus. Experimental knowledge received the support of the newly acquired insights into its constructs and observations and in its turn enriched theoretical understanding. Knowing and making began to aid each other, and it did not take very long before physical science and technology discovered that they essentially belonged together.

What made the new situation differ from that of previous times was the fact that it was no longer a question of connecting purely experiential knowledge with technique but of the mutual compenetration of scientific knowledge and technique guided by science. The vacuum which hitherto had existed between *epistēmē* and *technē* became filled with a form of science which was based on both knowing and making. The gap separating intellectual science, which used only a minimum of material reality, from material practical knowledge, which was poor in understanding, was bridged by a form of activity in which a wealth of insights goes hand in hand with the actual working with matter. For this reason one could justly call physical science a genuinely *human* science, because the unity of the intellect, the senses, and the hand finds expression in it.

Thus it is not surprising that in philosophy the dualistic view of man gradually began to lose its power and that there arose a more lively awareness of man's unity as spirit-in-matter. This assertion

---

[10]St. Thomas, for example, called this science a *scientia media,* an intermediary science, because it proceeded in a mathematical fashion despite the fact that materially it was a physical science.

is not contradicted by the fact that Descartes, the spiritual father of the modern era, rigorously maintained the dualistic concept of man. For Descartes lived in the first phase of the new physical science, and in this phase the inner connection of physical science and technique did not yet sufficiently express itself. There still seemed to remain an unbridgeable gap between the possibilities of the spirit and those of the body.

The fact that man's cognitive and technical abilities gradually approached one another does not mean that they became identical. There remains a difference between technical procedures and philosophical reflection, between physical science and mathematics, and in spite of their close connection also between physical science and technology. Let us examine the last-named difference.

7. *Physical Science and Technology*

Discovery and Invention. According to Dessauer, physical science is characterized by discovery, and technology by invention.[11] Discovery refers to something that existed already before the discovery but had not yet been brought to light. Invention, on the other hand, is concerned with making for the first time something which did not yet exist. Electricity, for instance, was discovered, but the incandescent bulb was invented. Thus physical science and technology reveal themselves as two clearly distinct things, of which the former refers to the discovery of nature and the latter to the finding of the ways to combine the data of nature in such fashion that something new arises which can be of service to man. This finding of something new may refer to the invention of a *thing* which as such does not exist in nature, e.g., an incandescent bulb, or also to a *process* by which man can produce things which occur in nature in insufficient quantities. An example of the latter is the production of fertilizer or soda.[12]

Despite the fact that the distinction between discovery and invention does point to an essential aspect of the difference between physical science and technology, it should be clear that the distinction in question is purely relative. For the progress of physical science is not determined only by the discovery of the hitherto unknown, but

---

[11]*Streit um die Technik,* Frankfurt a.M., 1956, Ch. II, sect. 8 and 9.

[12]Dessauer speaks here of the distinction between the invention of a *Raumform,* a technical thing, and that of a *Zeitform,* a technical process. Cf. op. cit., Ch. II, sect. 4.

also by seeing what was already known in a new light. And this second point is more important then the first. The two, moreover, are closely connected. The discovery of new phenomena usually is the result of a new way of looking at what was previously known. For instance, a new view of light—that light is an electromagnetic phenomenon—gave rise to the discovery that radio waves were possible.

It is likewise a new way of viewing old things which lies at the basis of invention. Invention consists in the discovery of possibilities, and this is ultimately nothing else than seeing something new in what is already given. To return to the same example of the radio waves, after they had become known as "artificial" waves through the invention of emitters, it was discovered that there were also natural emitters and natural radio waves. It could have happened that these natural waves would have been discovered first, just as the discovery of radioactivity did precede the invention of means to produce radioactivity.

Discovery and invention, therefore, are closely connected, or rather, they compenetrate each other. Invention requires discovery, a new mode of seeing things. Discovery, in its turn, demands the finding of technical means, and these means, surprising as it may seem, are not solely means having a material character. For discovery does not only require instruments which make new observations possible, not only experimental constructions to analyze the phenomena, but also needs conceptual constructs, models in which the newly acquired knowledge can be suitably represented.

The Model as Construct. Above knowledge has been spoken of as an appropriation and assimilation of the object known. This appropriation takes place by means of an image. Although this image is directed to reality, it itself *is not* this reality. Hence physical knowledge demands experimental confirmation, i.e., effective action upon the material world. The cognitive image in question, however, is not simply a reproduction, made possible after the discovery of a reality, somewhat like a photograph which an aerial observer can take when the clouds have disappeared and the unknown landscape lies uncovered. The cognitive image of physical science discloses a greater resemblance with a constructed *model* than with a picture—an immanent model, of course, but nonetheless a constructed model.

This model constructed in the mind is often formed by way of analogy with transient models. We may refer here, for instance, to explanations through mechanical models, which have dominated physical science for such a long time and continue even now to exercise a powerful, though somewhat diminished, attraction. The immanent models in question, moreover, are often materially expressed in the form of sketches or even more "realistic" material structures. These material structures serve to illustrate the immanent model which itself, however, is never directly *seen* in nature but merely made in thought from already-known material. Accordingly, making plays a role not only as transient making in support of immanent knowledge, but has also an analogon in knowledge itself, insofar as this knowledge constructs immanent models.

Conclusion. Although physical science in the first instance can be distinguished from technology by pointing to the difference between immanent knowing and transient making, characterized respectively by discovery and invention, nevertheless the two appear to be closely related. For the knowing proper to physical science includes making, and making implies knowing; discovery demands the finding of models, and the invention of technical constructions requires the seeing, the discovering of new possibilities. This reciprocal implication of knowing and making, however, does not prevent that there remains a difference between physical science and technology, because the distinction between immanent knowing and transient making cannot be eliminated.

Physical science remains directed to the understanding of nature, i.e., to make immanently one's own the other which is called nature. Physical science, therefore, is primarily formation of the spirit, man's immanent self-realization. Technology, on the other hand, aims at arranging the data of nature in such a way that they lead to an effective control of matter with respect to the needs and desires of man. It remains a transient activity. Technique, to quote a definition of Dessauer, "is a mode of being arising from ideas and brought to reality by working and shaping into a final form that which is given in nature."[13]

No matter how much truth there may be in this definition, it does not satisfy us entirely, because it does not sufficiently express the meaning which technical activity has in the totality of human existence. Any definition is inevitably colored by the way in which it has been reached. This is the reason why there are so many

---

[13]"Technik ist reales Sein aus Ideen durch finale Gestaltung und Bearbeitung aus naturgegebenen Beständen." *Op. cit.,* p. 234.

definitions of technique and technology.[14] Insofar as these definitions arise from different approaches, they do not necessarily have to be contradictory, but the same cannot be said insofar as these definitions owe their origin to fundamentally different philosophical standpoints. The definition presented above results from the confrontation of immanent knowledge with transient making. This aspect is important, of course, but not at all the only one that makes itself felt when there is question of technology. It does not sufficiently pay attention to the ultimate value of technology for mankind. It does not show the place technology occupies in man's endeavor to realize his own nature.

Where is the place in question? The many tensions which technology justly or unjustly is accused of causing and all of which somehow are connected with the intrinsic value of technology for mankind show that this value is not at all easy to define. We may ask, for example, to what extent technical making serves also man's intellectual formation and his immanent self-realization, which traditionally are considered to be the core of any real culture. This question aims not only at the subservient function which technology fulfills with respect to physical science, but also at a proper function of technology, in which physical science in its turn plays a subservient role. We must ask ourselves whether or not technology has its own intrinsic cultural value. This question forces us to delve deeper into the essence of technology than would be possible if we limited ourselves to the opposition of knowing and making. The essence of technology has to be seen in the light of man's own essence. The next chapter will be dedicated to this purpose.

---

[14]Dessauer himself presents several of them and elaborates the various viewpoints taken with respect to technology. A comprehensive explanation of the different philosophies of technology and their historical roots may be found in H. van Riessen, *Philosophie en techniek*, Kampen, 1949.

CHAPTER ELEVEN

THE ESSENCE OF TECHNOLOGY

1. *The Determinants of Technical Activity*

The Essence of Technology and the Essence of Man. Asking about the essence of technology is asking about the essence of man. Thus it would seem logical that the question about the essence of technology be preceded by a reply to the question of what man is. In this way the philosophy of technology appears to be a branch of philosophical anthropology which, of course, could hardly be denied. However, we are faced with the peculiar situation that a satisfactory anthropology is not possible without a profound reflection upon the essence of technology, especially as this essence manifests itself in the development of technology. For man is an historical being who only gradually arrives at the discovery of his own proper essence by developing himself and his world.

On the other hand, it is true, of course, that man himself takes the initiative in this development and in taking this initiative proves that he is aware of what it means to be man. However, he does not at all foresee all the consequences of what he initiates. We may refer here to what has happened in the pursuit of science. Initiated by the Greeks, this pursuit took a different course than was expected and explicitly intended by man, but its result served to enrich man's understanding of himself.

A striking example to the point is the fact that in our time the dualistic view of man lost much of its importance. As we have pointed out several times, the dualistic conception of man in the past was in part the result of the distinction between the possibilities of the spirit and those of the body which manifested itself clearly in the situation of science and technique in former ages. When this situation was changed by the rise of physical science and of the technology based upon this science, the view taken of man likewise underwent a change.

Accordingly, we are justified in attempting to throw light upon the question of what man is by means of the reply to the question regarding the essence of technology. True, the very reply to this question cannot avoid raising anthropological problems, but this is a situation that cannot be avoided. For by its very purpose philosophy is always directed to the totality, yet a philosophical study can never be anything else than a limited approach to this totality.

Because this book is intended not as an anthropology but as a reflection upon physical science and technology, we will not specifically devote our attention to the general anthropological questions but concentrate our efforts upon technique or technology as human activity. We may start by asking questions about the determinants of technology, i.e., that in man which makes him necessarily the technical being which he is. What makes man take the initiative in his self-development as a technical being?

The Biological Determinant. If we pay attention to the fact that animals also make and modify things, it appears justified to consider as the first determinant of all technical activity human nature itself as it is biologically constituted. As Gehlen correctly remarks, man's technical activity does not flow entirely from his rationality. He quotes approvingly Hermann Schmidt who emphasized that "the objectivation of labor which takes place in technical activity is the result of an unconscious process inherent in the species, whose motivation springs from the sensitive part of our nature."[1] Or, to quote Rathenau, mechanization "did not arise from a free and deliberate agreement, from the ethically purified will of mankind, but grew up unintentionally and even unnoticed. Despite its rational and casuistic structure, it is an instinctive process, a dumb natural event."[2]

Gehlen himself sees technology as a kind of resonance phenomenon, especially insofar as technology tends to automatisms. Man experiences automatisms in himself, e.g., his pulse, and in certain natural phenomena, such as the course of celestial bodies, and endeavors to realize automatism.[3] Thus the technical is in resonance with the natural. Others see technology more as an extension of natural evolu-

---

[1] A. Gehlen, *Die Seele im technischen Zeitalter,* Hamburg, 1957, p. 17: ". . . dass die Objektivation der Arbeit, die im technischen Geschehen vorliegt, das Ergebnis eines nicht bewussten, von der Gattung getragenen Prozesses ist, dass ihre Motivation aus dem sinnlichen Teil unser Natur entpringt."

[2] Quoted by Gehlen, *op. cit.,* p. 17: ". . . nicht aus freier, bewusster Vereinbarung aus dem ethisch geläuterten Willen der Menschheit entstanden, sonder unbeabsichtigt, ja unbemerkt erwachsen. Trotz ihres rationalen und kasuistischen Aufbaus ist sie ein unwillkürlicher Prozess, ein dumpfer Naturvorgang."

[3] Gehlen, *op. cit.,* p. 16.

tion, as a progressive projection of human organs.[4] Just as living nature seems to tend to progressive differentiation and to produce constantly more refined organs, so also the same tendency operates in man when he creates technical forms as developments of nature's possibilities.

This general biological foundation in nature may be admitted, provided one does not draw from it the undue conclusion that such a foundation suffices fully to explain man's technical activity. While the biological foundation is a determinant which sets this activity in motion, it does not fully determine it. For human activity is characterized precisely by the fact that man deliberately seizes and cultivates its natural foundation, as he experiences it in himself. Thus, this activity may remain a "natural event," but it ceases to be a "dumb natural event."

We may recall here what has been said in Chapter Seven regarding the relationship of determinism and freedom. There is determinism in freedom, because man's being is an unfolding of material being; nevertheless, his freedom is not submerged in determinism. Likewise, it is through man's higher level of being, as it manifests itself in his intellectual knowledge that technique obtains its specific character of human technique. We must therefore examine the various aspects of intellectual knowledge in order to discover the determinants of technique and technology. Because several of the preceding chapters have already presented fairly extensive analyses of knowledge, we may restrict ourselves here to a few brief indications.

Man's Urge to Know. Let us begin with man's urge to know and to explain. By speaking of an urge to know and to explain, we intend at once to draw attention to a distinction in man's cognitive urge by virtue of which he tends to both *multa,* the many in their plurality, and *multum,* the many in their unity. These two essentially go together. Man's cognitive urge is stimulated by everything which he encounters. Nothing escapes the restless curiosity of his inquiring mind. Man exhibits in his intellectual activity a kind of collector's enthusiasm which aims at things in their endless plurality and multiformity, things as *multa.* When Hillary was asked why he wanted to climb Mount Everest, his simple reply to the point was: "Because it is there." Whatever exists arouses man, he wants to make it his own by

---

[4]For instance, E. Kapp in his work, *Grundlinien einer Philosophie der Technik,* Braunschweig, 1877, one of the first philosophies of technology.

investigating it and adding it to his collection. However, he is not interested only in collecting the many, but also wants to reduce this multiplicity to unity, i.e., to embrace the many from a single or from a few viewpoints.

The classical principle which of old has acted as a norm of education, *non multa sed multum* (not many things but much), clearly shows the preference of the scientific attitude of mind. The aim is not the many as many, but the many as reduced to unity. Although this preference is justified, it should not make us lose sight of the essential value pertaining to the search for the many. For otherwise there will be great danger—as is graphically demonstrated by ancient science —that the urge for unification may lead to undue simplification of the actually given plurality. For this reason man's intellectual curiosity which wants to collect everything constitutes an indispensable element of the pursuit of science, because it keeps science in touch with reality and stimulates theoretical investigation.

The great contribution which was made to physical science in the past by empirically gathered technical knowledge of matter bears witness to the truth of these assertions. Likewise, even nowadays a "dumb little fact" which does not fit the theory may become the starting point of the most important theoretical developments. In this way the *multa* are indispensable to bring about the *multum,* the many reduced to unity, as we could describe the content of this untranslatable term. For unity in multiplicity is what all science aims at and what makes it fruitful.

This was also the way in which things went in the history of physical science. At first the two aspects of knowledge, the urge to explain and the urge to know, went their own ways: the former that of pure science and the latter that of empirical technical knowledge. Nevertheless, they were destined to meet again, and it was precisely their meeting in the seventeenth century which became of decisive importance for both pure science and technology.

Although it is true that man's interest extends to all things, one may reasonably expect that a certain sequence will manifest itself in his interest. For instance, by virtue of man's sensitive-spiritual nature it is to be expected that his attention will go first of all to what he sensitively experiences, to nature around him. This knowledge, moreover, is immediately useful for him in his struggle to maintain himself in this nature. Nevertheless, in the background of all knowledge, no matter what its immediate scope may be, there is always man's desire to understand himself. The history of Greek thought illustrates this point: started as a philosophy of nature, with Socrates it began to direct its attention to man. The point is made clear also by the fact that in the course of history new discoveries in the realm of physical science constantly became the starting point of a new reflection upon man. We have seen several examples of this in Chapter Nine. Changes in the world view mean always also modifications in the picture of man. This idea leads us to another determinant of technical activity—man's desire for self-knowledge.

Man's Self-Knowledge. Man's awareness of himself as spirit-in-matter is one of the most potent impulses driving him to technical reshaping of matter. Because of this awareness he knows that there exists a large discrepancy between spirit and matter, between, on the one hand, the unlimited and unrestricted possibilities of the spirit and, on the other, the limitations, the restrictions, and the closedness of matter. True, at first this awareness led precisely to the pursuit of pure science and the rejection of technical skills as inferior. Nevertheless, ultimately this awareness of the discrepancy between mind and matter has to be considered to be an important determinant of technology. The reason is that this awareness not only influenced all those who, disregarding official science, devoted themselves to technical endeavors, but also began to make itself felt at a rapidly increasing rate once it became clear that the discrepancy in question could be overcome. As soon as this possibility became clear, the awareness of the limiting function exercised by matter with respect to the spirit was changed into the will to overcome this limitation.

The first beginnings of this will and desire may be seen in the fairy tale. Despite its irrationality, it expressed what man could be if he were not limited by matter, if the spirit would be capable of exercising real mastership over material forces. It is in part also through the perspective of how things could be that man's technical activity is not a "dumb natural event" but a consciously guided process. Superficially considered, technology and fairy tale may appear to be miles apart, nevertheless, it is true that without fairy tales there would have been no modern technology, without fairy tales technical activity would have remained a "dumb natural event" without any driving force. It is to the fairy tale that technical activity owes its inspiration, for this tale expressed graphically a very important aspect of man's self-knowledge—namely, the tension between what actually is and what could be. Thus the opinion that in the technological age there is no longer room for the fairy tale in a most serious fashion misapprehends the essence of technology.

The Awareness of Ethical Values. Another determinant of technical activity is closely connected with the preceding one—namely, man's awareness of the distinction not only between what actually is and what could be but also between what actually is and what *ought* to be. This is the awareness that being-man is a task, that being-man is a having to be man. As an ethical awareness, as knowing the distinction between what is and what ought to be, it urges man on toward ideals embodying an existence worthy of man for all. It finds its expression in the utopia. While the fairy tale concentrates upon the control over the forces of nature, the utopia points especially to an ideal society which ought to exist if there were no obstacles.

The obstacles find their source partially in man's evil dispositions and partially in his impotence to control natural conditions in such a way that a truly human existence becomes possible for all. Nature simply does not supply all that is necessary. Strictly speaking, therefore, it is not so much the distinction between what actually is and what ought to be which acts as a technical determinant as the distinction between what actually is and what ought to be if nature would offer greater possibilities. For the last-named distinction makes the tendency to technical progress an essential component of the ethical obligation and renders this obligation less static and more dynamic.

What we mean by this expression is the following. In a certain sense it is true that the ethical obligation is absolute and independent of concrete conditions, for it is an obligation which has to be fulfilled as best as possible, regardless of any concrete situations. Thus the concrete realization of this ethical demand may be brought about in quite different fashions in different sets of circumstances, but it is an obligation which holds for *all* circumstances. It is not suspended by any particular combination of conditions. For instance, an elementary ethical demand is that man has the duty to be just in *all* situations. If the situation itself *can be changed,* then changing the situation itself becomes an additional ethical obligation, but it does not suspend the first-named duty. On the other hand, man is not obliged to the impossible and, therefore he is not responsible for conditions of nature, in the strict sense, for these are precisely conditions which he cannot change. If there is a shortage of food, whatever is available ought to be distributed justly, but if nature does not supply enough food, no man can be held responsible for the resulting chronic shortage. Thus many ancient civilizations hardly viewed this shortage as a shortage, because it was a *natural* shortage. To speak of a natural shortage is almost a contradiction if one adheres to a certain view of nature.

The utopia, however, does not view the shortage of nature as a contradiction, and it is in this that lies its permanent value. The fairy tale and the utopia thus anticipated a view of nature which in later times would become a determinant factor of man's ethical awareness. This view of nature is the will not to be resigned to the natural scope allotted to man's ethical activity but to enlarge it and thus to realize not only what ought to be now but also what ideally ought to be. This will and this desire to realize what ideally ought to be have been unbreakably connected since the time when man discovered that his pursuit of science and his technical achievements resulted in an enormous increase of the latitude allowed by nature. He then began to realize how little he could appeal to nature to fix his ethical obligations at a stable level. In this way we are led to a consideration of the last and, in a sense, most important determinant.

The Workability of Matter. Considered in themselves, neither man's urge to know, his self-knowledge, his ethical awareness, nor any combination of these determinants suffice to give rise to technical activity, for all of them are too much concentrated upon man's spirit. They either remain within the sphere of contemplation, the sphere of spiritual self-realization in science and art, including the fairy tale and the utopia, or if they give rise to action, they remain in the realm of ethical activity. Although they are potent determinants of technical activity, they could become actual only when the most specific determinant of technical activity, the workability of nature, with all its implications was understood.

Nature, of course, had always been seen as workable. A simple reflection upon man's technical occupation, a natural occupation of man, as we have seen, showed that nature was workable and invited man to work it. The reflection, however, upon this natural technical activity did not yet make man realize that the totality of nature had to be seen as workable down to its most profound depth. It is this realization which lies at the basis of contemporary technology. This realization is the result of the encounter between, on the one hand, man's theoretical activity as embodied in pure science and philosophical reflection and, on the other, the technical activity of man resulting from his biological nature. Although man did not at once realize that the whole of nature was workable as soon as positive physical science was born, it remains true that this science saw nature as in principle subject to change and control. Hence it was merely a question of time before the consequences of this view would be drawn.

2. *Anthropological Consequences*

The view that nature was workable caused man to see this nature no longer as the adversary of the spirit. Matter is no longer the limiting factor which makes impossible what the mind sees to be fitting and suitable for man, but matter is seen now precisely as making the ideals of the spirit capable of realization. It was not really matter which had imposed limitation. Man's own spirit had been the cause of it, because it had not yet sufficiently become aware of itself, it had not yet sufficiently learned to see itself as spirit-in-matter rather than as spirit limited by matter.

Thanks to the new view, man began to experience his being a *homo faber* as a necessary complement of his spiritual functions. He has to work not so much to stay alive as to develop himself into the man which he ought to be because he is capable of becoming such a man. To become human does not mean only to form and enrich the spirit, but also to work nature so as to put it under the control of the spirit, because it is in this control that lies the destiny of matter. This more profound anthropological vision is the ultimate consequence of the view that nature can be reworked by man.

Man the Unveiler of Nature. In a sharp analysis of the essence of technical activity Heidegger remarks that man in his modern technology is not so much the reworker of nature as the unveiler of its possibilities.[5] He makes this remark in connection with a consideration of Aristotle's famous theory of the four causes. As a matter of fact, the reworking of nature, the being an efficient cause, is only one of the aspects found in technical activity. This reworking is essential, of course, for whatever natural possibilities man unveils, whatever he

---

[5] *Die Frage nach der Technik,* pp. 50f.

draws forth from nature results from his work on nature. However, this reworking of nature is consequent upon man's discovery of a possibility. Invention always precedes construction, but it is never complete without this construction. This is true not only in the sense that without the construction the invention is not actually realized, but also and especially because only the actual realization proves that a genuine possibility has been discovered.

Considered merely as a reworker of nature, man remains on the same level as the animal, although he is capable of more refined reworking. It is precisely in the interplay of seeing possibilities and realizing them in his labor that man's technical activity expresses the unity of spirit and matter existing in man. Just as in the human body matter is organized in such a way that it becomes the embodiment of the spirit, so also the body as permeated with the spirit acts upon nature outside the body to organize this nature in such a way that it begins to function as an extension of the body so as to make possible in a limited fashion the realization of man's spiritual desires which go beyond the power of the body alone.

What these spiritual desires are should be clear. They flow from what the spirit experiences in itself as unlimitedness. In its cognitive function, for example, the mind experiences something of the transcendence of space and time. It is aware of this transcendence, as we have seen even in the simple formation of concepts, because a concept as a concept no longer clings to the perceived object in its concrete presence in the here and now. Most of all, however, the spirit experiences its transcendence with respect to the limitations of matter in realizing that these limitations are limitations.

In a previous chapter we have pointed out the consequences which this realization has for the pursuit of science. Thanks to the fact that man, despite all the limitations of his knowledge, has to some extent an outlook upon unlimited knowledge, he continues to be urged on in his pursuit of science. He is not satisfied with what has been reached. He is aware of it that every concrete status of science is limited and thus falls short of the ideal of all science. It is this ambivalence of, on the one hand, being limited by matter and, on the other seeing through this limitation, which constitutes the spiritual strength of man and is at work also in his technical activity.

The Naturalness of Technical Activity. Man's technical endeavor is really nothing else but an effort to utilize the possibilities of matter, despite its limitation, in such a way that its limitation is transcended. A clear illustration of the point is offered by tele-communication. In communicating with his fellow men from a distance the mind is clearly aware of its dependence upon the limited possibilities offered by the senses but nevertheless endeavors to raise sense knowledge to the universal level proper to the spirit. Because of its universality, intellectual knowledge has something which we may call a kind of omnipresence. This omnipresence, however, is obtained by means of abstraction, which alone places this knowledge beyond space and time. However, thanks to the technical construction of, e.g., a television apparatus, man is capable of conquering space in a new fashion, without abstracting from space. Television enables man's eye to know what happens at a distance. The eye remains exactly as it was before, and its natural range is not changed in any way.[6]

The natural limitation and dependence remain, but the technical apparatus eliminates something of this limitation, and in this way the senses participate to some extent in the unlimited possibilities and perspectives of the spirit. Ultimately, however, it is not the sense which is enriched but the spirit itself, for the sense is subservient to the spirit which depends upon it. We have to rely upon our voice, our ear and our eye to enter into spiritual contact with one another, because otherwise such a contact would remain purely abstract. We have to rely upon our senses to arrive at understanding of material reality. But by opening new possibilities for his senses, man creates also new perspectives for his spiritual desire to understand, just as also his loving concern for his suffering fellow men receives new dimensions from the technical possibilities opened for medical science.

Nevertheless, technology does not overcome time and space in the sense of eliminating them as it were. Technology does not eliminate anything of matter's fundamental characteristics but merely makes a new use of them. In a telephone conversation, for instance, the spatial distance remains, but it is more quickly overcome. An airplane does not eliminate gravitation, but takes advantage of this phenomenon in a new fashion. Technology does not create or eliminate any possibilities but merely unveils them. For this reason the character of technical inventions reveals very little arbitrariness. To

------

[6]At least, *de facto* this is still the case. However, it is not a matter of being so in principle. It is quite possible that the human body still contains hidden possibilities which are waiting to be discovered. For man's knowledge of his own sensitivity is still exceedingly small.

attain a certain goal, e.g., to fly, only a few forms of construction offer any possibilities. The evolution of the airplane shows this very clearly, inasmuch as the plane gradually more and more approaches its most proper form. One would almost be inclined to think here along Platonic lines as if the idea of the airplane exists in itself and is slowly more closely approximated by concrete planes. In reality, however, this idea lies contained in the possibilities of nature and has to be developed from them.

The more one reflects upon technology along the lines drawn in this chapter, the more one is impressed by the naturalness of technology. Man's technical endeavor is the realization of the possibilities of nature in accord with the natural aspirations of the human mind. It constitutes the natural complement of man's bodily possibilities and serves the spirit-in-matter to organize the world into a human world. Nevertheless, it is true that one of the main objections against technology lies precisely in its unnatural and inhuman character. Must we say, therefore, that our analysis has gone astray when it led us to conclude to the human and natural character of technology? To find out, let us first examine the objections raised against technology and then revert to the essence of man's technical endeavor.

CHAPTER TWELVE

TECHNOLOGY AS A DANGER

1. *The Ambivalent Character of Technology*

Anyone who wishes to analyze the dangers of technology should keep in mind that from the very beginning two kinds of dangers are to be distinguished—namely, dangers which actually have been caused by technology although they do not flow from its very nature, and dangers which are really inherent in technology as such. As we will see, this distinction cannot always be rigorously adhered to, but this does not take away from the fact that it is very important.

General Ambivalence. It is not difficult to see that some of the dangers connected with technology do not necessarily flow from its very nature. Evidently, man's technical knowledge and ability can be put to good and to evil use. This possibility gives technology its ambivalent character, but it is a feature which technology shares with many other human endeavors. There is no human activity which cannot be put to wrong use and thus denatured. In this sense man's whole existence is ambivalent, and this ambivalence is merely participated in by technical activity, whether it be of a primitive type or scientific.

In this respect, therefore, nuclear energy as a source of power does not differ from muscular power armed with a knife. Both are capable of being used constructively as well as destructively. In other words, the ambivalence implied in good and evil usage is not a specific aspect of modern technology. This assertion, however, does not mean that man does not have now a greater responsibility to prevent abuse because of the enormously increased possibilities for good and for evil which technology has placed at his disposal. Nevertheless, this responsibility does not concern the essence of modern technology. Modern technology as such does not lead more easily to abuse than did ancient more primitive technical knowledge.[1] It is true, of course, that the

---

[1] It is interesting to note here that man has always been greatly dismayed by any new development of technical means. Striking examples of this dismay from all periods of history may be found in Klemm, *Technik, eine Geschichte ihrer Probleme*, Freiburg, 1954.

consequences of abuse are much more catastrophic nowadays than they used to be, but this situation, as we will see, may be considered an advantage rather than a disadvantage.

Specific Ambivalence. Accordingly, when modern technology is viewed as a danger for the humanity of mankind, the reason must be sought elsewhere—namely, in the conviction that, whether used for good or for evil, modern technology means of necessity a loss of humanity because, to cite Guardini again, it leads to a non-human man in an unnatural nature. Its specific ambivalence is that, while liberating man's spirit from material limitations, it enslaves his spirit to matter. Modern technology, therefore, is at the same time spiritualization and materialization of man. The following analysis will show that this ambivalence really does exist.

2. *The Autonomy of the Technological Order*

The Reason for the Autonomy of the Technological Order. Technology is the realization and consequently the embodiment of human ideas in matter. A machine objectifies a certain purpose pursued by man. The material parts are arranged in such a way that the inherent forces of nature will realize the purpose in question. Man's finality thus makes use, as it necessarily has to, of the inner orientation of the forces of nature. As a result, the machine will never operate directly in accord with the intentions of its maker, but only insofar as the forces of nature are arranged in it in such a way that they really reflect the maker's intentions. As a material mechanism, therefore, the machine remains autonomous. What is at work in the machine is not the human idea but the artificial form given to matter.

In this form the idea which inspired it leads, so to speak, its own life, which is not necessarily fully in harmony with the intention of its maker. In the operation of the machine certain properties may reveal themselves which its maker did not foresee, because he did not sufficiently know the materials and forces composing it or because it was built from other materials and in another way than he had in mind. What is true of any machine applies *a fortiori* to the entire technical world created by man. While a single machine remains to some extent subject to man's comprehensive grasp, the same is true only to an extremely small degree of the composite whole which we call the technological world. This world, then, leads a life of its own in accord with the arrangements which have actually been made in it. It thus becomes an autonomous technological order.

The consequence is that any human ignorance as well as all of man's hidden or open wickedness, once it is embodied in this order, continues to operate independently of man's will. Of course, man is able again to interfere in this order to correct it and make it correspond more closely to his intentions. But even with respect to this interference it remains true that what does happen does not depend on what the intervention intended to realize but on what it actually did accomplish.

Technological Autonomy in Ancient and in Modern Times. This kind of autonomy is not specifically proper to the contemporary technological order, but applies to all technical activity, even in its most primitive forms. The arrow shot by the archer does not travel toward the target intended by him, but to the target to which it was directed by virtue of its actual position in the bow. Nevertheless, there is a qualitative difference between the autonomy of the technological order and that of ancient technical implements. The pioneer who built his cabin with tools he himself had fashioned had a comprehensive view of his labor in all its successive phases. He knew exactly the meaning which the things he made had in his world, for his practical knowledge was concrete and not abstract science. Of course, there were many things which he did not know; for example, why the various materials he used had the properties which they did have. However, this ignorance did not trouble him, because he knew that they did have these natural properties and that he could make use of them for the concrete purposes for which he did use them.

Contemporary science, on the other hand, is characterized, as we have seen in Chapter Three, by abstractness and partiality. To the extent that technical activity becomes more scientific it increasingly shares more in the abstractness of science: it too becomes abstract and partial, directed to a single aspect or a connected group of aspects. For this reason the modern industrial worker, whether he be a designer or a common laborer, no longer has a comprehensive grasp of the social effects flowing from his products. If, for instance, he makes motor cars, he does not comprehend the traffic problems which they create. For the construction of a reliable car differs greatly from the solution of traffic problems and demands an entirely different kind of scientific or practical knowledge from that of regulating traffic. Or to give another example, realizing the idea of seeing at a distance in the form of television demands a kind of knowledge the orientation of which differs entirely from that of understanding the pedagogical problems created by this new means of communication.

Evidently, we do not want to say that the inventor, designer, or laborer does not have to be concerned about the social results produced by his activity. All we intend to assert is that within the framework of the knowledge and skill needed for the realization of the idea "television" pedagogical problems do not arise, just as traffic problems do not manifest themselves in the realization of the idea "motor car."

In a motor car factory the laborer whose job it is to make the chassis is not responsible for the performance of the engine because his work and his knowledge are not concerned with this part of the car. In a similar fashion, with respect to the whole technological order, it is true that anyone working in it understands and is concerned only with an abstract part of it. This assertion applies even to those who occupy the highest positions. Although it may be their specific task to understand and grasp the whole, they do so only in an abstract fashion. The top executive sees the total course of affairs only by means of graphs and reports, just as also the man in the control tower of an airport has the landing and departing planes present to himself only in an abstract fashion by means of a radar screen or radio phone. There is no one who ever sees the *concrete* whole.

Rationalization of Labor and the Autonomy of the Technological Order. Accordingly, as labor becomes progressively more rationalized, the abstractness of knowledge which is always concerned with mere aspects is extended to the building of the world in which we live. Thus this world becomes constantly less easy to comprehend, because each of its partial processes is based upon its own abstract way of knowing and a corresponding way of acting or doing things. New ideas are thus continually embodied in the technological order and their effect in certain realms cannot be foreseen, simply because this effect was unknown within the framework of the knowledge and the activity to which these ideas owed their realization. Yet once they are embodied in the order, they exercise their influence in an autonomous fashion. They are integrated into the objectively existing field of forces in which they operate.

For this reason the evolution of modern society as a technological order takes place in a convulsive fashion. Because of a scientific discovery or a technical invention a certain realm suddenly develops enormously and disrupts the whole existing pattern of society. Contrary to the ancient world in which nature appeared to man as a cosmos, i.e., an orderly whole to which man's life could be adapted in accord with fixed patterns, the technological order is structured unharmoniously. Disproportions make themselves felt constantly and compel man feverishly to hurry on along the road he has taken in order to solve the problems raised by these disproportions.

Man was able to rely upon nature, even though he did not comprehend it. Nature was stable. It did not give much scope to his life, but within the available scope he could be free. Although he often felt himself in the power of nature, because he could not control its action, he was not responsible for nature's being what it was. Nature was hard, but it did not absorb his spiritual energy, because it was independent of him. Thus he could devote his spiritual powers fully to the formation of the mind and to cultural creations within the limits accorded to him by nature.

The technological order, on the other hand, for which man feels himself to be responsible, is not a stable and harmonious world. It is continuously disrupted and, because man knows that he is responsible for this world, it demands constantly that he devote his full attention and personal efforts to retain his control and to correct the disproportions resulting unexpectedly from his technological creations. Man cannot reserve sufficient time for spiritual peace in which he would be able to be himself. He feels himself the victim and the slave of the technological order which he has created.

General Disproportions. The disproportions in question do not remain limited to the technical realm in the narrow sense, for human society is too closely connected with these technical achievements. Thus it may happen that a certain technological development may disrupt the whole social structure without the technologist as such being able to do anything about it. For such disproportions and effects do not lie within the abstract field of his vision. He merely tries to perfect his technical products.

The brief history of industrial technology offers striking examples of the unharmonious development which took place in the social order under the influence of technology. The industrialization of the nineteenth century gave rise to enormous social problems and to a veritable revolution in the traditional patterns of life. Nevertheless, the nineteenth century should not be blamed as much as is usually done for its inability to check at once the disastrous consequences of the industrial revolution. It simply was not prepared to cope with these consequences. Social adaptation to the revolution had perforce to lag behind, because its problems do not lie on the same level as that of building steam engines and mechanical looms.

At present man again finds himself in a phase of technological evolution the consequences of which he cannot sufficiently foresee. Our human care still continues to go out to the effects resulting from the monotony of work at the conveyer belt, which forces man to adapt himself in his work to the machine and thus is a symptom of his subordination to the technological order. Yet the new development of technology now brings us face to face with an entirely different situation. Increasing automation confronts us with a future in which monotonous labor could be eliminated so radically that whatever human labor would still be needed would impose intellectual demands that the large majority of laborers would be unable to meet.

The world faces a huge shortage of capable physicists and technologists as well as of well-trained technicians. For any type of labor which is objectified in the machine, whether this labor formerly was intellectual or manual, operative or directive, can remain fruitful only if there are human beings who intellectually and materially control this objectivation and thus make it human again. The reason lies not only in the above-mentioned necessity of constant control but also in the necessity of putting the objective achievements of the machine to good use. Thus there is a great shortage of well-trained laborers on all levels. To the extent that more of man's spirit is embodied in the technological order in the form of ideas, this order demands more and more of man's attention. Like an insatiable dragon, it demands the whole of man.

The Danger of the Technological Order with Respect to Man's Human Existence. Thus the evolution of the technological order impresses man as a process running its course independently of his will. In part this impression is correct, for the forces which develop technology, despite their human character, have to work in an abstract fashion and thus are blind with respect to the total results of their work. The automatic execution of what man has embodied in the technological order constantly gives rise to unexpected effects, thus forcing him to renewed and steadily accelerated efforts. It prevents him from paying attention to anything else but the functioning of the technological order.

At present this functioning requires more and better trained technologists and technicians. As befits a technological order, modern society views this situation in a technical fashion. If the human material falls short of requirements, something has to be done about it, just as something has to be done when traditional materials no longer satisfy the demands made by modern products. If, therefore, new materials are created to remedy the last-named deficiency, then the human shortage has to be solved, as is the custom in physics and technology, by "producing" new human beings, adapted to the demands imposed by the technological order. If man now threatens to fall short intellectually, i.e., if instead of a shortage of materials energy, or laborers there is now an intellectual shortage, a shortage of intellectual manpower, then the educational system has to be changed to remedy this deficiency.

It is not surprising that the perspective of such an omnivorous technological order which sees nature as well as man himself as a composite of modifiable units causes our contemporaries to feel that in this order man will lose his human existence. The danger is not at all imaginary, but is inherent in technology itself because it arises from the inner dynamism proper to technology. Nevertheless, the existence of such a danger does not necessarily mean that everything is lost. Man's human existence can still be saved, but only if this inevitable danger is recognized as such. For this reason it is important to analyze the dangers inherent in technology. The essential question is whether the technological order necessarily disregards man's nature or merely contains a danger of disregarding this nature. In the first case the only salvation lies in a radical renouncement of technology. In the second we have to evaluate the danger of technology in a realistic way.

3. *The Unnaturalness of Technology*

a. The Ambiguity of the Qualifier "Natural"

Nearly all attacks on technology are directed against its allegedly unnatural character which is supposed to disrupt the natural situation of man's life. It is accused of dehumanizing man by making an unnatural man grow up in an unnatural nature. The accusation may appear rather harsh, at least to those who still consider nature the ultimate and decisive norm. That this norm is not arbitrary is shown by history. No matter how much the concept and evaluation of nature have changed from antiquity until our time, this concept has always retained a certain normative character.

The difficulty, however, is that "nature" is a typically ambiguous term having a whole spectrum of meanings, so that it is not very easy to determine exactly in what sense the natural is normative. For this reason it is possible to indicate not only reasons which may justify calling technology unnatural but also others showing that it is wholly natural. In ancient technical activity this natural character revealed itself so strongly that no one would seriously think of calling it unnatural. One has only to look at a human hand to see that it is naturally adapted to the manipulation of tools. As was pointed out in the preceding chapter, the basis of ancient technical activity was at least as biologically natural as it was rational.

Accordingly, the reproach of being unnatural could be meaningful only with respect to modern technology. Nevertheless, even of contemporary technological activity it is true that its development from that of the ancients does not manifest anything unnatural. Although its method is analytic and therefore onesided, this method is wholly a natural consequence of the structure of human knowledge which, because of the unity of knowing and making, permeates also man's technical activity. Hence there is no reason for calling the development of ancient technique into modern technology an unnatural process.

Frightening Naturalness. It is precisely this last conclusion which causes many to be frightened by this evolution. If it is true that the characteristic features of the technological order are not based upon any aberration but in harmony both with the nature of man's cognitive and operative powers and with the nature of matter, then the situation rightfully causes dismay and anxiety, for in that case there must be something wrong with the very nature of man. Pointing in this direction is the fact that practically no one among the opponents of modern technology ventures to reject it radically as unsuitable for man's nature as this nature really is, because the inner logic controlling the evolution of ancient technical skills into modern technology and the contemporary technological order testifies too eloquently to the contrary.

Some, therefore, claim that technology is natural but at the same time sinful. The technological order is the consequence of man's setting himself up against God and is doomed forever to bear the effects of his fall into sin. Others, to whom the concept of sin no longer says anything, think that what reveals itself in technology is the utter meaninglessness of man's entire existence. Thus it is not surprising that, precisely at a time when man has managed to realize some of the desires expressed in fairy tales and utopias, so many find themselves in sympathy with philosophical currents which proclaim that man's existence is devoid of meaning.

It would be wrong to seek the cause of this phenomenon exclusively in the two world wars and the threat of a third. The cause lies much deeper. Even when technology is not misused, the technological order seems quasi-naturally to dehumanize man and to reduce him to a thing. It is this which is a much more frightening indication of the meaninglessness of human existence than any kind of misuse, which always allows hope to remain that somehow it will be corrected. The dehumanization and reification of man, as inherent tendencies of the technological order itself, seem to characterize man's mode of existence as a being toward death, as a mode of existing which has ultimately to destroy itself. Or to express the same idea in terms of the evolutionary theory, the species *homo* is a design of nature that has failed and is bound to eliminate itself. As the initiator of the technological order, man seems predestined to perish in this order, just as certain prehistoric species of animals undermined their own chances of survival through disproportioned albeit natural evolution.

The cultural crisis of the West is largely rooted in the inner division of mankind in its attitude toward technology. The naturalness of technology forces man to pursue it with all his energy, but at the same time the ultimate perspective opened by technology makes many internally reject it, because technology dehumanizes and therefore ultimately seems to be unnatural.

Where does man find an indication of the unnatural character of technology? Only in its supposedly dehumanizing effect or also in a clear-cut opposition to nature? In other words, is technology against nature only when viewed from the standpoint of man or does it also go contrary to nature in the sense of material nature? Both of these points need to be examined more accurately.

b. Living Beings and Technical Things

In Chapter Nine we analyzed the modifications of the world view and of the concept of nature which took place under the influence of the development of physical science and technology. We saw there how from the viewpoint of physical science nature has lost its established form and is considered to consist of more or less random formations of elementary units. Evidently, this modification in the evaluation of nature does not extend to the whole of nature. Especially the realm of the living is excepted from it. True, mechanism has constantly gained ground on vitalism, but this fact does not mean that the realm of the living has lost its proper character.[2]

Naturalness Versus Artificiality. The truth of this assertion manifests itself most clearly when we compare a living being with a technical thing. Although the two have much in common and their operations are based upon the same forces of nature, the great difference is that a living body is organized from within, while a technical thing is organized from without. For the organization and operation of a technical object is based upon an artificial form given to the material of which it is built. This form is imposed upon matter. Iron does not naturally have the form of gears, wheels, or chassis. Such things do not originate spontaneously in nature, not even by chance. With respect to living organisms, on the other hand, while it may be a matter of dispute whether or not they originated by chance from non-living matter,[3] it is certain that their structures fit in harmoniously with the fundamental properties of matter. Once formed, they appear to be stable, with a dynamic kind of stability, for they develop and adapt themselves constantly more to their environment.

What is striking here is that the distinction between a living being and a technical thing assumes importance in direct ratio to the extent that one is inclined to a mechanistic viewpoint. From the standpoint of mechanism, which denies that there is an essential difference between a living organism and a mechanical object, a technical thing is exceedingly crude, because of the discrepancy between its microstructures and its macrostructure. Although its microstructures permit the macrostructure, this structure remains

---

[2]Cf. Ch. VII, sect. 2, pp. 136 ff.
[3]Cf. Andrew G. van Melsen, "Philosophical Aspects of Evolution," *Symposium on Evolution*, Pittsburgh, 1959, pp. 59 ff.

foreign to them. In a living body, on the other hand, the micro-structure and the macrostructure, as it were, call for each other.

A sign of the discrepancy in question is the fact that in the realm of the living no two individuals of the same species are alike. Although the species-individual structure holds also for the building blocks of living nature, nature plays with them in such a way that it constantly produces something unique without forcing anything and without diminishing the vital power of the living body. The endless variations of the same fundamental theme is one of the main charms of nature. No two human faces are the same, and no two trees are alike. With respect to technical objects, however, uniformity is the ideal. The artificial structure of the prototype, precisely because it is artificial, has to be imitated as accurately as possible, for otherwise the thing does not "fit." Accidental deviations from the type are troublesome, for they may spoil the product.

Versatility Versus Onesidedness. Secondly, as compared with the living body, the technical thing exhibits a strong onesidedness of functions. As we have pointed out previously, the closedness of matter, which always is exactly what it is, makes a complex structure necessary when it has to perform a multitude of functions. This rule applies to living organisms as well as to artificial mechanisms. However, these mechanisms are based upon structures that are "foreign" to matter, and for this reason technical structures are much cruder and less capable of intricate functions.[4]

c. Physical and Chemical Technique

In this connection it is interesting to point to a difference between what we may call, for the sake of easy reference, chemical and physical technique. Guided by his theoretical knowledge, the chemist also makes new compounds artificially. However, the chemist intuitively makes no distinction between compounds occurring in nature and others which, to the best of his knowledge, can be produced only in the laboratory. All he does is to bring substances together in a cer-

---

[4]Of course, we do not mean that a technical product may not be capable of functions which go beyond the possibilities of a living body. However, such a capacity is as a rule accompanied by troublesome onesidedness. A jet plane, for instance, can fly much faster than a bird, but is not capable of much else than flying fast and thus misses the mobility of a helicopter. How troublesome this is appears from the necessity to keep extending the runways of our airports.

tain set of circumstances and in a carefully determined sequence, and then the reaction follows "naturally."

He does not force his molecules into an artificial form, but merely compels the process of nature to take its course in a certain direction. The substances which he synthetizes in this way are in principle entirely similar to those of nature when he is engaged in the synthetic production of substances occurring in nature. Thus the work of the chemist resembles in many respects what we have called above, in Chapter Ten, the cultivation of nature. The chemist guides the processes of nature rather than forcing it to assume foreign forms.

Physical technique, on the contrary, is characterized precisely by imposing foreign forms upon matter. It too, of course, makes use of the possibilities offered by nature. Hence physical technique also may be said to create conditions in which matter is forced to assume a certain form. Nevertheless, the difference from chemical technique is striking. The physico-technical reworking of matter demands a constantly active interference in the process. The material is subjected to manipulations until it assumes the artificial form. The process does not have a natural terminus but ends only when the technician judges that the arbitrary form which he had in mind has been given to the object.[5]

4. *Technology and an Unnatural Way of Life*

The objection may be raised that the preceding characterization of the technical thing as unnatural is unjustified, because it considers this thing separately and not in relation to its user and to the purpose for which it has been made. However, even if this relationship is taken into consideration, there is ample reason for speaking about unnaturalness both from the biological viewpoint and from the specifically human standpoint.

a. The Biological Aspect

The excessive development of all kinds of technological means leads to the atrophy of human organs and thus undermines man's health. For the human body is a whole in which, as always in life, the various parts are marvellously attuned to one another. Hence there is a way of life which from the biological viewpoint may be called a

---

[5]The arbitrariness in question refers, of course, only to the form of the material and not to the purpose which the technician has in mind.

natural, healthy way of living, i.e., a way of life in which the whole body takes part and is active in a natural succession of motion and rest, of effort and detention. It follows, therefore, that the use of technical means through which some organs are overworked and others practically never used is unnatural and harmful. This situation is greatly favored by the modern process of labor. True, even of primitive forms of technique it is true that they could become an occasion for onesided development, but in these forms there was less division of labor and consequently less onesidedness and, in addition, the laborer himself could determine the speed of his operation. In the modern factory, however, these two factors are missing, for its rigid specialization leads to extreme onesidedness and to keeping up with the conveyer belt.

While it would be useless to deny the adduced facts, it should be evident that the biological objections against modern technology are not weighty enough to stamp it as unnatural. Because technical means possess striking advantages even for the health of the body, the disadvantages can easily be absorbed, especially because the resulting decrease of man's working hours offers him ample opportunity to compensate himself for the onesideness of his labor. Moreover, it is rather striking that the victims of the technological order nowadays must be sought among the executives of industry rather than the ordinary laborers. In other words, the dangerous tensions appear to be mental rather than biological.

b. The Human Aspect

The Burdening of the Spirit with Matter. For this reason the objection that technology makes man's whole way of life something artificial carries much more weight than the complaint that technology is unnatural with respect to man's body. Although enough time is available now for bodily rest, the technological order takes away from man the peace of mind which he needs even for his bodily well-being. The speed-up of labor to a biologically unhealthy level which was frequent in the past may have practically disappeared, but the technological order has plunged man into a hurried pursuit without respite. If through his technology man has managed to liberate himself to some extent from his natural bonds with nature, technology itself has tied him up even more and this time the bonds are unnatural. For, by creating the technological order, man has imposed upon himself the task of keeping this order functioning in accord with his desires.

The natural order may have been inhospitable in many respects, but at least it did not require constant care and allowed man to devote himself to his cultural pursuits within the narrow confines permitted by this order. The technological order, on the other hand, absorbs man's entire mental attention and working power. It seems as if, by embodying ideas in the material world, the spirit has burdened itself with the full weight of matter. The spirit now has to drag along so many material bonds that it no longer sees a possibility of really taking possession of its world. To illustrate this point, let us return once more to the example of tele-communication.

This invention, as we have seen, embodies a real human desire to let the senses participate in the universality of the spirit. However, we may ask, is not the actual result of this invention that man is confronted with so many impressions, so many facts, so many events that he simply lacks the capacity of assimilating all this and of making it his own spiritual possession? For instance, television with its enlarged perception does not lead to better understanding, to greater wisdom of life—for such wisdom is based upon broad and prolonged experience of life—but on the contrary it fritters away man's mental concentration and self-possession. It does not stimulate him to activity, but tempts him to being passive. Tele-communication, which in principle is universal communication with *all* human beings, concretely prevents authentic human contact. What has been gained in extension has been lost in depth.

Briefly, the natural relationship between man's turning to the world outside him by means of his senses and the assimilation of what he perceives has been lost. His inner self has become a vacuum and thus is wide open for all kinds of propaganda streaming in through modern channels of communication. It is hardly necessary to point out what all this may lead to.

The Loss of Spiritual Balance. The inner emptiness, filled artificially through technical means, is further promoted by a peculiar property of modern inventions which was pointed out by Marcel and Jaspers. All kinds of people learn to use things without understanding them at all and even without having to try to understand them in order to use them properly. The invention itself of a technical product is the result of a mental effort. It is a truly cultural deed, for it unveils the possibilities of nature. The use of this invention, however, does not demand any kind of mental effort that can even distantly be compared with that of making the invention itself. It requires merely that one turns the proper knobs in the proper direction. One does not even see what he does, at least not in the sense that he perceives what happens inside the box. There is, as it were, a short cut between turning the right knob and the effect resulting from it. Turn the lower knob and the picture becomes bright, turn the upper one and the volume increases, etc.

In the technical means, tools and instruments of former times the situation was radically different. They showed their structure fully, the idea embodied in them remained externally visible, and their use presupposed familiarity with this idea. In modern technical contraptions the only visible parts are control mechanisms which say next to nothing about what goes on inside and are simply attached to the side which produces the useful result of the inner process, such as a picture or sound. Whatever is visible expresses only the idea of usage and not of the inner structure which makes the usage possible. This inner structure is known only to the specialist, trained in the scientific and technical principles embodied in the set. This difference between ancient and modern technical means is, of course, connected with their respective character. Ancient technique was wholly based upon externally perceptible properties of matter, while modern technology is based upon scientific insights into its inner structure. For this reason it is wrong to condemn modern technical means as being nothing but "boxes," for their box-like appearance is very appropriate, because their inner workings are too complex to be understood by the average user.

On the other hand, however, it is true that, from the mental viewpoint, the user will very easily live "beyond his means" and thus become increasingly more impoverished. There is no longer any natural connection between what he does and what he understands, between his own effort and the effect it produces. In this way modern technology disrupts man's natural balance. Accordingly, when it is said that technology leads to an unnatural way of life, the reproach aims not so much at unhealthy aspects of technology on the purely biological level as at what is unhealthy on the specifically human level, on which lack of health is, of course, much more serious and dangerous.

Strictly speaking, one may make a distinction between bodily health and mental health, for it is possible to be bodily ill and mentally healthy, or vice versa. Nevertheless, such cases are relatively rare, because man is a spiritual-material unit.[6] If, therefore, technology deserves the reproach of leading to an unnatural way of life, this reproach must refer not only to man's biological and bodily aspect but to the whole of man.

The Culture of Means. It seems to be true that technology leads to a way of life which is unnatural for man, because it disrupts the equilibrium between exteriority and interiority, between controlling and understanding, between perceiving and mentally assimilating, between the creation of means and their human use. Modern technology seems to induce man to become so absorbed in the means that the goal no longer seems important to him. The man who has surrendered to the technological world may be compared to a housewife who does nothing else but cleaning and polishing and thus succeeds in making her house unfit as a dwelling place. Just as such a housewife suffers from a kind of cleaning neurosis, so the pursuit of modern technology appears to be a neurotic compulsion: once started, it does not want to let man do anything else. He has to go on with it and constantly becomes more deeply involved in it. He loses sight of all proportions and is interested in it alone.

A neurosis often begins with a flight from the real responsibilities to be faced in life. Was this the case also in man's technological pursuit? Did he want to escape from his real responsibility? Many do not hesitate to reply in the affirmative. They point out that technology is a secularization of the Christian idea of redemption and thus a pseudo-religion. Because the way to redemption preached by Christianity was the way of self-renouncement and detachment from the earth, it seemed too difficult, and therefore man sought his redemption on the earth itself, redemption by way of matter. This is undoubtedly an interesting view deserving close attention. We will consider it more in detail later in this work. At present we prefer to continue our analysis of the unnaturalness attributed to technology, considering now no longer man as an individual but rather the whole of human society.

---

[6]The fact that medical science has rediscovered this unity is one of those striking proofs for the "healthy" status of science itself which were spoken about when we considered the modifications of the scientific world view. The internal evolution of physical science corrected the onesidedness of the classical world view, and in a similar fashion medical science has been able to correct a faulty dualistic view of man not through the influence of philosophical trends of thought but by virtue of the purpose which it pursues in its research.

c. The Technological Order as a Secondary Social System

Characterization of the "Secondary Social System." In a fascinating cultural analysis, in which he proposes a theory of contemporary civilization, the sociologist H. Freyer sees the unnaturalness of technology mirrored in the unnatural character of modern society as a whole which, as he expresses it, is characterized by the "secondary system."[7] By this term he means a social structure in which "no established order is integrated, no previous autonomous rights are recognized, and in which one can neither rely nor count upon the validity of any structure in the future."[8]

The secondary system is nothing else but the technological order pursued till its ultimate social consequences. Just as the technical thing is an artificial construction, so also the secondary system is a structure in which natural bonds and historical growth are disregarded to make room for the perfectly working system, based upon abstract scientific principles. It is not borne by a natural ground but, like a bridge, merely supported here and there by a pillar.[9] In a secondary system "one no longer builds upon previously prepared ground, i.e., upon a social dimension which has an established form. There is no longer question of a structure which integrates and thus guarantees traditional possessions, special corporate rights, and regional freedoms."[10]

In the secondary system man is not integrated according to the full personality which he contributes to the whole, but is considered only according to a single aspect—the aspect, namely, which fits into the scheme. "In other words, secondary systems are systems of social organization which invade the innermost depth of man as a human being."[11] The secondary system divides man into functions, atomizes him. Man's natural unity of life is disrupted, as is illustrated, for instance, by the separation of his dwelling place from his place of labor. This separation, however, is merely a sign of a much greater division. Man is made to enter into all kinds of organizations, and in each of them he is the bearer of a number. As a number he takes care of a certain function in a particular organization. He is known in it only in this function, for the rest of him has no bearing upon the organization.

---

[7] H. Freyer, *Theorie des gegenwartigen Zeitalters,* Stuttgart, 1955.
[8] *Op. cit.,* p. 83.
[9] *Op. cit.,* p. 122.
[10] *Op. cit.,* p. 88.
[11] *Op. cit.,* p. 88.

The Secondary System as Effect of Technology. It is not difficult to recognize in the sociologist's characterization of the secondary system the effect produced by technology upon the social order. Inspired by physical science, modern technology no longer sees the things of nature as natural wholes, but considers them as instances in which certain abstract magnitudes go together. Within the framework of physical science a concrete piece of rock recedes as a reality to make room for an instance displaying a certain mass, form, specific weight, chemical composition, etc. By virtue of each of these magnitudes the stone obeys certain laws, is capable of being reworked in certain technical ways, and thus useful for certain purposes. In a similar way the secondary system does not see man as a concrete person, rooted in a network of natural relationships and living in historical traditions, but considers him as a producer, a consumer, or unemployed (he is entitled to compensation), a motorist, a street car rider or a pedestrian (check one), a possible orphan, widow or old-age pensioner, a taxpayer, a voter, a draftee, etc.

It is true, of course, that even in the old forms of society every concrete human being fulfilled many functions. However, these functions were not cut off from him. In each of his functions he was wholly known to all who came into contact with him in the exercise of the function. Otherwise he would be called a stranger or a foreigner. This situation still exists in small villages where everyone knows everybody.

In the secondary system, on the other hand, we are all in principle strangers for one another, except in relation to the aspects pertaining to the level on which we encounter one another. The neighbor is known as the man who lives close to us, but we know nothing about his work, his bowling club, his church, or the people with whom he travels to and from work. Thus our neighbor may remain in many respects a stranger for us, just as he is a stranger for all others whom he meets in a different social relationship. The natural unity of the person disintegrates and is divided into partial functions. Each one now leads many lives, none of which, however, is a full life. This situation, then, would explain the inner emptiness of modern life and the fundamental loneliness of man, despite the many social organizations to which he belongs.

Other Influences. As a social reality the secondary system is, of course, not solely the result of the technological evolution. Historians point also to economic changes, which began to manifest themselves as early as the end of the Middle Ages. Ancient economy did not work for a general anonymous market but supplied existing needs. It had a stable character, because it seemed meaningless to produce things for which there was not yet any need. Modern economy, on the other hand, *creates* needs. It has a special apparatus for this purpose—advertising. The producer labors for an anonymous market: what he is interested in is not the concrete existing needs but the needs he can create.

Like technology, modern economy does not know any natural boundaries. Both want to advance ceaselessly, both live on their belief in expansion. Does this belief reflect man's deepest nature or does it disown this nature? What is even more important, supposing that this belief reflects man's deepest nature, do expanding technology and economy lead man perhaps in the wrong direction, so that in his progress man really always lags behind himself? Is perhaps the entire secondary system nothing else but a monstrous growth of man's social nature, like a cancerous tumor in a healthy organism? Before replying to these questions, let us first analyze other unnatural aspects of technology, as they present themselves in human society.

d. The Leveling Influence of Technology

Depersonalized Production. One of the most serious reproaches addressed to technology is that it levels man and reduces mankind to an anonymous mass. Technology seems to disown even the way in which nature itself works with its elements. Nature manages to endow everything with something special to it, technology wants to standardize everything.

It is a fact that in this respect there is a great difference between ancient and modern technical production. The old technical product resulted from the labor of a single man and thus expressed something of his own personal being. The craftsman's product revealed the hand of its master and exhibited something of his personality. The machine-made object, on the other hand, results from the pre-calculated collaboration of many and merely expresses a function. Although it may be based upon the personal creations of a designer and an artist, in the industrial process of production these creations are subdivided into so many partial processes that no individual worker is any longer capable of grasping them as a whole and making them his own. All he has to do is perfectly to repeat a prescribed manipulation, carefully guarding against any variation from it.

Depersonalized Use of Products. The leveling influence of technology makes itself felt not only in the manufacturing of products but perhaps even more in their use. In principle, everyone drives the same car, which is the realization of the impersonal idea of swift surface transportation. This car travels in principle along the same kind of road. If, leaving aside certain functional differences, there still are various types of cars, the reason lies in competitive considerations rather than in the car's nature itself. Everyone watches the same television program or listens to the same music on the radio. The programs are standardized, attuned to the average taste, just as technology attunes its entire production to the average consumer, neatly divided perhaps into a few price classes and standard wishes.

What is peculiar here is that, because only standardized goods and services are available, the consumer himself becomes attuned to them and knows nothing else. In this way the theoretically average user, arrived at by considering many individual users with their distinct wishes and desires, ultimately becomes the real user. Every user gradually becomes a representative of the average user. He adapts himself to the demands of technology, viz., standardized goods for standardized users, mass production for the masses.

Standardization of Life. The tendency to standardized mass products is not limited to material goods, but extends to the whole of life. We have mentioned already the leveling influence exercised by radio and television. Man's entire life is becoming standardized, for the technological order absorbs everything. Education, for instance, is affected. Certificates and diplomas have to be standardized, because man has to be certain that their bearers fit exactly into the interlocking wheels of the technological order, just as the spare parts of an engine have to be exactly according to standard.

Nothing escapes this tendency to standardization. Administration procedures are full of it. Anyone who has to fill out forms—and who hasn't?—occasionally meets a situation in which the standard questions are inadequate to express his case properly. Of course, usually the form has foreseen such a situation and allotted a special place for supplementary remarks, but the implication is clear: anyone who cannot be analyzed and processed in the normal categories is a troublesome abnormality that does not fit into the existing order.[12] The order wants uniform human beings who can be addressed in the same way to produce the desired reactions.

The result is that in countries of high technological development, such as the United States, all kinds of refinements disappear, because they demand too much personal attention. Since they cannot be taken care of in a technical fashion, they are too expensive and therefore uneconomical and doomed to disappear. For the cuisinier with artistic inclinations there is no room in the standardized kitchen of the standardized restaurant. Being unable to practice his art, he gradually loses his special skill.

Disappearance of Cultural Differences. In this way personal culture, whether productive or appreciative, disappears. There is no room for it in the technological order with its leveling tendencies. This leveling influence manifests itself also in the disappearance of regional and local differences. Such differences are tied up with the natural possibilities offered by the soil, the geographical situation, climate and landscape and are rooted also in the proper history of the region. Such geographic and historical differences stimulate cultural wealth, because they offer distinct possible ways in which man may vary his reply to what is given in nature. In their differentiation they reflect the universality of man.

Technology tends to wipe out all these differences and to create a uniform technical culture which, no matter what its own value may be as a basis of human life, reduces everything to the same level. Many cultural manifestations which formerly lived as meaningful traditions now lack their natural basis. They may be kept alive artificially as a tourist attraction, but this artificiality soon makes them all look alike. Thus technology may be able to create greater possibilities of controlling nature, but this ability leads everywhere to a similar condition—namely, the one that is technically most desirable. And this tendency demands so much of man's attention that the lesser possibilities spontaneously offered by nature, because of their diversity, were actually able to offer greater scope to culture than the technological order is able to provide.

---

[12]In passing we may remark here that the much-criticized complexity of income tax forms is based upon the desire to do justice to all. Although two taxpayers may have the same gross income, it does not follow that they should be subject to the same amount of taxation. It would be dangerous to desire the introduction of simplified and uniform tax forms for all.

Everywhere, for instance, housing becomes more and more the same. Climatic differences no longer count, because technology eliminates them or reduces them to a common denominator. In regions where the climate demands full enclosure, the walls are made of glass, because air-conditioning and heating make the house independent of the surroundings. Scientific nutritionists determine the most desirable food, and modern preservation and transportation make this food in principle available all over the world. If we add to this modern means of beauty, body culture, and universal advertising through film, television and print, we see why it is possible that, for instance, the same type of woman can now be considered everywhere as ideal, just as everyone everywhere also admires the same kind of car, aeroplane, or refrigerator.

e. Conclusion

Summarizing these considerations of the dangers contained in technology, we may say that they constitute an impressive indictment, even if here or there it contains a certain amount of exaggeration. Modern technology, the indictment states, leads to dehumanization, materialism, unnaturalness, and general leveling of man. It dehumanizes, because technology becomes the norm and man is made subservient to it. It leads to materialism, because man's entire attention goes out to matter and to controlling matter in such an intense fashion that there remains no room for the things of the spirit, for reflection and contemplation. It leads to unnaturalness and general leveling, because it undermines the natural basis of culture and thus produces a kind of uniformity which chokes man's personality and reduces him to an anonymous entity, disposing of the same technical means and striving for the same ideals.

We have devoted much space here to the tendencies of the technological order, because they contain indeed dangers which are inherent in the very nature of technology. For this reason it does not matter too much if they are exaggerated in certain respects so far as the *actually existing* situation is concerned. For the technological order is still in its first stage, so that what now is not yet fully realized will later become reality, at least if the tendencies in question pertain, as appears to be undeniably the case, to the technological order as such.

Another question, however, is whether these tendencies lead of necessity to dehumanization, materialism, unnaturalness, and general leveling or merely contain a danger that these evils will follow. More precisely put, we would have to ask whether they contain such a danger merely in a certain respect. For the crucial question here is what norms we want to use when we speak of unnatural, inhuman, materialistic, leveled, and similar qualifications. The norms upon which these terms are based are evidently derived from the past, from the view of nature and of man which were considered ideal in the context of past possibilities.

But, we may ask, to what extent is the ideal of man pursued by the past normative for the future? Would it not be possible to say that, even though the technological order leads to an unnatural nature and a non-human man, ultimately this unnatural nature and this non-human man would be more natural and more human than what we, guided by the past, think to be human and natural? It will be necessary, therefore, first to reflect profoundly upon the concept "nature" and especially upon "human nature." Only after such a reflection will it be possible to evaluate the tendencies of the technological order both as dangers and as new possibilities of human existence.

Moreover, the very fact that the technological order forces us to rethink our concepts of nature and of human nature may be a first indication that this order is natural and human. For it demonstrates that the technological order interferes in the historically grown state of affairs in such a way that man finds himself in a crisis and forced to reconsider his position as a human being, i.e., this order arouses especially what is characteristic of man as man.

CHAPTER THIRTEEN

NATURE, MAN, AND TECHNOLOGY

1. *Technology as Natural and as Unnatural*

Technology and the technological order reveal themselves as paradoxical insofar as there are reasons both for calling them natural and for claiming that they are unnatural. The natural character of contemporary technology may be defended on the ground that it is simply the continuation of ancient technique. There is, of course, a great difference between the two, but this difference results from the fact that modern technology makes use of physical science. This use cannot at all be called unnatural; on the contrary, physical science and technology appear to belong together because of the *nature* of man's knowledge, which is rational-sensitive-operational. Physical science, therefore, is a typically *human* science, as we have noted in the preceding pages. Although its ideals and method may seem to deviate from the ancient Greek ideal of science, this deviation is merely a question of appearance and not of reality. The Greeks laid the foundation of physical science as well as of philosophy, and it was merely a natural consequence of man's cognitive status that physical science was not able to reach full development until later times. Other arguments still could be brought forward to show that the only possible conclusion is to confirm the natural character of physical science as well as of contemporary technology.

On the other hand, the preceding chapter has listed a number of impressive arguments leading to the inevitable conclusion that technology and the technological order are unnatural. They produce artificial arrangements which are clearly in opposition to the natural. They are unnatural, moreover, because they compel man to do violence to his natural bodily being and especially because they disturb the equilibrium of his material-spiritual nature, violating his inner unity, by dividing him into functions. Finally, they uproot him from his natural surroundings and from the historical soil in which his way of living has developed.

It should be evident that these contradictory conclusions can be reached only because they do not take the term "nature" in the same meaning. We must therefore investigate somewhat more profoundly the meaning of "nature" and the various connotations attached to it. This investigation will complete the considerations which have been devoted to the meaning of nature in Chapter IX, Sect. 1.

2. *The Concept "Nature"*

a. Nature and Human Nature

Nature. The fundamental meaning of "nature" is always that which is, grows, comes to be, or takes place independently of man's influence. In this sense nature may refer to the whole cosmos, which is independently of man. It may refer also in a more detailed fashion to the nature of plants, trees, elements and compounds which inevitably are as they are and work as they work. This sense is used, for example, when we speak of natural history, i.e., the description of the various things of nature, of their essence and forms.

The term "nature," however, may be used also more abstractly; for instance, when we speak of the laws of nature or the science of nature. In this way it refers not so much to the existence of naturally *formed* things independently of man's influence as to the aspect of *all* material beings, whether natural or artificial, which lies beyond man's power of interference. For, through his knowledge of physical science, man now is capable of changing any existing element into any other one, but he can do so only by following the procedure prescribed by the general properties of nature as they are known in nature's laws. Or, to say it differently, man can intervene in nature only by taking nature as it is. He is capable of making iron rustproof, but only by combining it with other substances in such a way that the combination is naturally not subject to rust. In this special more profound sense of "nature" it is true that every technical product is natural by the very fact that it can be produced.

It should be clear, however, that this special sense of nature is not the point at issue when there is question of the natural or the unnatural character of technology. What this question aims at is always concerned with the interference in the spontaneously *formed* patterns of nature. It asked specifically to what extent man has the *right* to interfere in them. That man has the *possibility* of doing so is sufficiently evident.

Human Nature. There are two things which have to be kept in mind before this question can be answered. On the one hand, man has always realized that certain interventions in nature flow immediately from his own nature, i.e., from the natural needs which he himself has as a being of nature. On the other hand, man has also always been aware of the fact that not everything which presents itself to him as a possibility may actually be done. Sometimes the immediate bodily consequences deter him from actuating a possibility; for instance, it is possible to grasp a red-hot object, but it would eliminate the subsequent use of the grasping hand. Sometimes also special or general religious and ethical precepts accomplish the same goal: they appeal not to what man is and can do, but to what he ought to be and ought to do.

In both cases what *may* be done within the limits of what *can* be done finds its norm in something which by virtue of the fundamental meaning of "nature" may be called *human nature*. For there is question here of being normalized by something which as such lies beyond man's control. The case is quite clear with respect to the bodily consequences of certain actions. The bodily constitution of man is as it is and consequently is a norm of what is healthly or unhealthy for his body independently of man's control, for man has not made himself. For this reason medical science both in its curative and its preventive work knows that it is anchored in human nature, that it does not create nature but takes nature as a given norm in its research and medical task. Technology, likewise, finds natural norms in the given nature of man: artificially produced aids of organs are normalized by the natural structural and function of the organs. Spectacles, microscope, telescope, and television apparatus, for example, are adapted to the human eye.

Technology, however, does not find its norms merely in the bodily constitution of man. The normalizing in question is really only an aspect of a much broader normalization by the whole man as spirit-in-matter, as spiritualized body. Precisely because man is spirit-in-matter, precisely because being spirit-in-matter is man's nature, the pursuit of technology is a natural task of man. This point may be most conveniently illustrated by a comparison with man's urge to know. The urge to know, to understand, is a natural human urge. No matter how much the pursuit of science is a free deed of man, a deliberate pursuit, nevertheless the urge to pursue science is not the result of man's free decision, but flows from his nature, from his being a spirit-in-matter. The fact that man needs his senses in the pursuit of this urge and that these senses in their turn need the work of his hands—and therefore technology—again is something which belongs to man's nature, it is something which lies beyond the control of man.

What does lie within the control of man is whether or not concretely he will pursue physical science. But if he pursues it, it follows from the nature of human knowing that physical science has to proceed in the way experience has shown that it should proceed. For this reason we spoke above about the evolution of physical science, as it has taken place, as a natural development. It is a development which is in harmony with man's nature. Accordingly, that man is what he is and that he ought to be what he ought to be are things which belong to human nature. At the same time, however, it pertains also to human nature that what man ought to be is not automatically realized but only through man's own free activity.

Thus the concept "human nature" is a complex concept, a concept which agrees only in a certain respect—albeit a very important one— with "nature" as it is used with respect to the material world. Like nature, "human nature" expresses an original aspect which is beyond man's control, but what is special to it is that man's nature has the character of an "open" nature, i.e., every man as a person has to realize in himself what he ought to be according to his nature. In other words, we are dealing here with analogous concepts, as was mentioned already when we spoke about the problem of freedom and determinism.

Openness of Nature. Surprisingly, in the course of history something of the openness which is characteristic of human nature was attributed also to nature in the general sense. As we have noted repeatedly, man nowadays no longer conceives nature as *formed* nature but as *workable* nature, thus giving it a measure of openness. Of course, this does not mean that the difference between non-human and human nature has been eliminated. For it is precisely man who, guided by his human desires, unveils and realizes the possibilities of nature. Nature itself does not do so, at least not with respect to the possibilities discovered by technology. The restriction made here is not a mere tautology. For, according to the evolutionary theory we have to admit that in the evolutionary process nature itself also in a way gropes for and discovers is own possibilities. However, nature does not do so in the same way as man, because nature realizes its possibilities in an unconscious fashion, while man realizes them consciously and guided by what his intellect sees as possible. Thus the distinction between *nature* and *human nature* leads us to the opposition between nature and spirit. It will be necessary to devote here some attention to this contrast, because conceptual opposition throws light upon the proper content of the opposed concepts.

b. Nature and Spirit

As should be evident from the foregoing, in the contrast *nature—spirit* the comprehension of the concept of nature is restricted. For a spirit also has a nature—namely, his mode of being as man's spirit, as embodied spirit, with all the consequences flowing from this mode of being. One of these consequences is that what man experiences as his natural task belongs also to his nature. Hence the opposition nature—spirit expresses especially the difference between the nature which operates deterministically and the nature which acts freely, which acts *on its own*.

Or, to use again the terminology of Chapter Seven, the opposition nature—spirit refers to the difference between the nature whose activities are specifically determined and the nature which determines its own actions. This possibility of self-determination, however, can never refer to what man is by his very nature, for this nature is something which man simply has to accept. He cannot be non-man. He is capable, of course, of not realizing what a man ought to be, but even then he remains a man. Accordingly, the big question which arises in the evaluation of technology and of the technological order is whether or not technology is a deviation from what man ought to be. The realization of the technological order makes it evident that this order pertains to the possibilities of man. In this sense, of course, the order is natural. The crucial question, however, is whether technology and the technological order are also possibilities which man may realize if he wants to be faithful to his nature as spirit-in-matter.

c. Nature as Sacred

Divinely Established Nature. In the evaluation of this question another meaning of the term "nature" plays a role. It is a meaning which we have met before, in the historical survey of world views—namely, nature as sacred, as divine, as what has been divinely preordained for man. As van Peursen expresses it, nature means here the supernatural, because it points to the origin of the natural.[1]

A decisive answer, however, to the question what man may do with nature cannot be expected from this meaning. All depends upon the sense given to "nature as preordained for man": is it formed nature or nature as a workable basic datum? It depends, moreover, upon what is considered to be the ideal of man: is this ideal to be wholly controlled by what was considered possible in earlier periods of civilization or also by what has entered man's perspective at a later date? We should keep in mind here that the typical Greek view of spiritual culture and spiritual formation was at least in part based upon the then existing scientific and cultural possibilities. The discrepancy which was then experienced between the possibilities of the spirit and those of the body led to a dualistic view of man and to contempt for bodily labor, slave labor. The education of the spirit with a minimum of bodily labor thus became the ideal, i.e., it became that which was held suitable for man and ordained for him by nature. Of course, man could disregard this ideal, but in doing so he would become unfaithful to what man ought to be, with all the penalties inherent in this unfaithfulness.

Even nowadays the idea is still alive that formed nature, nature as man encounters it untouched by human hands, is something sacred and untouchable. Even the advertisements of our technological age sometimes use the term "natural product" to indicate that the quality of a thing is unsurpassed. Or, to give another example, according to Freyer, there is an analogy between the catastrophic results which the secondary system as an unnatural system produces in the human sphere and those which flow from the disturbance of the equilibrium of nature through deforestation etc. In both cases, he says, man resorts to countermeasures, but these measures can lead only to an artificial equilibrium and never to a natural balance.[2] Exactly what he means is not too clear, however. We have the impression that by natural equilibrium he means something like a natural order which has a primordial and sacred character, something which has been assigned to man and which he may not disturb with impunity.

Violation of Nature. Meanwhile it would be useful to keep in mind that, even if we do not consider the actually existing order

---

[1] C. A. van Peursen, "Natuur en mens wijsgerig gezien," *Natuur en Mens,* Groningen, 1957, p. 15.

[2] *Theorie des gegenwartigen Zeitalters,* p. 195.

of nature and the actually existing natural equilibria as sacred, they may nevertheless contain certain indications which we may not neglect with impunity. For the existing equilibrium is the result of countless factors which in a prolonged struggle for life have become carefully adapted to one another. The elimination of a single factor or group of factors often has repercussions that were not foreseen. In its original stages agricultural science all too frequently was discomfited, because it did not sufficiently pay attention to this natural equilibrium. Among the factors which contribute to the balance of nature we must reckon also man's technical and cultivating labor. Sudden shifts in this labor likewise disturb the equilibrium in question.

Nevertheless, one cannot accuse modern technology of severely upsetting the balance of nature. True, as man progresses in science, his technological intervention becomes more radical, but it is true also that he understands more what he is doing and acquires a greater knowledge of the existing natural equilibrium. Moreover, it is in principle wrong to make an essential distinction between the conditions and balance existing in "virgin" nature and those in which man's interference and cultivation have produced all kinds of shifts. In denying this essential distinction we are not thinking of the well-known epistemological problem concerning the extent to which nature can exist without man, but we are simply referring to the fact that man himself also belongs to nature and therefore must be considered to be a natural factor. The problem, therefore, is whether there is a distinction between man as inserting himself into nature, i.e., as remaining always within the natural order, and modern technical man who, by doing violence to the natural order, places himself outside and above this order.

d. The Relative Character of the Distinction Between Nature and Culture

Natural and Unnatural Cultivation of Nature. It is the above-mentioned distinction which continues to be alive somehow in modern man. When he seeks to escape from the city to take refuge in God's free nature, he does not go to the jungle, but to nature as it has become through centuries of man's dwelling in nature.[4] Although this

---

[4]It is interesting to note here that even virgin forests, as we know them, exist now only as "natural parks," i.e., as products of culture, albeit only through a kind of negative culture.

nature is cultivated by man and as such a product of culture, it is held to be a nature which has been cultivated in a natural fashion. The super highway with its speeding car belongs to the unnatural technological order, but the country road with the farmer's cart pertains to nature. The apartment building and the factory are unnatural, but the humble old farm blending with the landscape is nature.

It is not without importance for the ambivalent attitude taken toward technology that modern man who utilizes the most refined technical means shows a marked preference for the very primitive which, he feels, brings him closer to nature. Modern European dwellings know not only air-conditioning but also the open fireplace, a primitive form of heating, which affects man as something natural. Camping proves very attractive, not only because it is cheaper but also because man has the feeling that in this way he remains closer to nature. Even when he has recourse to the airplane for his vacation, he often prefers to fly to remote regions where he can leave civilization behind and enjoy nature and human beings untouched by technology. The natural romanticism of the eighteenth century is not at all dead. Man continues to seek nature, stripped of all its human overgrowth and additions. He is homesick for life in and with nature.

Of course, even this kind of life is not devoid of techniques. But whatever technique there is in it is sober and limited to the use of natural things and forces which, as it were, spontaneously offer themselves for man's use. The distinction which we made in Chapter X between ancient technique as accepting nature's invitation and modern technology as forcing nature, therefore, is not an *a posteriori* rationalization, but lives fully in modern man's feeling about life. The old technique of heating by means of an open fire is felt to be natural, while invisible air-conditioning impresses man as unnatural.

Historical Aspect of Nature. Thus is appears that we meet here a new meaning of the term "nature." Although this meaning remains within the general range attached to the term, it shows an aspect of its own. Nature here no longer means what somehow is independent of man, but includes also cultural labor—namely, the kind of labor which remains within the natural order because it is in harmony with the original order. History, however, shows very clearly that important modifications take place in what *de facto* is considered to belong to the original order of nature. The Dutch polders once were most revolutionary reclamation schemes, but now they form part and parcel of the natural landscape. The narrow country road winding its way from farm to farm lies deserted and devoid of fast-moving motor-cars. It now impresses us as belonging to nature. In a way this is true, for it follows the contours of the landscape and does not force its way through mountains and over vales, as the modern super highway does.

What is called "nature" here has, therefore, a strongly historical connotation. It is always a cultivated nature, but one which because of its greater or lesser permanence and stability seems more familiar and thus suggests that we have to do with nature alone. It is only in historical retrospect that we discover how cultural this nature is.

Unnatural Technological Order. Nevertheless, the realization that the distinction between nature and culture is merely relative does not take away the unnatural character that is attributed to the technological order. The same remark may be made with respect to its acultural character. For cultivated nature may appear to man as nature un-qualified because he has the time to fuse, as it were, with it. When such a fusion can take place, cultivated nature and the human so-cieties which have historically taken root in harmony with this nature constitute a natural milieu for subsequent generations and therefore a starting point of their cultural labor. But it is typical of the techno-logical order that it does not leave man the necessary time to grow accustomed to it. The process of modifications is so fast that man does not have the opportunity to adapt himself to his new world in such a way that it becomes a second nature for him. It is, moreover, not only the speed of the development which disconcerts man, but also the fact that the direction which the technological order takes is not clear to him.

3. *The Technological Order as a Culture of Means*

a. The Relationship of End and Means

Ancient and Modern Technological Development. The old culture developed because certain needs became apparent and demanded to be satisfied. There was a more or less immediate connection between what was seen as a natural need and the way leading to its satisfac-tion. The end determined the means and thus indicated also the direction in which the old culture tended to develop. Insofar as applied science plays a role in the technological order, the situation is not much different, for applied science endeavors to discover how available scientific knowledge can be used to find a solution for particular concrete needs and desires. In the technological order, however, not only applied science plays an important role, but also pure science, i.e., science which is pursued without any utilitarian motive, purely for the sake of understanding. Paradoxically, it is precisely this pure science which is the main culprit with respect to the fact that the technological order develops so unnaturally and so little in harmony with the existing state of affairs. For pure science continually discovers entirely new possibilities in nature and the resulting desire to realize these possibilites constantly causes wholly new situations to arise.

Accordingly, the evolution of the technological order is very strongly influenced by the unending discovery of new means for which man subsequently seeks a suitable purpose. This is the reason why this evolution exhibits the disrupted character mentioned above. There is no clear-cut direction in its development, and thus there constantly occur disproportions between the different aspects of the technological order. Contrary to the old culture, the technological order is a genuine culture of the *means*. The ancient culture was determined by ends which appeared suitable and worthy of being attained. Guided by these ends, man then began to seek the means to realize the ends in question. This procedure seems to be the natural course of affairs. Thus the typical feature of being a culture of means which characterizes the technological order once more confronts us with the unnatural character of this order.

The Influence of Man's Cognitive Situation. On the other hand, it should be noted that the evolution of the technological order as a more or less independent culture of means is a natural consequence of man's cognitive situation and of the human activity connected with this situation. For this reason it is not true that the means are pursued for their own sake. Although an initial and somewhat superficial consideration of technology may give such an impression, a more profound examination shows that ultimately the means are developed for the sake of the general human ends which they serve. As was pointed out when we spoke about the determinant factors of technology, precisely the general ends pursued by man influenced his preoccupation with technical matters. Man, however, has experience that in the long run greater expectations can be built upon an apparently autonomous scientific development of technical means than upon the direct search for means to attain concrete purposes.

Following the first line of approach, man even found at his disposal means which gave rise to new ends. In former ages the control of natural disasters, such as periodic famines and decimating epidemics, seemed just as utopian as the idea that an existence worthy of man was the destiny of every human being. As a utopian ideal, it belonged to the purposes envisaged by man, but it did not constitute, of course, a concrete ethical task, because ethics moved within the confines of what was naturally pre-ordained for man. The control, therefore, of such natural disasters was not the result of a deliberate search for means to accomplish this purpose, but just the opposite. Thanks to the pursuit of science, to the search for an understanding of nature, man discovered the means to intervene in nature, and it was only because these means were now at his disposal that the control of these disasters became an ethical task and consequently a human purpose.

It is also the formerly unsuspected fruitfulness of pure science which causes constantly increasing interest in pure science among organizations whose purpose is not the pursuit of science but the production of technical means. The fact that the technical laboratories of large industries have become research institutes eloquently testifies in favor of our assertions. This fact implies a recognition that there is a fundamental relationship between man's knowing and man's making. At one time in the history of Greek thought these two went their own ways and their independent course proved fruitful for mankind. What happened then on a major scale in the history of science and technology repeats itself on a smaller scale every day in every laboratory: the search for understanding constantly opens up new perspectives.

The Natural Character of the Technological Order. Thus the independent culture of means which the technological order seems to be, viewed as a whole, reveals itself as the best and most efficient means to serve the general human end which inspires all technique. In this respect, therefore, the technological order is a natural order. It merely seems to reverse the relationship of means and end. Viewed, however, in the proper perspective, the order shows that end and means retain their natural relationship. The apparently disoriented developments occurring in the technological order, which seem to be without any connection with what man has grown accustomed to in the course of history, clearly reveal their main direction when they are seen in a broader perspective. They cut loose the ties binding them to the latest offshoots of what has, as it were, grown up naturally in history, and they are entitled to do so, because they are firmly rooted in the end to which all cultural labor tends—viz., to make nature more and more adapted to the desires of man.

b. Natural Function and the Use of Technical Means

A Curious Objection. A few remarks may be added here concerning an objection against technology which is often raised and which we have touched in the preceding chapter. It is claimed that technology places powerful technological means into the hands of the masses which have no understanding at all of the ideas embodied in these means and therefore are bound to use them carelessly and thoughtlessly.

This is a rather curious objection, for it really points to an aspect in which the technological order very clearly shows its inner relationship with the natural order. Would we perhaps have to require that man understand the working of his eyes before he be allowed to see or his digestive system before he may eat? Let us assume that at least the physiologists would receive a passing grade as far as their knowledge of vital functions is concerned—although even this grade would be given more from the desire not to have only failures rather than from an objective evaluation of their knowledge. Yet even with respect to these physiologists we would have to face the strange situation that these ladies and gentlemen would have to exercise their vital functions for many years without being qualified in order to prepare themselves for their qualification.

If, then, man spontaneously exercises his vital functions, one can hardly reproach him for doing the same with technical means. One who wears spectacles does not have to know the laws of optics to understand the meaning of the technical means bridging his nose. He experiences this meaning in their use, just as also he is familiar with the meaning of his television set even if he has no notion of electronics. Likewise, one cannot reproach the producer of technical apparatus for concealing the construction lay-out in a box, so long as its use and function are clear and adapted to the natural build of the human body. If this condition is fulfilled, the technical apparatus is soon experienced as a kind of extension of one's own body, just as familiar as this body itself and just as unknown.

Moreover, just as it is only in sickness that the body or a part of it is the object of experience, so also the technical instrument becomes the center of attention only when there is something wrong with it. Generally speaking, when it works as it should, we do not pay attention to it but integrate it into the reality of our subjectivity. For a tennis player, for example, the racket in his hand is wholly integrated into the natural whole of his body movement and belongs to his body. For the automobilist, likewise, the car has become, as it were, a part of himself. In driving he does not so much guide his car as himself. This pressure on the pedal means the acceleration of his own motion, and that one its deceleration. By quickly turning the steering wheel, he prevents damage to *his* left mudguard. His attention should not even go out to the technical structures which cause him to influence his motion through certain manipulations, for otherwise he does not drive properly.

Of course, he must have a technical feeling of what he can or cannot do, for what constitutes torturing his engine and his tires, just as also he must have a feeling of what he may demand of his body and what would be excessive. Even as he understands the symptoms indicating these things in his own body, so also he can evaluate them in the mechanism which has become, as it were, a part of him. It may be true, of course, that a certain amount of technical knowledge is required for understanding these signs, but the same is true also of the symptoms exhibited by his body.

Scientific Study and Spontaneous Use. Evidently, in the whole of human activities there is room for abstract scientific attention to the structure and function of the body as well as of the technical apparatus. However, this attention is not required of everyone and, moreover, it cannot be the normal attitude toward the body and the apparatus. For even this abstract attention proper to the pursuit of science demands the spontaneous use of other functions than the one which is being investigated. The tennis player, for example, who studies his "foot work" by means of a film, spontaneously uses his eyes, just as the physiologist does when he experimentally studies the eye itself. The same is true of any technical investigation: there remains a difference between the means and the object of perception.

There is, for instance, a difference between a technical trial run of a car on proving grounds and the simple use of a car as a means of locomotion. One who does not see the difference in question suffers from the same kind of neurosis as a man who during his meal thinks only about his digestive system. Accordingly, the spontaneous use of technical means without the scientific and technological knowledge of the expert is wholly natural, at least if we may take the natural use of the body as a norm. For the understanding of how the body operates escapes man's mind. We must add, however, that, although such an understanding is naturally lacking, the intellect strives to acquire it. This tendency constitutes the driving force of the effort made by physical science to understand the relationship of mind and matter.[5]

c. The Progressive Relativation of the Concept "Nature"

The Untouchable Order of Nature. The preceding reflections on the various reasons which supposedly demonstrate the unnatural character of technology have in common that they show how relative the concept "natural" really is. With respect to the originally existing order of nature the technological order is, of course, artificial. However, this artificiality is such that it fully harmonizes with the natural order, to such an extent even that the artifacts of the past are experienced as wholly natural because they have been organically integrated into the natural order. This order demands to be completed with respect to both external nature and the nature of man. For this reason man naturally assimilates artifacts, i.e., man discovers more and more that, if nature is a condition of his human existence, it is so especially as a nature whose possibilities have to be unveiled. Man, however, does not know *a priori* all the possibilities that are concealed in nature. Looking upon history, especially that of recent times, in retrospect, he experiences that much which seemed to be part of a firmly established natural order, either in external things or in his own nature, has subsequently revealed itself as not so firmly established at all. On the other hand, he realizes also that despite the progressive relativation of the concept "nature" nature still remains for him the ultimate norm and as such is untouchable.

As to the question, however, of where this untouchable realm begins, modern man is far less certain than previous generations. He

---

[5]Cf. p. 304.

knows that this untouchable nucleus will appear to him in ever-changing forms. Nevertheless, there is one point of which he is certain, and this certainty drives him relentlessly forward and makes him abandon apparent certainties, apparently eternal natural relationships, and apparently eternal ideals of manhood: nature is not a final, unchangeable order of things within which he has to seek his spiritual self-realization, but nature is given to him as a task, as something which he has to assimilate and organize in harmony with the existing natural organization of his body and with his natural surroundings. The actual order of nature which makes human life possible is merely a first beginning, but contains a host of possibilities. These possibilities, however, do not manifest themselves spontaneously, but are an appeal to man to bring them to reality not for the sake of nature but for the sake of man himself. For the fact that man and nature are attuned to each other reveals itself not only in the original order of nature, found by man, which makes human life possible but also, and even more, in the ability of man to produce from nature artifacts which serve, or rather are able to serve man's existence in a most wonderful fashion.

The Cultural Ambiguity of Technology. It is precisely this last-named distinction which constitutes the crucial problem. No matter how much technology discloses nature's possibilities and by realizing these possibilities, is a condition on which man in his dependence upon nature relies in his efforts to attain fully to an existence worthy of man, technology is and remains a condition of a very special kind. It certainly is not a sufficient condition and, strictly speaking, not even a necessary condition for a fully human existence. There have been great civilizations with only a minimum of technical knowledge, at least as measured with our standards, and this proves that technology in the modern sense is not at all necessary. A cultural state of barbarism possessing a perfect technology, measured by our standards, likewise is possible. The ambivalent character of technology is further evidenced by the fact that, on the one hand, it has contributed mightily to the conviction that slavery does not have to be a "natural" condition while, on the other, it itself can lead to spiritual slavery.

All this seems to indicate that technology, as a typical culture of means, is ethically indifferent and therefore can be used for good as well as evil. However, the situation is not so simple as this conclusion may seem to suggest. For, as we have seen above, technology, as a more or less independent culture of means, reveals purposes and modes of fully human existence which otherwise would hardly have been thought of. This alone suffices to raise technology above the state of being ethically indifferent. Technology is a necessary task of man, his *Geschick,* destiny, as Heidegger expresses it very neatly.[6] Man is called to this task and discovers it in his own nature and in that of his surroundings. Both man and nature, as attuned to each other, demand technology for the realization of their possibilities. Technology, therefore, is a condition of culture. The question which arises here is, what is the basis of the peculiar character proper to technology as this condition, if technology is neither the sufficient nor unqualifiedly the necessary condition of culture?

4. *The Conditional Character of Technology*

a. Personal Sacrifice in Former Times and at Present

Man's Personal Being and the Future. To be man is to be a person. Consequently, in the development of technology it is never permissible to be solely interested in the supposed ascent toward a future ideal relationship of man and nature and for the sake of this ideal to sacrifice the human beings living during the period of ascent to the demands of progress. No future ideal can justify that the people upon whom the technical order is based be reduced to mere cogs in a machine, so that their personal life is destroyed. For the ascent in question is not an abstract ascent of mankind but the ascent of concrete human beings. Ideologies, however, as Freyer says, do not hesitate to sacrifice the present to the future.[7] It is, of course, wholly human, i.e., in harmony with human nature, to keep the eye fixed upon the future, for man lives toward the future. All human undertakings take place in time, they know successive phases, and it must be the final phase which dominates the whole, for only in that case can there be question of a conscious human tendency.

The above-mentioned objection against technological ideology, therefore, does not blame it for its orientation to the future, but argues that the sacrifices made for the future destroy precisely the core of the goal pursued—namely, man freed *from* material

---

[6] *Die Frage nach der Technik,* p. 63. Dessauer also rejects the neutrality of technology, which is defended by Karl Jaspers. Cf. F. Dessauer, *Streit um die Technik,* Ch. 2, sect. 19 and 20; Jaspers, *Vom Ursprung und Ziel der Geschichte,* Frankfurt a. M., 1955, p. 122.
[7] *Theorie des gegenwärtigen Zeitalters,* pp. 206 ff.

wants *and* therefore free *for* a personal life that is worthy of man. The sacrifices in question are wholly unlike the personal sacrifices made, for example, by parents who deny themselves many things in order to give their children access to possibilities which otherwise would have remained closed to them. Although such personal sacrifices may prevent the growth of a parent's personality in certain directions, they strengthen it fundamentally because they are made in freedom and thus make man free. What seems to be sacrificed, however, to the technological order is precisely the personal being of man, because man makes himself subservient to the demands of the autonomous matter in which the order is embodied. There is no technological order, no matter how ideal it be, which will ever render man his personality, because by its very character such an order is impersonal.

The Withering Away of Man's Spiritual Life. Moreover, the paradoxical aspect of the technological order consists in this that through its abundance of material means it has caused such an unbridled desire of material comforts and pleasures that no one is really satisfied. At least, this order seems to have eliminated as meaningful the personal sacrifice, in the above-described sense. One may legitimately ask the question whether thus the technological order has not sacrificed one of the required conditions of personal life and especially of personal happiness. Concepts such as asceticism and detachment seem to have become antiquated. The personal sacrifices, based upon these concepts, such as those made by parents for the education of their children, are no longer needed. The state, i.e., the technological order, increasingly takes care of them. The order likewise assumes responsibility for the sick, the aged, the incapacitated, and the victims of disasters. Of course, we all pay for these services through taxes, but taxes are not a personal sacrifice, for they are simply imposed by the technological society. In this way this society effects a maximum of human development on the material level and its shrivelling-away on the spiritual level. It thus stands in the sharpest possible contrast with the ancient and medieval picture of the ideal man.

b. The Ancient and Medieval Picture of Man

The ideal of ancient times and of the Middle Ages was the man who interpreted his being spirit-in-matter as the subservience of matter to the spirit, in such a way that no more material means should be used than were necessary to allow the spirit to be itself and to be free with respect to matter. For this reason detachment was fundamental; hence poverty and want were not considered disastrous but means to form the personality. The ideal was, if we may use the expression, to become human with a minimum of materiality. Science, consequently, was formation of the spirit, spiritual control over, and liberation from nature and not material control of nature.

A sign of this ideal of science lies in the fact that all the ancient sciences, philosophy, mathematics, and theology—needed only a minimum of material being. And if art sometimes made use of powerful material means, e.g., in architecture, the purpose was to make matter rise above itself and point to God. Art expressed ideas which reminded man of spiritual reality. The entire culture bore the stamp of spiritualization and through matter reminded man of his spiritual being.

Of course, even antiquity and the Middle Ages knew the temptation to surrender to material pleasures. This temptation, however, was seen as something that had to be overcome. Asceticism was the key to a truly human existence.

c. The Premises of the Technological Order

The technological order starts from entirely different premises. It believes in an ideal of humanity which includes a maximum of materiality. Its science is science of nature, which has to make use of powerful material means to realize its cognitive ideal. The cultural ideal of the technological order is to embody in nature ideas which will make it possible for man to attain a maximum of development in the material aspect, so that the necessity to deny himself anything will be wholly eliminated. If the technological order sometimes preaches economy and thus appeals to something resembling detachment and sacrifice, its reason lies merely in the desire to secure the future supply of the necessary materials to satisfy the needs. Appeals to economy and to massive consumption are means which this order uses in turn as required by the economic situation. These appeals remain subordinate to the general aim pursued by the technological order—namely, creating and satisfying a maximum of material needs.

d. Evaluation of the Divergences of These Ideals

Inevitable and Free Asceticism. In criticizing the contrasting ideals of former times and of the technological order, it must be kept in mind that ancient and medieval man could hardly have done otherwise than consider asceticism a natural attitude of man, simply because nature did not offer him any alternative. The material means nature placed at man's disposal barely sufficed to allow the large majority of mankind to lead a sober life of hard and constant labor. It was the actually existing state of affairs in man's relationship to nature which was mirrored not only in Plato's idea of controlling the passions to enable the spirit to live its life of contemplation and in the Stoic ideal of detachment and resignation to one's fate, but also in the christianized version of these ideas presented in the early stages of Catholic thought.

Through physical science and technology, however, the relationship in question has been modified. Man has discovered that new perspectives are open to his life. The picture, however, of these perspectives presented in the preceding pages is far too onesided. For it is very misleading to claim that the technological order is characterized by the fact that it offers no room for asceticism and detachment. On the contrary, we should say that it is only in this order that full justice is done to these categories. In the technological order asceticism and detachment no longer make virtues of necessity, but are attitudes assumed in full freedom.

As everyone knows, sickness and want are excellent means to purify man, for it is often only through sickness and want that man attains to a high level of human existence, to the acceptance of his situation, and to mastery of himself. Nevertheless, a physician will never strive to keep the patient ill because he admires the spiritual powers and self-control revealed by the sufferer, but he does his utmost to cure the patient. The reason is not only the primary and immediate motive that it is his task to do so. There is also another motive which goes beyond this—namely, not before the patient is again in the full possession of his bodily powers, will he be able to show the real value of his spiritual power. Man has naturally to be healthy and as a healthy being to show that he is truly human.

This simple example may serve to illustrate the peculiar way in which technology is a condition of existence that is worthy of man. In both sickness and disease he can and must be truly human. Nevertheless, he must strive for health, for a healthy state is natural to him. In certain respects it is more difficult to remain truly human during an illness, and in others the same difficulty is encountered while being healthy, but these difficulties do not determine whether one should strive to be ill or to be healthy. It is only too obvious that man is destined to be human in health, for only in a healthy condition does he have at his disposal all the conditions needed for his human existence. What he can accomplish as a sick man, he can do in principle also as a healthy man, but not vice versa. For this reason being-sick or being-healthy is not indifferent with respect to man's existence. Significantly, even the most austere religious orders take good care of their sick to cure them from their disease.

Technology and the Fully Human Life. The situation is somewhat similar with respect to technology as a condition of a fully human life. Such a life is possible in a technologically poor society as well as in one which is technologically rich, yet technology is not a matter of indifference, because it opens perspectives of a fully human existence which would not be possible otherwise. Just as the physician in his study of human nature sees in this nature that man ought to be healthy, so also the study of nature and the reflection upon man's being as spirit-in-matter teaches us that man is called to be fully human through the control of matter, for only through this control is it possible to secure health and the joy of life for every human being. Only a technological order can do full justice to human virtues.

For instance, it is generally admitted that any human society ought to be ruled by justice. It is, however, not merely a question of dividing material goods properly, but also of securing the goods themselves which are to be divided. Once man has discovered that nature can produce more in a technological order than in its original state, he sees this order as a demand of justice which he should endeavor to satisfy. The parable of the talents in St. Matthew's gospel (ch. 25) finds an application here. Although this parable makes us think first of all of the different ways in which individuals used the talents entrusted to them, why shouldn't it be applicable also to the different fashions in which the various eras have made use of these talents?

It may be of interest to add here a remark concerning Indian philosophy. Although this philosophy used to emphasize the idea of detachment perhaps even more strongly than ancient and medieval thought, now that it has discovered the possibilities given to man through modern technology, it does not hesitate to integrate the value of contemporary scientific and technological thinking into its ancient wisdom. It justifies this procedure on the basis of the above-mentioned social importance of technology.

e. Technology and Personality

The Technological Order and Personal Sacrifice. Even with respect to asceticism and self-denial it is true, as we have said above, that only in the technological order full justice is done to such virtues. Only in this order does their most intimate meaning become clear, for it is precisely the abundance of possibilities, placed at man's disposal in this order, which emphasizes the meaningfulness of asceticism. In this order asceticism becomes truly a free deed, while at the same time also it becomes more than ever necessary. For if the individual man wants to realize the possibilities of his personal self-unfolding, he will have to make a careful choice from among the available means. He faces a very real difficulty, which we have described above as one of the serious dangers of the technological age—namely, the senses may become overwhelmed by such an abundance of material goods that the spirit can no longer cope with the situation. The danger in question, however, is not one in which man will automatically and inevitably perish. What it does is appeal to man's old virtues in a new fashion.

Even for personal sacrifice there remains much room in the technological order. Its place, however, will increasingly lie less in the material sphere and more in that of the spirit. The truth of this assertion reveals itself, for example, when one pays attention to the difference between the factory owner of the past and the modern industrial leader. The old-style paternalistic factory owner—we do not speak of the others—may have been like a true father for his laborers, but they remained fully his subordinates, his inferiors. In times of sickness or misfortune he may have helped them even at the cost of personal sacrifice, but he was the absolute ruler of his kingdom or empire, the benefactor of *his* people. Moreover, it should not be forgotten that what formerly was done through philanthropy constituted only a small part of what should have been done then and is being done in our time.

The personal sacrifices which nowadays are demanded of the industrial leader lie in a different area. He must, as the French express it, *payer de sa personne,* he has to meet the others as fellow-workers not merely in words but in reality. He has to see to it that a truly human atmosphere prevails in the sector of the technological order which is entrusted to his care and that his personnel understands what is required of them. Where formerly orders sufficed, there must now be conviction, and this requires that both sides, the employer as well as the employees, become more personally involved in their work.

The interesting point in the modification of the relationship between employer and employee described above is that it has not arisen merely from humanitarian considerations which lie outside the technological order or which go contrary to it. As we have pointed out, the very development of technology demands that the emphasis shift from bodily to intellectual labor. It is for this reason that simple orders constantly lose more and more of their meaning in labor relationships. Their place is taken by mutual consultation.

Similar considerations apply to the above-mentioned example of parents and the education of their children. The personal financial sacrifices of the parents have become less necessary than in former times—they would, moreover, be unable to guarantee the number of students required by present-day society—but nevertheless, the sacrifices demanded of modern parents are no less than those of the past. One has to think here only of the sacrifices involved in adapting themselves to the rapidly changing conditions in which the growing generation has to live and work. They can no longer be satisfied with viewing life from age-old traditions and with letting their attitude toward the younger generation be determined by the wisdom of the past.

Personal Thinking and Choice. The evolution of physical science and the consequent technological and social changes again and again compel man to personal reflection upon the fundamental values of human existence. The traditional forms of culture, in which this reflection was, as it were, objectified, retain only a relative value. They are important only insofar as they invite man to reflect upon fundamentals, but no longer insofar as they embody the reflection of former ages and, by transmitting it, secure its permanence. Life, even ordinary everyday life, has lost its obvious character. Trusted and familiar patterns of life have become antiquated, and the new patterns do not even get a chance to become traditional before they disappear in the rapid stream of new developments. All this means that the progressive character of the technological order compels man, far more than did the ancient stable order of nature, to personal reflection and personal choice from the abundance of material means.

Dangers of the Technological Order. These observations do not mean that the technological age does not include great dangers for man's personal existence. These dangers are very real—we have analyzed them in the preceding chapter—but, on the other hand, it is just as real that the technological order demands precisely of man that he be a person. The order has no use for people who are "stuck in the rut." The objection is often heard that the technological order makes man a mere cog in the social machine, just as it degrades him to being an extension of a mechanism in its factories, so that the entire life of man becomes nothing but humdrum and routine. This objection, however, does injustice to technology in two ways. First of all, it fails to recognize that the progressive character of modern technique excludes humdrum routine and, secondly, it pays no attention to the fact that technology is often forced to make its machines in such a way that they can be handled even by the unskilled: they are "foolproof." Increasing automation, however, gradually eliminates the need of unskilled labor and demands more understanding and more skill. Humdrum routine work is slowly becoming less and less important.

Accordingly, so far as the present development of technology is concerned, it is not true that it necessarily will change man into a kind of automaton. On the contrary, the more machines are automated, the less automatism will be required of man, for this kind of action can be safely delegated to machines. A question of real concern, however, is whether man will be able to cope with this new situation, because he is used to living in the routine of the non-technological order, in which he could pass a great deal of his working hours in routine occupations. Just as the technological evolution forces man to be more human, to perform more specifically human actions, so also the technological transformation of society forces him to become more specifically human and to rely less on routine. This undermining of tradition may include dangers, but it also demands personal reflection and personal attitudes. The main argument to which one could always appeal in any type of traditional social order —the fact that it had always been done so and therefore was good— is no longer valid, but, we may ask, must we really regret that this argument is gone?

Rather than being a threat, technology and the technological order are a challenge for man to show his real worth: to be an animal governed by patterns like other animals with an added degree of intelligence or to be really a person. Accordingly, just as man's technology discloses the possibilities of nature and consequently also its essence, so also does it disclose new possibilities of man, insofar as it compels him to be more man, to be more a person. Of course, we do not want to assert that man's personal existence has been discovered only by technology. In this respect also technology reveals its peculiar character as a condition of man's fully developed humanity. For technology itself arises from man insofar as it is based upon man's nature; hence it is always man himself who takes the initiative. On the other hand, however, it is also by means of technology and his reflection upon technology that man succeeds in penetrating somewhat more profoundly into his own nature.

f. Technology and War

This revealing character of technology finds a particularly pregnant expression in the catastrophic dangers which the misuse of its powerful means contain for the whole of mankind. What technology does here is nothing else than disclose on an immense scale something of the true nature proper to human malice. It projects this malice, as it were, on a giant screen. In former ages war could still appear to some as a kind of rough and tumble social sport, but technological terrors such as the thermonuclear bomb make it clear what war really is. The awful power of material annihilation presented by present-day technology for the settlement of human conflicts suddenly makes it abundantly clear how senseless it is to undertake such a settlement with the aid of material means of destruction. Technology is powerless to eliminate human malice and sinfulness, but it enlarges their effects and thus makes them more clearly visible. Here too it does not deny its character: as the discloser of nature's possibilities, it challenges man to be more man and a better man.

For this reason the elimination of the catastrophic menace given in nuclear energy cannot be found in banning such technological means or in declaring their use illicit. True, such a ban may be the first step in the right direction. Once, however, nuclear bombs have been invented, the human race has to live with them, i.e., it must come to such a legal organization that war itself is excluded. The universal and radical nature of the technological means forces mankind to adopt universal and radical solutions. Neither a prohibition nor a careful inspection of its execution will ultimately be able to suffice, for what would remain of such a prohibition and inspection in times of war? Thus the technological means demand a legal order which is adapted to their proper nature, and this order can exist only among human beings who realize how horrible warfare really is.

In this way technology always reveals itself as a condition of man's fully human existence, but a condition which does not automatically produce the status whose condition it is. Man himself will have to ban war. Technology cannot do so. Likewise, one cannot say that it is only in and through technological means that war manifests itself as an evil. Even without these means man knew that war was evil and that he should prevent it. However, this evil seemed so deeply rooted in the nature of man that the banning of war appeared to be wholly utopian. The dearth of the natural goods needed by man seemed bound to drive men of ill will constantly to deprive others of their share, so that war appeared inevitable. Modern technology, however, shows that there really is no natural scarcity and it enlarges the consequences of the evil in question so much that war seems to repel rather than to attract.

5. *Conclusion*

The Paradox of Technology. If in concluding this investigation of the disputed natural status proper to technology we glance in retrospect at the many problems which it raises, we easily understand why it had to become a "sign of contradiction." Technology constantly forced us to draw contradictory conclusions about its nature. On the one hand, it has a spiritualizing influence upon matter but, on the other, it seems to make man subservient to matter. In one section we had to conclude that technology was unnatural, but in another it manifested itself as wholly natural, i.e., in harmony with the nature of the cosmos and of man. Again, technology seems to have a tendency to eliminate certain virtues, but on the other hand, it calls for others.

Does not, we may ask, this ambivalent character of technology and of the technological order connected with it contain a feature that is human *par excellence?* For technology is not subservient to man of necessity, it does not automatically lead him to a higher level, but constantly appeals to him to become more human. It is this which makes technology human, even though it adversely affects certain traditional values. Strictly speaking, moreover, it does not affect these values themselves, but only some of the forms in which they traditionally expressed themselves. Technology may appear unnatural to the superficial observer, but on closer inspection it is more consonant with truth that technology reveals the nature of nature more clearly.

Technology and the Ideal Man. The only conclusion which imposes itself here is that to despair of technology is to despair of man. While technology has lightened the burden which human life implied in a very real fashion, it has also placed man face to face with a more serious problem on a new level. The big question is, will man be able to cope with this problem or must we despair of him?

Those who despair whether man, as he is, will be intellectually, and especially spiritually and morally suitable for the task awaiting him in the technological order would do well to study the lesson which can be learned from the history of the changing world view. This history shows clearly how flexible formed nature was, despite all the original appearances to the contrary. Is perhaps, we may ask, human nature, as we know it historically with its distribution of talents apparently fixed in all areas, also such a changeable datum of nature? The affirmative answer would mean that human nature contains a reserve of spiritual powers whose very existence would still be concealed from us—just as former generations had no inkling of the material forces of which we now dispose.

The comparison may seem dangerous, because it may appear to imply that cosmic nature and the nature of man are put on the same line, and because it seems to base its hope upon a reshaping and improving of man in a physical and technical fashion. However, there is no need to push the comparison to such an extreme before we can doubt the rock-like conviction of many that so far as human nature is concerned nothing will ever change. For never before has there been such a powerful appeal to man as there is now in the technological age with all its dangers and possibilities. It is possible that precisely in this appeal technology will demonstrate the peculiar way in which it is the condition of man's fully human existence. Technology does not produce the ideal man, but demands him more insistently and more loudly than ever before. And, what is just as important, it offers the necessary means. This is a point which will be discussed in the subsequent chapters of this book.

CHAPTER FOURTEEN

THE TECHNOLOGICAL ORDER AND THE FORMER IDEAL OF KNOWLEDGE

1. *The Problem of Cultural Continuity*

A Break With the Greek Ideal? The preceding considerations of the evolution of technology and its function in the self-development of man constantly led to the conclusion that, despite the initial appearance to the contrary, the development of technology is wholly in harmony with the character of nature and of man. It was pointed out repeatedly, moreover, how intimately physical science, conceived as the theory of nature, is connected with technique as the cultivation of nature for practical purposes, and that this connection is so strong that physical science and technology imply each other. Finally, we saw over and over again how the Greek beginning of science contained the view of nature and of man which later was to lead to physical science and technology. True, the Greeks did not see pure science as capable of bearing fruit in technical labor, but this situation was connected with the level reached by science in their time, with the concrete possibilities of pursuing science that were open to them.

Another question, however, is whether the Greek view that immanent speculation is superior to the transient making of things must be explained solely by the level which scientific knowledge had reached in their time. This question is important for more than one reason. If the Greeks actually erred in their evaluation of science, there could still be, of course, *de facto* cultural continuity insofar as later science arose from earlier science, but there would be at the same time a complete break insofar as the Greek ideal of science and the consequent picture of the whole man would differ fundamentally from the idea pursued by contemporary science.

The investigation of the question whether such a break actually did occur does not derive its importance merely from an historical interest in the origin and development of our culture but ranks, as we noted in the Introduction, also among the most urgent cultural problems of our time. Even nowadays it still is *de facto* true that the superiority of pure science is considered to be the foundation and the purpose of authentic academic education. Thus the question arises whether there is not a great discrepancy between the way we actually use the sciences, their actual influence upon society, and the officially professed philosophy of science.

A question that is connected with this problem is the value of the humanities programs of the European gymnasium and of many American High Schools and Junior Colleges as a preparation for university studies. What is the use of maintaining a preparation for university study, if this preparation aims at making us familiar with a cultural world which is no longer our world and which thrived on other ideals than those inspiring the pursuits of contemporary science?[1] Such a preparation can only lead to confusion: the scientist who has been educated in this way will either feel that the time and labor spent in studying the old culture is a total loss or pursue his science with a bad conscience, i.e., have the impression that what he is actually doing in his science means an apostasy from the authentic ideal of science. Neither horn of this dilemma offers much comfort.

The Two Aspects of this Investigation. The investigation of the alleged discrepancy between the professed ideal of science and the actual pursuit of science will, therefore, have to be twofold. First of all, we must see what exacly the arguments were which the Greeks put forward in support of their preference for pure science. Special attention will have to be paid, of course, to the question whether these arguments were wholly determined by the actual level science had reached in their time. We say "wholly," for it is quite obvious that the actual level exercised some influence upon their view. For instance, given the type of science which was at their disposal, they could hardly have foreseen the usefulness of pure science for the control of nature. Nevertheless, it remains quite possible that their arguments in favor of the superiority of pure science contain also elements having a permanent value which, therefore, remain in force today.

In the second place, we must analyze the relationship between theory and practice in contemporary science. In this analysis the important point is not so much the fact that the quest for understanding the phenomena of nature ultimately produces more practical results than the direct search for applications. Of course, this aspect of pure science is very interesting, but it does not con-

---

[1]The question has been raised with all desirable clarity by H. J. Pos in his article "Theoria en Praxis," *Universiteit en Hogeschool,* vol. 1, 1954, pp. 5-14.

tribute anything to the question which concerns us here—namely, the real value of pure science. If pure science were to be considered superior on this ground alone, the argument would be extremely weak, for the norm of evaluation would be taken from the applicability of pure science, so that this science would still be subordinated to the application itself and therefore not superior.

Moreover, pursuing this same line of thought, one could profess the greatest admiration for the Greeks, because of the genial intuition which made them opt for pure science, and at the same time reject the basis on which they founded their preference for pure science. For, if nowadays the government or an industrial enterprise promotes pure science, they are motivated by the practical results which they expect from it in the form of new technological possibilities, and they do not *a priori* exclude these possibilities as belonging to an inferior order.

Accordingly, what we have to investigate here is whether the whole of contemporary science, in both its speculative and its practical aspects, demands the superiority of the theoretical over the practical on the same grounds as those which were put forward by the Greeks. Or to say it differently, does contemporary science ultimately drive man to a kind of reflection which, while taking into account the evolution that has taken place, still corresponds somewhat with what the Greeks called pure contemplation?

2. *The Relationship Between Theory and Practice Among the Greeks*

It would be out of the question to present here a complete survey of Greek thinking about science and its value. We will therefore limit ourselves to a brief statement of the view held by Aristotle, because it is this view which exercised the strongest influence upon the philosophy of science in the West. The Philosopher speaks about the value of speculative science, of *sophia,* in several places of his *Ethics.* To establish its high value, he makes use of two arguments or rather two series of arguments. The first series is concerned with the nobility of the object considered in speculative knowledge. They are contained in *Ethics,* bk. X, ch. 7.

Aristotle's First Argument. In this chapter Aristotle points out the following:

1. "Not only is reason the best thing in us, but the objects of reason are the best of knowable objects."

2. Contemplative activity "is the most continuous, since we can contemplate truth more continuously than we can do anything."

3. Contemplation "is admittedly the pleasantest of virtuous activities . . . and it is to be expected that those who know will pass their time more pleasantly than those who inquire."

4. "Self-sufficiency . . . must belong to the contemplative activity." While ethical activity needs fellow men in relation to whom a man can act justly, contemplative activity has no need of others.

5. Contemplative "activity alone would seem to be loved for its own sake." No other activity surpasses it in nobility, and all other pursuits of man ultimately aim at making contemplation possible.

6. Strictly speaking, a contemplative life will be lived by man not "insofar as he is man . . . but insofar as something divine is present in him."[2]

For a good understanding of these arguments it is necessary to keep in mind that Aristotle is speaking here about *eudaemonia,* happiness. Through contemplation man reaches his supreme happiness. This, however, does not mean that happiness is the end of contemplative wisdom as something extrinsic to it which is to be reached by contemplation as an external means. On the contrary, happiness finds its origin in wisdom not as through an intermediary but as directly emanating from it.

The whole context, moreover, clearly shows that in speaking about theoretical contemplative knowledge Aristotle thinks primarily of what we would call philosophy. Nevertheless, it would not be correct to exclude the theoretical knowledge of our time entirely, for elsewhere Aristotle explicitly includes knowledge of celestial bodies when he speaks of theoretical contemplative knowledge.[3]

The main reason why Aristotle in this context considers practical science to be of a lower rank than contemplative science is that prac-

---

[2]This translation has been taken from W. D. Ross, *The Works of Aristotle,* Oxford University Press, vol. IX, *Ethica Nicomachea,* bk. X, ch. 7.

[3]*Ethics,* bk. VI, ch. 7. It is to be noted that for Aristotle celestial bodies had a higher rank than terrestrial bodies. This made them more suitable for a purely scientific consideration.

tical science never finds its goal in itself but always in something else; hence this science cannot be highest, for it is subordinated. *Sophia,* wisdom, on the other hand, does not aim at something else, but carries its goal (happiness) within its bosom. Wisdom provides man with what he ultimately aims at.

In this connection there is another interesting consideration, which Aristotle presents in the first book of his *Metaphysics* (Ch. 2). He argues there that it was only after securing the necessities of life in a reasonable fashion that man could rise to the level of science. Only then was he able to indulge in the luxury of contemplation. Science, therefore, is not concerned with the useful, for man's needs must be provided for before he can reach science. Science is pursued for its own sake. It has its purpose within itself. For the same reason political skill, which the Greeks valued very highly, is not the supreme virtue, for its purpose is to render secure public peace and order, which are the conditions of contemplation.

The background of Aristotle's thought—and the same applies to St. Thomas' commentary on these texts—constantly reveals the idea that the material conditions of man's existence have been immutably established for once and for all. There is, moreover, a rather strong dualism, insofar as he speaks of the life of the spirit in contradistinction with that of the body. Genuine science has little or nothing to do with the material conditions of life, except insofar as they are factors limiting the life of the spirit.

The Second Argument. In addition to this line of arguments, Aristotle uses another kind to substantiate the superiority of wisdom. He points out that its object is universal and immutable. Practical science cannot be supreme, because its object changes constantly and prevents this science from reaching the universal. Medical science, for example, is concerned with health. But what is healthy for a fish is not healthy for man.[4] The same applies to all practical sciences, whether they are concerned with making things or with doing deeds: they never aim at the universal and the necessary but always at something which is or can be different in its concrete cases and its concrete applications.

It is important to keep in mind that what Aristotle considered here to be characteristic of practical sciences and which made him place them in a lower rank no longer remained valid in later times. For

---

[4]*Ethics,* bk. VI, ch. 7.

in the course of the evolution of science the practical sciences also began to consider the universal, by virtue of their connection with the new positive science of nature. For instance, modern biology, as a general theory of life, is capable of accounting for the differences between what is healthy for a fish and what is healthy for man by means of general physiological principles. Accordingly, the second argument of Aristotle can no longer serve to relegate practical or applicable sciences to the second rank.

Epistēmē, Nous, and Sophia. There is, however, another remark of Aristotle concerning *sophia,* theoretical wisdom, which has not at all lost its force, at least not in any essential point. Let us begin with the Aristotelian distinction of knowledge into five forms of intellectual virtues. These virtues are *epistēmē* (theoretical science), *technē* (skill as practical science), *phronēsis* (practical wisdom, e.g., political economy), *nous* (the contemplative reason), and *sophia* (theoretical wisdom). Two of these, the *technē* and the *phronēsis,* as theoretical aspects of practical science, do not directly concern us here, but we are interested in the relationship of the other three, *epistēmē, nous* and *sophia.*

By *epistēmē* Aristotle means the logically connected whole of theses and conclusions which is deduced from the first principles of a science. He assumes that the first principles of any science do not fall under this science itself, because they cannot be proved by means of this science. These principles pertain to the contemplative insight of the *nous.* Obviously, Aristotle was thinking here especially of mathematics, whose axioms, the Greeks held, were intuitively understood and served as the foundation from which the science itself was deduced. *Sophia,* however, was concerned with both principles and conclusions and, therefore, united *nous* with *epistēmē.* "The wise man must not only know what follows from the first principles, but must also possess truth about the first principles."[5] Wisdom, therefore, is the perfect science, an absolute ideal of all knowledge.

Science and Its First Principles. It is very interesting to see here how this view of Aristotle shows both how he was dependent upon his time and how he managed to transcend this limitation and propose something of lasting value. As to the former aspect, the present state of science does not allow us any longer to say that science itself does

---

[5]*Ethics,* bk. VI, ch. 7.

not establish its principles. This assertion is certainly true of physical science, which considers the discovery of general principles one of its main functions. Aristotle's view is not even any longer true with respect to mathematics, in which—to abstract from abstract mathematics—Euclid's intuitively understood axioms may be replaced by others.

Nevertheless, it would not do to claim that Artistotle was entirely wrong when he stated that the principles of a science do not fall under this science itself. For the expression "the principles of a science" is an ambiguous concept. To limit ourselves to physical science, it may refer to the fundamental laws of this science, such as those of classical mechanics or of classical chemistry (Lavoisier, Dalton, Proust), but it may also refer to what we have called the presuppositions of physical science. While the fundamental laws in question lie within the reach and the competence of physical science, the same cannot be asserted, as we have stated repeatedly, with respect to the presuppositions.

Let us explain the point. If physical science at a given moment finds it necessary to revise the fundamental laws of classical mechanics, as actually did happen in the theory of relativity and in quantum mechanics, it does so on the basis of exactly the same methodic principles on which formerly it felt justified in formulating these classical fundamental laws. There is no question of a modification in the methodic fundamental principle that experience must be the ultimate norm of any change to be made in the teachings of physical science, but broadened experience shows new aspects which the old theory could not explain. The experimental method as such has not undergone any change, but there are now new experimental means available, which permit us to apply the method in a more refined way.[6]

Accordingly, if we keep in mind the distinction between principles (presuppositions) which make physical science the science which it is and those which determine the actual content of this science, we must admit that Aristotle was right when he claimed that the principles (presuppositions) of a science do not belong to the subject matter of this science itself. This conclusion is very important for the question which we are considering here—namely,

---

[6]In ordinary speech one will easily say that new experimental methods have constantly been discovered throughout the course of history; for instance, the use of the electron microscope and of radioactive isotopes. These new methods, however, are nothing else but new means of applying the experimental method as such.

the value of contemplative science even in the contemporary scientific and technological order. Let us examine first what this value is and return subsequently again to the view of the Greeks.

3. *Theory and Practice in Contemporary Science*

a. Changing Perspectives

To evaluate the contemporary relationship between theory and practice, between the theoretical cognitive aspect and the practical aspect of application of contemporary science, it is necessary first to realize that the relationship between theory and practice is not given for once and for all but undergoes modifications constantly. Or, to say it differently, what is called theory and what practice depends largely upon the viewpoint one takes. For this reason there exist now a number of distinctions in this matter which would have been almost irrelevant to the old Greek situation.

Without attempting to enumerate all possibilities, we will list here a few of these distinctions.

1. Within the framework of technology itself it is meaningful to distinguish between the actual scientific application of a technical science (practice) and the pursuit of this science itself (theory). The former is the concern of the industrial engineer, the latter that of, e.g., the professor of a technological institute. In this sense the professor undoubtedly is a theorist, and the engineer a practicer, who may on occasion quarrel in a similar fashion as other men of theory and practice.

2. With respect to physical science technology as a whole has the character of being concerned with the practical order and is opposed to it as practice is to theory.

3. Within the framework of physical science, however, one may pay attention, for example, to the position of mathematics. From the viewpoint of pure mathematics, physical science appears to have the character of being a realm of mathematical applicability. Thus mathematics, pursued for its own sake, is related to physical science as theory is to practice.

4. In pure mathematics one may distinguish between the ordinary mathematician who aims at developing the theory of mathe-

matics and the one who examines the foundations of this science. For the former the latter is a pure theorist and he himself is a man who pursues mathematics in practice. For the ordinary mathematician aims at a mathematical theory, while the examiner of the foundation aims at the theory of mathematics.

5. Finally, all the above forms of pure positive science may be placed in contrast with philosophy. In this way all forms of positive science bear the stamp of being practical, because in principle they reveal themselves fruitful with respect to man's activity. Even though the mathematician does not think about the applicability of his theory to physical science, *de facto* what he is doing has its applications. This is true even for the investigation of the foundations on which mathematics is based; for instance, the results of mathematical logic have rendered good service to computer technique. What applies to mathematics is *a fortiori* true of physical science, for pure physical science was and still is the most important driving force of technological development.

Compared with all these sciences which are in principle fruitful in practical applications, philosophy alone bears the mark of being a strictly useless science. True, in the past it has contributed insofar as it made it possible for physical science to arise as a science, and in this sense it could be called fruitful. However, the fruitfulness in question is precisely something which can no longer be attributed to contemporary philosophy. For the vision of man and of nature which it developed in the past and which created the intellectual climate in which science could bloom has long since been embodied in the method of physical science. Thus the practical usefulness of philosophy is a thing of the past. Must we say therefore that philosophy now is no longer meaningful?

b. The Meaning of Theory

Practical Value is Not the Aim of Theory. It is tempting to seek the meaning of the theoretical attitude, as it manifests itself in the above-mentioned contrasts and in the whole development of science, with respect to its practical value. It seems that man's urge to understanding is a kind of primitive instinct which has made him unconsciously develop science in such a way that its actual evolution would reveal practical value as its ultimate aim. This line of thought, however, logically leads to an impasse. For it ends up with a consideration of the meaning to be attributed to the relationship between theory and practice and thus becomes a reflection upon the meaning of man's being, as it manifests itself in the evolution of science.

Self-Knowledge as the Aim of Theory. As soon as one realizes this point, it becomes possible to view the relationship between theory and practice in each of the five above-mentioned meanings also from a different angle than that of orientation to practice. It is then no longer necessary to view, for example, the meaning of the investigation of the foundations upon which mathematics is based in the light of the fact that ultimately this investigation will reveal itself somehow useful. The interest in this investigation now becomes a sign that in pure mathematics man is not only concerned with following his mathematical instinct but also with learning something about himself by means of this human activity. For the investigation of the mathematical method, which is performed in examining the foundations of mathematics, in its own way throws some light upon man's cognitive possibilities. The same applies to physical science, as pure science. What motivates man here is, as we have pointed out before, the desire to attain to an understanding not only of nature but also of himself.

What applies to these two theoretical sciences is valid also in a very special way for the whole of technology. In developing technique, in utilizing all possibilities which present themselves in theory, man is driven by a desire which ultimately again is nothing else than his universal urge to self-knowledge. If, contrary to Greek thought, theoretical science has shown itself fruitful for practical life, the meaning of this phenomenon is not only that theory has received a new aim—practical usefulness—but also that practice itself has changed its aim and possesses now also an extremely important theoretical purpose. We do not mean so much that technology can be of great service to physical science, but refer to that of which this usefulness is a symptom, the fundamental fact that the powerful possibilities offered by technology are revelations of what being-man really means.

Behind the entire creative activity of man who restlessly investigates and exploits all possibilities stands as the motive and driving force the desire to penetrate more deeply into his own nature by means of the world which he builds for himself. As we have seen above, physical science in its own specific realm needs the experiment, i.e., it needs experience which is made more differentiated by means of man's intervention in the realm of material reality.   In a similar way one may view man's entire transformation and recreation of the world as one huge experiment in which he gropingly tries to develop the world and himself for the purpose of discovering more about himself than was originally given to him.

Viewed in this fashion, knowing and making lie in the same line; both mean man's self-realization, one in an immanent way and the other in a transient fashion.   Both go out to the world, but both also revert to man.   For in knowledge man appropriates the world to himself immanently as an enrichment of his spirit; in technological making he appropriates the same world to himself to humanize it, and at the same time he learns to know himself in a new way, provided he reflects upon this activity.   This reflection cannot be dispensed with; it is, as it were, the key-stone of the edifice, but is not supplied by man's technical activity itself.   In this respect also technology does not negate its inner bond with physical science.   For, as we have seen in Chapter One, physical science is a non-reflective science, i.e., a science which in its abstraction does not understand itself.   Hence, although physical science and technology necessarily have to be reflected upon, they themselves do not supply this reflection.

The Grandeur of the Greek View.   The ancient Greeks were very much aware of the meaning of *sophia* as the all-embracing wisdom which extends not only to science itself but also to the principles upon which science is based.   Because their view prevailed in the West, a tradition of many centuries required the study of philosophy as the understructure and upperstructure of science.   Until the seventeenth century it was thought that philosophical reflection was necessary for the pursuit of any science whatsoever.   This idea, however, proved to be a mistake: the positive science which has arisen since proved that it is possible to pursue science fruitfully, both theoretically and practically, without philosophical reflection, because the necessary philosophical presuppositions could, as it were, be embodied in the method of the science in question.   Nevertheless, the Greeks were not mistaken in the fact that human knowledge which is fully worthy of man requires not only the pursuit of science but also the philosophical evaluation of this science.   Scientific concepts have to be supplemented by a concept of science if man's knowledge is to be integral.

The pursuit of technology, likewise, if it is to be a genuinely human activity, demands understanding of the technological activity, for otherwise it becomes an activity in which man loses sight of himself. But the understanding of technological activity is a matter of theory, something which differs in character from technological activity itself.

Considering all this, one is struck by the grandeur of the Greek view which attributed superiority to the theoretical element. Man is a being in quest of himself, in quest of enlightenment about his own nature. It was a first idea of his own essence which made him pursue theoretical science. The results of this science, especially the practical results in later times, did not merely contribute to a better understanding of what man is, but also found their profound meaning in this understanding. Thus contemplative activity stands at the beginning as well as at the end of all human activity. It directs all activities and has to assign them their reason, for the other activities do not find their purpose in themselves but expect it from man's contemplative activity. No matter how much man develops nature and society, transforming them into something which serves him and is more worthy of a human existence, it should be evident that the accomplishments of science and technology do not supply the answer to the fundamental question regarding the meaning of human existence, although they may be able to throw considerable light on it. One could even say that rather than to reply to this question, they have made the question itself all the more urgent.

The Ultimate Question is Made More Urgent by Science and Technology. The reason for this assertion is as follows. The contribution which science and technology make toward a more human way of life reveals its typical character of being a culture of means in direct proportion to its success. As we have pointed out before, the technological order is a culture of means, and consequently cannot be a goal in itself. Thus the question regarding the meaning of human existence imposes itself the more strongly according as the necessity to work in order to maintain life absorbs less and less of the entire activity of a society. Here lies also the real problem of leisure. Formerly the large majority of mankind was so much occupied by the care for its daily bread that their life and work was given meaning in a simple and direct fashion: they had to work to remain alive. The more human, however, man's existence becomes, the more man is liberated from this daily care, the more vehemently is he thrown back upon the question of what meaning his existence has.

For without a reply to this question man cannot lead a life worthy of himself, because man is and remains the being which is concerned with the meaning of his existence and that of his world. Now that the necessity to care for the preservation of our lives leaves us time to spare, we may, of course, attempt to evade this question by seeking distraction, by losing ourselves in all kinds of freely chosen work, by the intellectual pursuit of science, by devoting ourselves to art or sports. Anyone, however, who reflects only for a moment on the meaning of his occupation, whether it be vocational or avocational, is confronted with the problem of the ultimate meaning. For the meaning of any effort and any relaxation, of any particular science and any social activity always points to something which transcends these things. They have meaning only insofar as they derive it from a general and ultimate meaning of human existence.

In this connection it is interesting to revert for a moment to Aristotle's argument in which he attributes priority to pure science on the ground that it has a non-utilitarian character. In a sense this argument must be said to be to the point. For reflection itself upon the historical evolution which has taken place under the influence of physical science, upon technical activity and social progress, does not have the utilitarian character proper to physical science as a practical science. This reflection, as reflection, may be compared to a keystone: it gives meaning to all other forms of activity.

On the other hand, however, there is a great difference between Aristotle's view and our times. We are no longer able to separate what he called "wisdom" from the reflection upon technical activity which is the giver of meaning. For it is precisely through this technical activity that man learns to know himself better. His self-realization in reflection demands technical activity, not merely as a condition of life, but as an intrinsic constituent element of his reflection.

Meanwhile, however, one could seriously ask whether modern man, living in the technological order, is not absorbed so much by it that he *de facto* never manages to reflect upon the ultimate meaning of human existence. The question is all the more urgent, because the pursuit of science and technology itself is such a fascinating intellectual occupation and has, moreover, the tendency to absorb man's attention to such an extent that it is at least just as much an obstacle to reflection as the grinding care for the daily bread used to be in former ages. One may justly ask whether the "natural" life of the past, which was physically more difficult but also more stable, did not really offer more opportunities for reflection than the raging torrent of modern life which restlessly drives man to more perfect control of matter and the development of new possibilities. Is it really true, as we have stated above, that physical science and technology by their very nature demand reflection upon the ultimate meaning of human existence? All these questions refer to the hold which physical science and technology increasingly have upon man's attention. We will devote the next section to reply to them.

4. *The Shift in Intellectual Attention*

Ancient Culture. In the world of Greek culture there was a strong connection between existing scientific insights and philosophical reflection upon these insights. This was true especially of physical science. The physical science of the Greeks was not an independent science having its own specific method, but constituted a part of a study of nature which was preponderantly philosophical in its orientation. This study of nature in its turn was indissolubly connected with the study of man in which man strove for an understanding of himself. It is typical, for instance, that Aristotle's works contain alongside physical science and philosophy of nature at least an equal amount of philosophy of science, in the broad sense of the term. In other words, the actual pursuit of science was deliberately placed in the perspective of metaphysics and philosophy of science.

The Middle Ages. This intimate bond between philosophy and science continued to exist in the Middle Ages. This era remained faithful to the ideal of ancient Greek *sophia* or wisdom, but viewed this ideal in the light of theology. Like the whole of profane life, so also the pursuit of science was viewed and evaluated in the awareness that man and nature are creatures and the work of God. Concretely speaking, this meant that the study of nature, by way of the philosophy of nature, tended toward a natural theology. The medieval theologians, who were the men pursuing philosophy, took seriously the Aristotelian view that man will live a contemplative life not "insofar as he is man ... but insofar as something divine is present in him." Wisdom was destined above all to make man more clearly aware of his place with respect to God. For what man's essence was and what the ultimate meaning of human existence was appeared to be dependent upon the intention for which God had created man. Man was what God willed him to be.

The Middle Ages, however, did more than place Greek science in a theological perspective. Attention to specific problems of physical science became increasingly more intense and slowly there developed something like a method to satisfy this attention. This method ultimately had to come into conflict with the prevailing philosophical and theological methods which, despite the high intrinsic value of their objects and of their viewpoints, were unsuitable for raising and solving the problems proper to physical science. For the newly developing science of nature was characterized precisely by its positive, i.e., non-philosophical character.

Modern Times. However, this non-philosophical character did not reveal itself immediately. We may even say that neither the protagonists nor the opponents of the new science were fully aware of what was really new in it. The theologians of the seventeenth century combated the new science by means of theological and philosophical arguments—an endeavor which was, of course, doomed to failure. But the conflict resulted in placing physical science in a very peculiar position. It became a doctrine which competed with philosophy and theology in their own fields. It became a struggle between science and faith, a question of choosing between the new science and the old one, integrally and without any deletions. This struggle was the reason also why the world view of the new science, as we have pointed out in Chapter Nine, could become the world view *par excellence.*

Whatever may have been the disastrous results of this conflict, it had at least the advantage that everyone pursuing science was confronted with general philosophical and theological issues and thus was forced to reflect upon the ultimate meaning of his science. In this way positive science at first remained in contact with the most profound questions of life. However, according as physical science developed and grew, it became clearer where its inner boundaries lie. The same happened to philosophy and theology. Meanwhile the effects of the initial struggle became apparent. Physical science did not merely become the non-philosophical science enjoying autonomy within its own realm, as was demanded by its very method, but also made many of its pursuers lose contact with philosophical and theological life.

It is, of course, difficult to judge how the cultural history of Europe would have developed if the seventeenth century had known theologians equal to St. Albert the Great and St. Thomas Aquinas, who in the thirteenth century managed to assign a place to Greco-Arabian science in Christian thought. Such intellectual giants would have been capable of recognizing the proper character of the new science which arose in the seventeenth century. Thus physical science would perhaps not have exercised the same secularizing influence which now became its role or at least this influence would not have been exercised in the same fashion. For we should keep in mind that not every influence which physics actually did have upon the course of history has to be considered as a natural result of this science itself.

Evaluation of the Modern Shift in Attention. Be this as it may, there is one thing which would have remained the same regardless of this historical situation—namely, the enormous intellectual attention which physical science and technology would have demanded in later times. For the shift of intellectual attention from philosophical to positive matters which is discernible from the Middle Ages seems to be connected with the internal possibilities proper to the evolution of man's thinking and power rather than with what actually did happen in the course of this development. Although the actual events may have played a role and may have led temporarily to an overevaluation of positive science of nature, they did not affect or change the character of this science and its inherent applicability. For this reason it is difficult to see the shift in attention from philosophy and theology to positive science and technology as an aberration of the human spirit and as an attempt to avoid the ultimate issue, the meaning of human existence—an attempt which was, of course, doomed to failure but meanwhile could deprive entire generations of the happiness that was their due.

For a correct appreciation of the shift in attention toward positive science it is necessary constantly to keep in mind that the discovery of this science and its practical applicability is such a great good precisely and especially because it raised the whole of man's busyness in the world to a higher level. To say it differently, it is not correct to view the interest in physics and technology as a backsliding of man's intellectual attention from the spiritual to the material sphere. Rather the opposite is true: man's actual busyness comes to lie on a higher level. Of course, there exists a very real danger that the attention of many will be so absorbed by science and technology that they seem to retain no interest in the ultimate questions regarding human existence. Nevertheless, this danger may not be blamed upon science and technology, for their typical abstractness does at least as much if not more than man's former labor "in the sweat of his brow" to press these questions.

Evidently, the temptation to be fully absorbed by the intellectually fascinating pursuit of physical science or the development of new technical inventions is greater than the danger of a similar absorption by hard labor for a precarious living. We may ask, however, whether this temptation is really as dangerous as it is made out to be. Moreover, is it not true that much of the philosophical interest of former ages was more appearance than reality? This interest arose from man's general desire to know and to explain. It was certainly not specifically philosophical, although the contemporary state of science gave this desire a philosophical orientation. Thus we may say that the development of physical science exercised a purifying influence upon philosophy, because it managed to separate the various elements composing the undifferentiated quest for explanation proper to former times. In the history of philosophy one can easily see how the rise of physical science gave philosophers a better understanding of the specific fashion in which philosophy views its problems. This thought leads us to the consideration of another point which is closely connected with the preceding.

5. *Technological Evolution as the Secularization of the Christian Idea of Redemption*

A much-disputed question concerns the extent to which the Christian concept of redemption is connected with the scientific and technological evolution which occurred in the Christian West and which did not originate anywhere else. The connection is none too clear. On the one hand, Christian faith reminded man that he was called to another and better life than that offered to him in this valley of tears but, on the other, it also postponed the possible attainment of such a better life to another existence than that of earthly reality. From early childhood the Christian was trained not to consider the earth as his permanent abode and to live for heaven. Thus Christianity is somewhat embarrassed by the technological and social development of the western world. It feels somewhat like a father whose son has deviated from what he considers the right path but somehow has become famous and thus still is an honor to the family, although not in the way which was judged to be fitting.

For to all appearance the improvement of man's earthly status which began in modern times is a secularization of Christian thought. The belief in progress which supports the evolution of society is born from the conviction that the redemption of man from his earthly misery can be accomplished by man himself here on earth. It is an undeniable fact that belief in progress in the above-mentioned sense was most lively in circles that were the least orthodox Christian or even wholly estranged from Christianity—viz., the eighteenth century philosophers of the Enlightenment and the Marxists of the nineteenth and twentieth centuries. Thus it seems that we really have to do here with a secularization of the idea of redemption which draws man away from heaven and toward the earth. There is, moreover, the fact established by experience that church affiliation usually decreases in direct ratio to the prosperity of a nation.[7]

Technology de Facto *Exercised a Secularizing Influence.* What interests us especially here is the question to what extent the secularizing influence of the technological and social evolution must be considered as being an influence which merely happened to exist *de facto* or as an influence which flows of necessity from the nature of this evolution. No one will deny that, concretely speaking, the influence in question possessed aspects which were merely *de facto* present. The effects of the struggle between faith and science at first made themselves felt especially on the level of knowing, i.e., of theory, which was entirely in accord with the fact that in the new physical science the theoretical aspect originally stood in the center of attention.[8]

However, according as physical science began to reveal its true nature, in which theory and practice go hand in hand, and according as, more than anything else had done in the past, it opened perspectives which breached the natural order and the natural social relationships, the struggle between faith and science shifted to the realm

---

[7]It is, however, often wholly overlooked that the situation is different in the most prosperous country in the world—the U. S. A. Precisely the opposite appears to be happening there.

[8]The seventeenth century space novels, which we mentioned on p. 181, were not only intended to depict the theoretical cognitive power of the new science, but served also as weapons in the struggle between faith and science. They had to make it clear to man that the true picture of the world was the one presented by the astronomers and not that of the theologians.

of practical life. Faith seemed to demand that the natural order and the social relationships based upon it be considered as holy and untouchable, because they were the created order of God, while science, on the other hand, lived in the conviction that this order, whether created by God or not, had to be modified to deliver man from his chains.

The Purifying Influence of Technology upon Christian Ideas. De facto, therefore, science and technology exercised a secularizing influence but, we may ask, did this have to be so of necessity? In our opinion, this question has to be answered in the affirmative. As we have pointed out above, in ancient times philosophy fulfilled in practice more than a single function and the rise of physical science as a positive science served to purify philosophy from functions that were really beyond its calling. The same effect, moreover, may be observed in theology. One has to think here only of the benefit exegesis derived from the theologians' realization that the Bible was not meant to provide mankind with physical explanations. The growth of this insight was calculated to strengthen the receptivity of the faithful to the true nature of the Glad Tidings, despite the fact that many lost their faith in the ensuing crisis. This loss, however, may not be debited to physical science, for it merely provoked decisions which sooner or later had to be made anyhow.

Physical science, therefore, exercised a purifying influence, as far as the realm of knowledge was concerned, upon philosophy as well as theology. It would have exercised this influence even if there had been no conflict between faith and science. In a similar fashion it has likewise purified the Christian idea of redemption and the entire Christian view of life. Anyone doomed to a wretched life on earth, upon hearing about man's future glory in heaven, is likely to conceive this glory in earthly terms. His desire for a better life on earth makes him long for heaven, but this heaven is an earthly heaven. On the other hand, according as man's earthly existence becomes more worthy of man and more glorified for all, the Christian idea of redemption gains in depth and meaning, its proper dimensions become more clearly visible.

Superficially speaking, the petition of Our Lord's prayer, "Give us this day our daily bread," may speak more strongly to us in times of famine, but it is an entirely different question whether this situation makes us more vividly realize the authentic meaning of this prayer. Only when man through scientific, technological, and social means has banished famine, does he realize how much of his achievement, in breaching the order of nature that included famine, remains fundamentally based upon the givenness of nature, upon a nature which God has given to man to change by his labor. It is true, of course, that material need is a means that may lead man to prayer, but it is a dangerous means of doubtful value, for it threatens to make prayer degenerate into a magic formula rather than being the humble bowing of the creature before an almighty and transcendent God. God is the mighty Lord of heaven and earth, but not a Lord in the fashion of man and cut down to human standards.

These considerations lead us to venture the opinion that, although science and technology may temporarily obscure the question of the meaning proper to human existence and diminish man's sensitivity to this question, this situation is not a permanent feature of the new order. As their development reveals more clearly the characteristic inner limitations of physical science and technological progress, the ultimate question will impose itself again but in a more purified way, unmixed with other motives. Thus physical science and technology appear to provoke a radicalism insofar as they throw man back to essentials even in the religious aspect. For they radically manifest how much man remains dependent upon the givenness of nature and how much all his activity springs from his own inner nature which as such also is something given to him. Thus man will become aware of his own radical dependence, but now really as a dependence which is *radical*.

6. *The Secularization of Charity*

All realms, even those which are far removed from the immediate reach of physical science and technology, manifest the beneficial influence of the evolution initiated by physical science and of the way in which this evolution tends to secularize many of man's aspirations and to throw him back to essentials. In this connection it should be kept in mind that the collaboration of physical science and technology in the strict sense has given birth to a development which did not stay confined to the realm of physical science. When it appeared that nature was not a fixed and immutable order, the immutable permanence of the social order likewise became subject to doubt. Thus all kinds of social sciences were born or, if they had existed before as theoretical disciplines, were given a practical orientation. In this way the technological element began to radiate over many different areas of life. To illustrate the point, we will examine here the secularization of charity, especially because this secularization is often adduced as one of the essential objections against the technological order.

Samaritan Charity or Secularized Services? The technological age no longer recognizes good Samaritans but only smoothly functioning impersonal services. What, however, was the reason why Christ praised the Samaritan? He was recommended because he did not heedlessly pass by, but lovingly looked down upon his fellow man in his desperate need and took care of him as best he could. Charity, then, has two essential aspects: love and care. Love urges us to provide the best of care, and this care must be inspired by love if it is to be genuinely human care, care of a man for his fellow man. Once, therefore, man has discovered the possibilities offered by science, love of his fellow man urges him to make use of these possibilities and to develop them even further. Anyone who nowadays, even with the best intentions, would do materially just what the Samaritan did, would fail gravely in love of his fellow man. What he should do now is call for an ambulance.

A society which is deeply concerned with real care for concrete man in distress has to embody this care in suitable and efficient services and may not leave it to good Samaritans who happen to pass that way. As a theologian recently wrote: "In this realm Christian charity, as secularized and laicized, has permeated human consciousness to such an extent that it has assumed the form of an inalienable human right. What in former ages sprang as a work of charity from a Christian virtue has now become so normal that it is a right of man."[9]

Secularized Services and the Fundamental Idea of Charity. It is not possible that what began as Christian charity prescribed by the Gospel and grew up thanks to the possibilities offered by science would really contradict the fundamental idea of charity. Superficially, of course, it may seem as if Christianity has lost its meaning now that secular agencies have taken over its inspiring initiatives. This appearance finds additional support in numerous utterances of Christians who take it for granted that the secularization in question is not a gain but a loss for the Church. The Church, they proclaim, has been de-

---

[9] E. Schillebeeckx, *Op zoek naar de levende God,* Utrecht, 1958, p. 4.

prived of a potent means which gave it access to the human heart and
rendered man more accessible to the message of the Gospel.

As has been pointed out above when we spoke of the secularization of the Christian idea of redemption, there is a serious misunderstanding here. Even from the Christian viewpoint, the secularization
of charity work is a great good, both because it has made this charity
more effective, more real, and because it forces the Christian to concentrate his attention upon the source of this charity rather than upon
its effects. Thus he is forced to live the ideal of charity in a more
radical way, for it can no longer be embodied in isolated deeds, such
as caring for the sick and the poor, but has to be extended over his
entire life. Charity must now be embodied in all aspects of human
togetherness, and one can no longer, so to speak, get away with
practicing it on occasion.

The view put forward here broadly contradicts the usual interpretation given to contemporary social developments. For it seems
that precisely nowadays one buys off charity by paying taxes which
the government uses for charitable work in established institutes
staffed by professionally trained personnel. As a matter of fact, it is
possible to take this view of the matter and—what is even worse—one
can coldly substitute one's tax contribution for the duty of charity. In
such a case, however, the blame does not fall upon the institutionalization of what was formerly done by charity, but upon a lack of genuine
understanding of what charity really means.

As loving care of our fellow men, charity has to extend to *all* areas
of life and not only to those which traditionally were called "charitable works." It has to embrace, moreover, *all* our fellow men and not
only those who find themselves afflicted with a few classified needs.[10]
Thus the institutionalization of charity does not mean that Christian
love of our neighbor is banished from society, but only that this love
is now compelled to become more universal and consequently also more
radical. It has now to dominate our lives in all their aspects, for everywhere we have to deal with our fellow men. In this way charity, just
as the personal sacrifice mentioned above, becomes more difficult, but

---

[10]The universalization of charity in question is not primarily concerned with
the fact that through the bridging of spatial distances charity can now be
effectively extended to all human beings because men now *de facto* constitute
a real community. This type of universality exists also, of course, and gives
a character of its own to the duty of charity. What we are referring to above,
however, is especially the necessity caused by the technological order to make
charity permeate all sectors of life as the source from which man draws his
inspiration.

is also more human, more appealing to the spirit which has to dominate human existence.

All this should not be taken to mean that there are no longer any special sectors in which to pursue particular types of charity. Likewise, we do not want to decide all kinds of issues as to who is best suited to take the initiative: the churches, the government, or private organizations. No matter who undertakes the task, for each one it means equally that, to be done properly, the work has to assume the character of a social professional function. Care for our fellow men has to be based upon specialized knowledge and skill which, in addition to years of study and training, demands great experience. A social organization which takes its purpose and the charity implied by it seriously has to be ready to appeal to this specialized skill. No one any longer has any doubts about this point with respect to the bodily care of the ill and the infirm, but the same rule applies with equal force to social and spiritual care.

In the past priests, ministers and their helpers have rendered immense services because of their generous and amateurish[11] efforts to lighten all kinds of social and moral evils. But they lacked the required skill and specialized knowledge to cure specific needs. In primitive areas of the world missionaries continue to perform medical work, simply because there is no one else to do it. Medical societies in civilized countries willingly offer them their aid and assistance to make their work more effective. Nevertheless, the situation is not normal or healthy. In the home country no doctor would tolerate the practice of medicine by an unskilled priest or minister. Of course, there is no danger that they would even attempt to do so, for physician and priest or minister know too well how much they complement each other's work.

Just as the minister of religion has long since become accustomed to the physician and his specific function, so also he realizes now that the sociologist, the psychologist, and the pedagogist work side by side with him. Thanks to their labor, the task of the priest or minister has become more specifically religious and charitable work more effective. How all these various social tasks have to be organized concretely is a question which we do not have to consider here.

11The term is used here not in a pejorative sense but according to its etymological meaning, as derived from the Latin *amare,* to love. They acted out of real love.

Suffice it to mention that, as experience teaches, there are many ways to organize such matters, each of which has its own advantages and disadvantages.

7. *Conclusion*

The Contribution of Science and Technology to Man's Self-Realization. The secularization of the Christian idea of redemption and of Christian charity justifies the conclusion that physical science and technology are capable of making an important contribution to man's self-knowledge and self-realization, although this contribution can never be *direct* because by its very nature it is directed toward matter. Science and technology constitute, as it were, the starting point of man's development, the point where he begins to become himself. Urged on by the forces developed in science and technology, man is forced constantly to renew his inner life by unceasing reflection upon his existence and by living ever more radically in accord with the fundamental meaning of his being.

This force is, of course, not a physical compulsion which leads of necessity to its effect. It is more in the nature of an invitation, but a very pressing invitation. The history of science and technology and the results produced by them confirm once more, but this time in an entirely different perspective, the old philosophical saying that "for the human intellect which is bound up with a body the proper and primary object is material nature."[12] When St. Thomas wrote these words, he was concerned especially with the origin of intellectual knowledge through abstraction from the senses. He was thinking of the development of knowledge in concrete and individual man, but his words possess a far greater range of validity. They apply not only to the individual, but also to the development of the whole of mankind on the intellectual as well as the moral level.

The Pursuit of Science and Technology and Authentic Existence. For this reason the pursuit of science and technology and the resulting shift of attention is not an apostasy from authentic human existence. This pursuit participates in the proper life of the spirit, it is the road which the embodied spirit, the spirit-in-matter, must take to arrive at self-realization in knowledge and love. On the other hand, it is true that, historically speaking, philosophical reflection also has prepared

---

[12]Thomas Aquinas, *Summa theol.*, p. I, q. 84, a. 7.

the way for physical science. Thus philosophical reflection embraces the beginning and the end of the historical development—a clear sign that, although for man, the spirit-in-matter, knowledge and handling of matter is essential, his self-realization becomes fully self-realization only when, in his reflection upon the pursuit of science and technology and their consequences, man attains to knowledge of who and what he is and embodies this knowledge in his life.

By doing so, he retains his spiritual control of physical science and technology and of all positive sciences and techniques which are connected with them, for in this way he achieves the *sophia,* the wisdom, spoken of by Aristotle, which knows not only science but also the principles of science. Appropriately adapted to the contemporary situation, this saying becomes: wisdom knows not only all sciences and the techniques which they use, but also their meaning for man.

At the same time, however, it follows that wisdom realizes that, in using science and technology, it has to accept their inherent properties for what they are, because they are consequences of what man is and of what matter is. This idea will be worked out in the subsequent chapter.

CHAPTER FIFTEEN

THE INTRINSIC CONSEQUENCES OF THE TECHNOLOGICAL ORDER

1. *Introduction*

Thinking from the "Viewpoint" of Things. It is an old saying that one cannot make a silk purse out of a sow's ear. In his use of any materials man has to take into account the inherent properties of the material as well as the bodily forces which are at his disposal. He cannot, for example, break iron with his hands. This same fundamental idea of technical wisdom applies to man's entire endeavor to attain greater possibilities of self-realization by means of the development of his world. He will have to take into consideration the intrinsic demands of matter as well as the typical features of human knowledge and power. These demands and these features include both obstacles and possibilities, both dangers and means to overcome them.

This situation makes itself felt first of all on the technical level in the strict sense. The technician has to accept the workable material as a givenness of nature, although by doing so systematically he does not have to stop with nature as it is given, but can make it do what he wants. This power, however, has as its condition that man by knowing appropriate nature in such a way that he is, as it were, capable of thinking from the viewpoint of nature. For instance, let us say that he wants to give iron a shape which it does not have naturally. Iron does not allow itself to be kneaded like wax or clay. Man, therefore, must make himself familiar with the inherent properties of iron to such an extent that he knows the conditions under which iron becomes like clay for him.

What was described here on the level of making things, on the level of practical thinking, repeats itself on that of pure thought. Fruitful science has to begin by taking things as they are if it is ever to understand why they are as they are. In this way what first was merely a brute fact of reality will be illuminated in man's understanding and seen as the necessary consequence of a more fundamental structure which makes also other consequences possible.

The same basic structures, therefore, are always present in both knowing and making. The potentiality of things is practically unbounded, but its realization demands that there be thinking from the things toward man. Since things themselves do not think, man has, as it were, to think for them to make them become what he wants them to be. If, however, man is to think for things, he has to make them intellectually his own. To repeat once again Aristotle's striking expression, man has "to become" the things. Only then will he be able to unveil their possibilities, but these possibilities remain *their* possibilities. If man wants actually to bring about these possibilities not only in himself but also in reality, he must let the process of realization run its course from the "viewpoint" of the things themselves. It is only when the proper possibilities of the things are realized that they become possibilities which work for man, possibilities which are of service to him.

Thinking Toward Man. Although thinking has to be from the "viewpoint" of things, it is, on the other hand, also a thinking toward man. For when man thinks for things to make them become something else than what they are, he does so for the sake of himself, for the sake of his self-unfolding. For it is only in man that there is self-presence and freedom and consequently awareness of the distance between what man and his world actually are and what they ought to be. This distance, however, as such, as well as the two poles separated by it, did not arise from the creativity of man himself. What is typical of man is that he has to discover all this but does not invent it. Or rather—for invention also is always governed by norms—he does not create it from nothing.

In one way or another man reads what he is and what he ought to be in what he is and does spontaneously. In other words, as we have expressed it previously, man is also a nature. What is special about his nature is that it is not a nature alongside material nature but, no matter how much his nature differs from material nature, the latter finds its unfolding in the former. Thus man's spiritual being is not an essentially foreign addition to material nature, but its most profound self, its intrinsic unfolding. For this reason it is meaningful also to say that man has to think for nature from the "viewpoint" of nature to lead it to its unfolding. What is naturally present in man is thus brought to a more perfect condition through man's thinking and doing. Such a development, however, is possible only if man pays attention to both himself and nature in continuous and constantly renewed reflection.

The optimistic belief in progress of past centuries thought that scientific and technical advances would automatically lead to a better world and better human beings, somewhat like a process of evolution in which man plays a purely executive role. There is a grain of truth in this idea, for in every phase of scientific and technical realization new perspectives which previously were invisible reveal themselves. We may compare this situation with the climbing of a new hitherto unknown mountain top: the higher one climbs, the clearer it becomes how he can continue his progress to the top.

Nevertheless, not every pathway which delineates itself leads actually to the goal pursued. The possibilities to go forward have to be evaluated constantly in reference to the goal. The optimistic belief in progress of past ages did not fail to recognize that there was a way to the top and to grasp man's real position in the world as well as the importance of science and technology but, on the other hand, it was mistaken in the idea that this progress would be achieved automatically as a kind of natural process. Just as virgin nature contains a challenge to man to become familiar with it and to control it, so also every new phase of knowledge and control of nature constantly appeals to man in an even stronger way to realize his human existence in a new fashion. Thus man is continuously forced to think from nature toward himself and to reflect over and over again upon himself.

Man's Self-Unfolding and Nature. In this chapter, however, we are concerned not so much with emphasizing again the necessity for man to reflect upon what he is and what he ought to be as with showing that all self-unfolding is at the same time an unfolding of nature and therefore remains bound up with what nature is—we mean, nature as it is in him and outside him. Man is not able to break iron with his bare hands, because of nature, the nature of the iron and that of his hands. When we speak of the nature of the hand in this context, we do not mean merely its physical nature as endowed with limited muscular power and limited possibilities of manipulation, but also the nature of the hand as the executive organ of the whole man with all his limited cognitive and operative possibilities.

Accordingly, in evaluating and directing the technological order, as it actually develops, the important point is not merely constantly to refer to a human ideal but also to attain a good understanding of the intrinsic possibilities and limitations which are connected with the realization of the ideal in the material or spiritual-material world.

In the preceding chapters, where we spoke about the dangers connected with the technological order, we had an opportunity to mention certain aspects of this problem. Here we intend to present these fragmentary considerations in a more systematic fashion.

2. *The Complexity of the Technological Order*

a. The Fundamental Law of All Material Structures

Physical Complexity. Modern society has become much more complex than it was in former times and, according to many, it has therefore become also much more unnatural. This complexity, however, should not be viewed isolated from a fundamental property of matter, which we have considered previously, namely, the necessary complexity of higher material structures. Because matter is of a closed nature, i.e., because a material thing is always only exactly what it is, the realization of ideas in matter will always demand complex structures.

To give an example, the arrangement of matter which makes flying possible is unsuitable for riding on land or navigating on water. If one wants to build an all-purpose vehicle, it will be either exceptionally complex and expensive or lag far behind more specialized vehicles in each of its functions. Thus, no matter how one approaches the problem of transportation, it is and remains a complex problem. It is necessary to build many types of vehicles and to create a complex whole of distinct means of transportation, such as bicycles, motor cars, trains, ships, and aeroplanes. If man wants to avoid the complexity of the traffic situation arising from this multiplicity, he may have recourse to the building of a single type of vehicle for all purposes, but in implementing this theoretical possibility he does not eliminate the complexity in question but merely transfers it to the vehicle itself. For, to be able to fulfill the many transportation functions desired by man in the world in which he lives, such an all-purpose vehicle would have to be technically extremely complicated, although it would remain less effective than single purpose vehicles. (Of course, amphibious vehicles may have specific advantages for certain purposes.) Without wanting to play the role of a prophet and to predict the technical possibilities that are still hidden in the laps of the gods, we may assume that all technological achievements will remain complex, at least if they are not to be reduced to absolute uniformity of function. The refined structural complexity of living bodies confirms the solidity of this assumption and constitutes, as it were, its living demonstration.

Social Complexity. The law that structures realizing ideas in matter have to be complex does not apply only to technological products, but holds also for the entire social order in which these products function. The above-mentioned example of traffic was a first example of this truth. According as a society wants to realize more material possibilities for its members, it has to become naturally more complex. This assertion is true not only with respect to the realization of *material* possibilities, but also of *all* ideas embodied in the social order, because in one way or another all ideas have to be brought to realization in matter. We have seen an example of this in the preceding chapter when we spoke about the embodiment of charity in the social order. When a human being is in need, he requires expert assistance, and this assistance demands an organization of material means which can bring the man in need into contact with the one who can effectively help him.

Accordingly, if comparisons are made between the social life of the past and that of the present, it is unjust to qualify the latter as unnaturally complex in relation to the natural simplicity of the former. For the complexity in question is the natural consequence flowing from the character of material nature. Of course, we do not want to affirm that there do not exist unnatural and unnecessary complexities which ought to be avoided, but this merely means that the complexities in question are not the right ones. In one way or the other, there has to be complexity. What we gain on one side, we lose on the other. The problem is to avoid complexities which are difficult to handle. For instance, modern motor cars are more simple to drive than old-fashioned types, partly because the complexity of the traffic now demands greater manoeuverability. A car must now be able to start, accelerate, and brake very rapidly. The simplicity of handling it, however, has been attained as a rule by making the car itself more complex, but this new complexity does not cause any serious inconvenience because thanks to the progress of technology its dependability has increased.

b. The Abstractness of All Knowing and Making

The "Scientification" of the Process of Production. The complexity of the social order does not find its cause only in the nature of matter, but also in the nature of man's knowing and power. This second cause is not isolated from the first, for what man's knowledge and power contribute to the complexity in question is itself anchored in the spiritual-material being of man. Because it is bound up with sensitivity, human knowledge is abstract, and thus science as well as the technology based upon this science is inevitably specialized. This point has been sufficiently emphasized in the preceding chapters, so that we may be satisfied here with a few concluding remarks regarding the complexity of the social order.

The specialization in question leads to the finding of partial solutions, applicable only to certain problems, which cause new problems to arise especially because of the resulting disproportions. For this reason the question of coordination has become of crucial importance in our time. In former ages the situation was much more simple. In the building of a technical product or the execution of something in which many collaborated, the direction was assumed by someone having great experience, capable of taking over the function of any of his subordinates or at least thoroughly acquainted with it, and possessing at the same time a comprehensive view of the whole by virtue of his previous experience. He did not have to coordinate *post factum,* but directed and guided *a priori.* Knowing what had to be done and how it had to be done down to the smallest details, he was personally capable of judging to what extent the partial achievements of others could be integrated into the whole.

In our time, however, even within the relatively narrow confines of a single industry, there are many branches of service, which are taken care of by specialists who alone are capable of evaluating their own work, but at the same time only this work and not any other. The central direction depends upon their work and advice. Moreover, this advice usually does not aim so much at parts as at aspects of the whole. It is concerned, therefore, with the whole, but in an abstract way. For instance, the industrial economist, psychologist, and technologist each take care of aspects pertaining to the whole process of production, without knowing this process as a totality. The evaluation of the whole, moreover, is rendered even more difficult, because we live in a society which is no longer stable but undergoing dynamic development. Thus not even the specialist himself can be certain that his advice is correct until its content has undergone the test of experience. Past experiences now offer but little guarantee that things will run the same course.

All this indicates that coordinating direction, first of all, becomes a matter of coordinating *post factum,* on the basis of the effects actually produced and, secondly, that it must be the task of many. Thus it becomes extremely complex, demanding frequent consultations and careful registration of exactly what does take place. It is not for nothing that statistics play such an essential role in all control, coordination, and planning. The necessity of relying upon statistics in its turn demands that everything be recorded in the way determined by the statistician. In this way the whole order becomes even more complex. Records have to be kept in such a way that the statistician can transform the data into a realistic picture of the course taken by the affairs.

The "Scientification" of Society. The situation which prevails within the confines of the single enterprise, having as a rule a rather uniform and restricted purpose, is found *a fortiori* in the much more complex reality which we call society or the social order. Nevertheless, despite all its intrinsic difficulties, even in the social order there is a need for coordination. The old saying that to govern is to foresee has lost none of its force, but nowadays much greater care is needed to have the necessary foresight. First, because so much more can now be foreseen, so that one can no longer justify one's failures by appealing to the unforeseeable. Secondly,—and this is equally important, despite its paradoxical character—because it is frequently impossible to be certain how things will work out in practice. Thus governing with foresight includes essentially an empirical aspect, i.e., the governing authority has to pay careful attention to the way in which things work out in practice and to attune its guiding hand in accord with this practice.

In this way the governing of society begins to show somewhat the character which is typical of experimental physics: there is a constant interaction between, on the one hand, the predicting theory which indicates what results are to be expected and, on the other, the perception of the actually achieved result, which in its turn is fruitful for the theory. As far as social life is concerned, the necessity of constant verification of the actual effects produced by a policy which is theoretically justified is all the more urgent, because some people are always ready to misuse new possibilities or, even worse, to lead their development into a direction which is unduly to the advantage of certain groups.

Another point of essential importance for a correct and fair evaluation of the complexity which the "scientification" of life in the technological order implies is that what this order offers us is not at all limited to so-called comfort and luxury. As soon as we speak of modern technology, many think immediately in terms of refrigerators, airconditioning, television, motor cars, airplanes and similar things —each of which is a product which makes life perhaps more agreeable but, on the other hand, justifies the question whether it is worth the sacrifices which it entails.

In reality, however, the technological order is concerned primarily with the necessities of life. The bread we eat, the water we drink, the fire which keeps us warm, and the cloth which covers our body would not be available in sufficient quantities to provide for the elementary needs of the world population if it were not for the achievements of modern science and technology. One has to think here only of increased agricultural production made possible by man's chemical-biological knowledge of the process of growth and by his more refined technical methods of agriculture, or of the modern facilities of transportation which enable man to provide food for regions afflicted by crop failure. Numerous other examples could be added here to show that in the present situation the technological order cannot be dispensed with even with respect to most elementary needs. These needs have entered into the very structure of this order and share in the inevitable complexity of the whole.

3. Effects of the Species-Individual Structure of Matter

a. Man as a Number

The Person Reduced to a Number. One of the most serious objections raised against the technical order is not so much its complexity itself as the way in which this complexity makes itself felt when one tries to master it. It is a general complaint that in the technological order man is no longer a person but a numbered individual. Strictly speaking, the situation is even worse: concrete man is not a single individual but a complex whole of individual aspects. Through the functionalization of society concrete man has become involved in the technical order in many fashions, but always only partially, always only with respect to aspects according to which he functions in a particular context.

Thus man is the bearer of not merely a single number but of an endless list of numbers. As an employee, a taxpayer, as the owner of a telephone connection, of a motor car, of a bank account, of an insurance policy, as the member of a political party, of a trade organization, of a labor union, and even of a church, as well as in many other partial respects and functions man is numbered. He is, moreover, a member of many "free" organizations, without which the modern world apparently is unable to function. In addition to these more or less fixed numbers, he has many others on a temporary basis, e.g., as a patient in a hospital, a guest in a hotel, or a visitor of the cinema. Many of these numbers remain unknown to him, but they exist and from time to time clearly make their presence felt.

It is hardly necessary to point out that this number status is closely connected with the fundamentally analytic and abstract method of our scientific knowledge and that, therefore, this method will affect every technical order which is based upon this scientific knowledge. As was pointed out in Chapter Six, the analytic and abstract method of physical science is wholly attuned to a fundamental feature of matter—namely, its species-individual structure. Thus the utilization of material means will inevitably reveal the fundamental character of this structure. The remark must, of course, be added that the use of methods which are wholly based upon the species-individual structure to regulate human society is precisely the main objection which many have against the technical order: concrete man has to give way for an impersonal complex of instances representing magnitudes and functions. Living human society is reduced to a lifeless order by being reconstructed in this technical and scientific fashion.

The Inevitableness of Species-Individual Features in the Technological Order. Since the dangers of this situation have been sufficiently stressed in the preceding chapter, we may place the emphasis here upon the fact that inevitably features pertaining to the species-individual structure of matter will be present in the technological order. For man is a spiritual-material being, his spiritual level of being is therefore permeated with the fundamental characteristics of matter. His natural organic structure reveals these characteristics and therefore demands to be studied in the way that is proper to physical science. Just as we may not limit the study of man to the approach used in physical science, so also we may not neglect the source of knowledge which is available in the material structure of the human organism.

In philosophical circles there is often a danger of misunderstanding the psycho-somatic direction taken by medical science and of one-sidedly interpreting this new orientation. They place emphasis upon the psychical origin of somatic diseases, and forget that the material basis of many psychical abnormalities is just as important. For the spirit has to become itself in and through the body. Its freedom is bound up with the possibilities of the matter in which it has to realize itself. For this reason the method of physical science is so important for medical science in its study and treatment of man as man. For a clearer understanding of man's material possibilities may enable us to influence them in a physico-chemical way and thus to make it easier for the spirit to be itself, to be more spirit. We are referring here not merely to the removal of morbid conditions but also to the curing of natural deficiencies. Both of these are consequences of the embodiment of man's spirit, which has to attain to self-possession in and through matter.

It may not at all be excluded that one of the essential conditions for the fullest possible self-possession of the human spirit consists in this that the spirit arrives at an understanding of these material structures and thus at controlling them more perfectly. Such a condition would not be contrary to the subsistence of the spirit, which was spoken about when we considered the problem of matter—spirit. For it is the human spirit itself which in the pursuit of science undertakes the endeavor to arrive at such an insight into its own dependence upon matter; consequently, such an attempt would merely serve to confirm its sovereign status, its subsistence.

Although scientists of the past thought differently, the study of the internal relationship of matter and spirit in man has not yet gone very far. Nevertheless, what has been reached thus far opens sufficient perspectives to make man labor intensively at the solution of the many problems involved in this relationship. Despite the fact that these problems as such are not problems of physical science, they have at least a physical aspect and thus can be approached by physical science. The fruitfulness of this approach shows clearly the truth of a remark which we have made earlier regarding the purpose of physical science, namely, that in this science also the human spirit is on the road to understanding itself not only in the theoretical order but also perhaps in the realm of practice.

The Technical Method and the Fallacy of Misplaced Concreteness. The theoretical and practical aid which physical science renders man in his endeavor to understand the spirit-in-matter which he himself is constitutes a sign of the aid which methods attuned to matter are capable of offering in all aspects of human life. This capacity explains and justifies the penetration of scientific analytic thinking and technical acting into realms where one would not readily expect any results from their use.[1] There is no human activity which does not have a technical aspect, because man does not have any activity which escapes realization in and through matter. For this reason social, psychological, and pedagogic techniques have an intrinsic value of their own, which cannot be neglected with impunity if man is to attain to a greater inner freedom and to social relations that are more in harmony with his human dignity.

Of course, wherever use is made of methods attuned to matter there is danger of the sophism which above has been called "the fallacy of misplaced concreteness." If no attention is paid to the abstractness of physical science and technology, their application implies the danger of doing violence to reality, of identifying physical science with science unqualified, of making the view of man attained by this science *the* view of man pure and simple, of equating technical activity with human activity, and of considering the scientific and technological world view as the one and only world view. The existence of this danger, however, may never be a reason for discarding the use of physical and technical methods in the study, education, and medical care of man or in the study and guidance of society. Such a procedure, moreover, would be a typical misunderstanding of the fallacy in question, which does not consist in attributing value to something valueless but in identifying the abstract with the concrete.

The fallacy could never act as a fallacy, it could never be a tempting sophism if the various images of man and of the world which it absolutizes did not possess an intrinsic value, i.e., if in their abstractness they were not true. The vision of material reality contained in the scientific world view really is a vision which makes

---

[1]We have given a few examples of this in Chapter X.

understanding of this reality possible, just as the technological world view connected with this vision leads really to the control of matter. The pursuit of physical science and technology flows from a correct view of what man is, viz., spirit-in-matter, i.e., a spirit which has to become itself through understanding and control of matter. The task, therefore, of being-man includes the pursuit of science and technology and for this reason a correct view of man and of society has to take the species-individual structure into account. Any attempt to regulate human affairs while disregarding this structure is wholly unrealistic. For man *is* an individual pertaining to a species, although he is not just an individual.

The Numbering of Man is Not Unnatural. Man's individuality permeates his entire being, his every expression and manifestation. For instance, every intelligible word spoken by man has a meaning which is posited every time he pronounces this word, although it may receive, of course, a very personal overtone. The term "beloved," for example, always expresses the same specific content, but necessarily refers to a wholly personal relationship. Alongside such cases in which the species-individual structure of language is present only in a fundamental way, there are in the spontaneous language of daily life also others in which this structure occupies a more prominent place as, for instance, when we say that the weather is dry or the milk has turned.[2] Nevertheless, whenever there is question of human language, the basic structure of species and individual is assumed into a personal context and thus given a particular overtone. On the other hand, it is equally true that if the basic structure were lacking in the personal use of language, the language would lose its character of being a language, just as a person who would not be an individual could not be a man. Man's being a person is rooted in his being an individual and for this reason he can also be pointed to and numbered.

Accordingly, when the technological order numbers man in many ways, it does not do something unnatural. The procedure becomes unnatural only when the order becomes submerged in its numbers and sees nothing else. In such a case an injustice is done to man, just as it would be unjust also to leave man entirely outside the realm of numerable beings. If everyone who is entitled to social security receives a personal check for his personal needs, he has to thank

---

[2]The personal element has been wholly banished from the technical language of physical science which pursues the material aspect of reality in a rigorously abstract fashion.

the punch card for making this attention to his needs possible. It is a similar punch card which makes it possible for the manager of a large trucking company to present his personal congratulation to every driver who has completed another million miles without an accident. Such personal attentions would be altogether impossible without the aid of modern technical means.

Technical Means and the Person. Of course, the technical means do not guarantee that this personal attention is really a sign of personal interest, for this interest is something which depends upon the character of the manager, upon his genuine love of his fellow men and upon the way in which he views his task. When there is question only of a small group, the personal attention to our fellow men may make use of the limited capacity of the brain to recall the past. (This capacity very likely functions in a way that is very similar to that of man's technical structures—at least, these structures help the physiologist to understand the functioning of the brain.) As soon, however, as personal attention has to be paid to a larger group, it becomes necessary to make use of technical means which retain the relevant data and make them easily accessible.

The more perfect such means or systems are, the less attention they require and the more this attention can be focussed upon the encounter with our fellow man as he *is*. A physician, for example, who treats his patients not as cases but as persons, realizes that the first requirement made of him is to be familiar with the medical history of his patient and with everything pertaining to this history. According as his file cards are better organized, he can have the necessary information more quickly at his disposal and thus gain time to reflect upon the needs of his patient. The same applies to the priest or minister, the teacher, the employer, and the business man.

The fact that a fellow man is registered on a file card does not necessarily reduce him to a mere number. On the contrary, the number makes it possible to meet him as a person, because it makes it possible for me to be familiar with his personal situation. One who wants to rely solely upon his native brain power is similar to a speaker who proclaims to be fully interested in his audience but neglects to make himself audible by using a public address system.

The objection could be raised that such means may be useful, but nevertheless are objectionable, precisely because they tend to reduce persons to members submerged in the anonymous mass. Such means would not be necessary if human togetherness continued to be primarily concerned with small groups. The manager of a small plant really gets to know all his workers and does not need a mechanical system of punch cards to know about their personal worries and joys. Parents, likewise, do not need cards to know everything about their children. The creation of mechanical means, which may be perhaps desirable and useful to aid failing memories—does not every family mark birthdays on a calendar?—causes a spiral movement that is characteristic of the technological order: means are developed for their own sake and no longer for the sake of the purpose. In other words, they do not aid man is keeping track of larger and more complicated social circles, but by their very existence tend to create mammoth organizations.

This objection is to the point insofar as the means in question do really have such a tendency, but not insofar as it suggests that the social bonds become more massive merely because these technical means are available, without offering any additional compensation for their massiveness. Let us consider, for example, medical care. The number of patients of which a family doctor takes care nowadays is likely to be more or less the same as formerly, but the depth of his medical care has enormously increased, especially because of the necessity to have recourse to all kinds of specialists and institutions. The specialist has, of course, far more patients than the family doctor. It is precisely the necessity, of which we spoke in connection with Christian charity, to provide for everyone the best of care which makes it necessary for the family physician to have recourse to the specialist and thus renders his own work more complex. The specialist, on the other hand, is enabled by modern technical administrative means to take personal care of many patients, despite the fact that he meets them only rarely and therefore cannot rely upon his memory to supply him with the necessary information. Without these technical means only the privileged few would receive personal care, while the rest of mankind would be reduced to nameless numbers.

Concluding Remarks. In considering the value and meaning of such technical means it is necessary not to lose sight of the following points. The technical means must work perfectly and without demanding attention, for only in this way will they be capable of being an extension of the working proper to man's brain, which does not require that we pay attention to it when we are thinking. Secondly, the technical means in question must be so flexible that they can contain a very large number of extremely varied data, so that the human entry is not entered into the wrong category. This requirement means that the instrument has to be inevitably very complex. The complexity in question, however, must not demand the attention of the user but should remain hidden. Finally—and this is the most important point—the user must have recourse to the instrument for the sake of his fellow man, i.e., the technical means must be such that it enables him to meet his fellow man as a person, in accordance with what is characteristic of such a personal encounter, which may vary from being purely business-like to being very intimate. In this way the numbered individual of the punch card becomes in the encounter a living person of whom, thanks to the card, one knows enough to make the meeting genuinely fruitful.

b. Leveling Influence

Technical Uniformity. The species-individual structure of matter has another effect which has to be considered here, because it makes itself particularly felt on the technical level. We mean the leveling influence which, as we have seen in Chapter Twelve, is proper to technical productions. Any mechanically produced object owes its origin to the constant, exact repetition of certain operations. By virtue of its deterministic way of working, which cannot make any contribution of its own but is wholly dependent upon the specific arrangements embodied in its construction, the machine cannot do anything else than repeat the same action over and over again. The entire modern technological order shares in this typical character of mechanical production because, if man is to profit from machines, he has to adapt himself to their ways of operating. Thus man's activity is likewise reduced to constantly repeated manipulations. In this way the leveling influence of the technical order may appear to be embedded in its very essence and consequently inescapable.

Nevertheless, there is reason to proceed cautiously in this matter. The species-individual structure is not an invention of technology, but a fundamental structure of material reality. As such, it permeates everything material, whether living or not, man included. Nevertheless, it is true that living nature manages to make use of the species-individual structure in such a way that it gives rise to endless variety. When in Chapter Twelve we spoke about the difference between the living body and the technical product we explained it *inter alia* by pointing to the discrepancy between the macro-structure and the micro-structure of technical products, which makes them always appear more or less artificial. This artificial character explains also why modern production must insist upon the strict repetition of the same operations, for otherwise the product would no longer fit. As compared with living bodies, technical products presumably will always continue to appear uniform, even though it is not at all excluded that the difference will become less striking according as technology becomes more perfect.

The main point, however, is whether in speaking of the leveling influence of technology the point of comparison has been chosen correctly. The things to be compared are not the technical product and the living body, but machine-made and hand-made products or rather machine-made mass products and hand-made mass products. For there have always been also mass-produced objects made by craftsmen, even though few of them may be found in a museum. The craftsman's mass product also originated from the constant remaking of the same object which had shown itself particularly adapted to a specific purpose. It was not without reason that the Greeks saw the element of routine as one of the essential aspects of technique. Of course, it was true, that the gifted craftsman had an opportunity for self-expression in all kinds of minute variations and that, in addition, local traditions provided a kind of differentiation remotely recalling the variety of nature with which it was closely connected anyhow.

Is Uniformity Essential to Technical Production? Thus the craftsman's mass product always managed to retain contact with art, as is indicated by the twofold meanings of such terms as *technē, ars,* and the modern term *art.* This connection was lost, however, at first in the mass production of the machine age. We must admit, therefore, that this kind of production has actually exercised a leveling influence. On the other hand, in all fairness we may ask whether this influence does not flow at least in part also from the primitive phase in which technology still finds itself. The term "primitive" should be understood here in a double sense: technical possibilities still are rather limited and, secondly, the human society whose needs are taken care of by technology is not yet capable of providing all human beings with an existence worthy of man, so that technology still remains relatively limited in its scope. It still has to work in an economy of scarcity rather than abundance. Even in countries, like the United States, in which technology has made the greatest progress and in which prac-

tically everyone enjoys a fairly decent standard of living, this happy
condition has come about in the lifetime of a single generation.

The three factors involved contribute, each in its own way, to the
leveling influence of technology. Because of its primitive condition,
technology has not yet reached more than a low level of flexibility;
because of the limited economic possibilities, it has to standardize as
much as possible; and because of its recent origin, it tends to replace
many other forms of human activity. Of course, machine production
will always remain based upon repetition, because its very essence
implies this, but this repetition allows many more possibilities than
are being exploited at present. If in a given area only one television
program can be received, all viewers are forced to watch the same
average show, but it would not do to claim that this situation is an
essential consequence of television as a means of communication.
Thus its leveling superficiality is something accidental. The same applies to the standardized production of all kinds of goods and services.
Provisionally they embody only what is useful for the masses, but it
remains possible also to make them embody other things, such as
beauty, and in this respect there is no necessity to have recourse to
uniformity. For, as soon as the first necessities are satisfied, it becomes
possible, thanks in part to technological progress, to produce many
small series of objects and to embody in each of them original artistic
ideas. Moreover, the constant shortening of the time required for
making a living can contribute to a renewed bloom of all kinds of
work which demands personal care and love and which has been
neglected in the first stages of technology and its leveling influence.
It could very well be that such work would be undertaken as "liberal
arts," i.e., as work of human beings who have been liberated by
technology.

Thus it could easily happen that the results of technology would
become wholly different from what at first sight should be expected.
A large part of man's activity has hitherto always been spent in constant hard labor—hard because it demanded much exertion, but also
and especially because for the majority of mankind it had to be repeated
every day in exactly the same fashion. Technology not only removes
this physical exertion, but also takes care of what is routine-like and
automatic, and this is at least just as important. Routine operations
can be more and more left to genuine automatons. Thus modern
technology creates room for man's creative activity in all realms, to
such an extent that its original leveling influence could easily change

into exactly the opposite. In other words, if at first the influence of technology tended to level man and to make him superficial, the reason for this must be sought in the fact that because of its imperfect status of development technology had to use man unduly as an automaton.

Concluding Remarks. Man will never be able to remove the species-individual structure from matter, but he is capable of using this structure in such a way that he can largely eliminate its harmful effects from his personal life. In this way the structure will become subservient to him instead of being a burden and limitation. The road leading to this ideal lies in the correct use and development of technical means. The same conclusion was reached above when we considered man as a number.

The question may be raised, however, whether the picture presented here is not unrealistic and overly idealistic. Does this picture truthfully express the reality of the technological order or at least its possible future development? The reply is that it may represent reality, because it expresses the inner meaning of technology and of the technological order. It is true, of course, that such a giving of meaning goes beyond concrete reality and aims at something which will never be reached fully. This should not surprise us, for the same is true of all human tendencies and endeavors. There always remains a distance between what man sees as the absolute ideal in a more or less vague perspective and that which he manages concretely to realize in his efforts to reach this ideal. In the natural order of the past, if we may use this expression, man did not fail less than he does now in the technological order. The difference is that in the latter order man's power is magnified enormously, so that his failure becomes much more visible. This greater awareness of his deficiency is all to the good, even though it means that man feels less happy because of it.

However, it is not merely the general deficiency of man which makes the technological order concretely fall short of what it could and should be. There is also another reason which is specifically proper to the technological order itself, or rather, this reason flows from a general characteristic of man but acquires a special weight in the technological order. This reason is that the technological order has of necessity an experimental character. We must consider this point now somewhat more in detail.

4. *The Consequences of the Experimental Character Proper to the Technological Order*

Characteristics of the Experimental Method. The experimental character proper to the technological order is a direct consequence of the intimate connection existing between technology and physical science. This connection has been sufficiently discussed in the preceding chapters, so that we may limit ourselves here to a consideration of the concrete consequences flowing from it in order to arrive at a correct evaluation of the technological order.

The experimental method is characterized by the fact that, on the one hand, it arises from a theoretical view and, on the other, gives rise to a new theoretical vision. The method puts a foundation under previously acquired knowledge, but at the same time also leads to new knowledge often of a wholly unexpected type. The same applies to the technological order. In part its achievements flow from a deliberate effort to make fruitful use of existing technical possibilities in order to realize certain ideals. On the other hand, however, it is true also that new possibilities reveal themselves, whose implications are fully understood only *a posteriori,* i.e., after exhaustive experiments with these possibilities.

Secondly, the experimental method is characterized by its specialization. Although it is subservient to the general investigation of nature, it functions in a fragmentary fashion within the framework of one or the other special theory. Physical science originated as a collection of partial theories, and it was only gradually that more comprehensive theories introduced a degree of unification. This fragmentary character has its repercussions in the technological order, especially in the lack of harmony manifested in the evolution of this order. The order does not develop according to a fixed and all-embracing plan, but proceeds by leaps and bounds in every direction according as new possibilities manifest themselves. The onesided development of these possibilities thus results in the disproportions of which we spoke in the preceding chapters.

Practical Consequences. The possibilities of the technological order overwhelm man: abstractly speaking, they may present him with new opportunities for self-realization, for becoming more human, *de facto,* however, they begin by contributing to mental confusion and loss of human existence. Man, so it seems, is unable to cope with all his possibilities.

Abstractly speaking, for example, nuclear energy is a great good, but concretely it should not be developed before man has managed to ban the specter of war. In the present situation nuclear energy means a mortal danger in the hands of political rulers. A single rash— or deliberate—deed may now mean the end of the human race. Similar remarks could be made with reference to almost any aspect of the technological order. This order tends to flood man with all kinds of luxury goods as by-products of its supplies in the realm of man's necessities. Man finds these luxuries at his disposal before he has learned to use them in freedom, and the result is that he becomes enslaved to these goods.

The technological order produces a level of prosperity which rapidly makes education possible for everyone, and the result is that education itself degenerates because there are not enough scientifically trained, morally outstanding, and pedagogically competent men available to staff such a massive program of education. If this situation is true in old civilized countries, in which the development of science and its application has been relatively gradual, what is bound to happen in countries which technological development enables to skip centuries of transition? One could continue almost endlessly with this kind of questions. To give just one additional example, the evolution of technology makes it possible to shorten the time devoted to labor, but what will be the result if man does not yet know how to employ his free time in a really useful fashion?

Undoubtedly, it sounds very nice to speak, as has been done in the preceding chapters, about the necessity which imposes itself upon man in the technological age to reflect upon the ultimate meaning of his existence. But, we may ask, is in practice all this not hollow theory when the technological order first fully absorbs man without leaving him any time for reflection and then suddenly confronts him with an abundance of leisure hours? A similar situation occurs here as in the rationalization of industry: first the conveyer belt reduces man to a machine, and then more radical rationalization eliminates this type of inhuman contribution of man and suddenly demands of him a level of education and training which is in the possession of only a few. Work now requires that the laborer assume responsibilities from which he was formerly excluded in a systematic fashion.

Thus whatever human meaning is given abstractly to the development of technology, concrete reality is quite different. There is, indeed, no point in denying the truth of this statement. Undoubtedly, abstractly speaking again, it would be ideal if man could control the entire development of the technological order and understand all its hidden possibilities but, concretely speaking, this ideal is beyond the reach of man. He will have to accept the fact that it is only through experiments that he can discover the possibilities of the technological order. The same situation exists also with respect to nature: man is unable to grasp nature in a single glance, but has to strive at understanding through experiments which allow him to form fragmentary but nonetheless effective concepts. In neither case, however, does this situation imply that, fundamentally speaking, man would not be able to control his possibilities. Let us examine this point.

Onesided Approach and Integral Knowledge of Nature. The discovery of the scientific method in the quest of knowledge *de facto* did not merely lead to an increase in scientific knowledge of nature, but became also an opportunity for more profound philosophical reflection. In manifold ways it contributed to man's increased self-knowledge. True, the estrangement of faith and science in the sixteenth and seventeenth centuries, brought about by misunderstanding and failure to evaluate the new science properly, has had disastrous consequences for the civilization of the West. Nevertheless, the resulting struggle most likely was necessary to eliminate all kinds of misconceptions. At any rate, it has become abundantly clear that, no matter how noble the motives may be, no results are to be expected from the suppression of science. Such a measure certainly cannot be motivated with an appeal to the fact that the human mind is not yet mature enough for new scientific data, for the maturity in question is to be acquired only through a confrontation with the new data.

The history of any science teaches us in retrospect that the greatest progress is always made in critical situations arising from its confrontation with different types of sciences. We have seen an example of it in philosophy. Its bloom, as well as that of theology, in the Middle Ages resulted to a large extent from the acquaintance made with the science of the Arabians, and this science itself reflourished through this confrontation. As soon as the crisis situation had passed, medieval philosophy became mired until the seventeenth century when philosophy experienced a new period of growth thanks to the encounter with the new physical science, which in turn exercised a stimulating influence upon mathematics. And history continues along the same lines.

We may repeat here what we have said before, while certain sciences may develop more or less autonomously, as philosophy, astronomy, and logic did among the Greeks, sooner or later their development comes to a stop because they lack the fertile encounter with other disciplines. Purely philosophical reflection may be able to satisfy man for a time, but its relative value is bound to make itself felt and thus lead to a correction of the situation. Likewise, physical science was able to loosen its moorings and to consider itself as science unqualified, but this aberration was unable to impress a permanent seal upon man's science of nature. The overevaluation has been corrected both by the ensuing philosophical and theological discussions and by the internal evolution of physical science itself.

The statement that this kind of correction of onesidedness takes place "spontaneously" should not be misunderstood. It does not mean that the correction occurs, so to speak, behind the back of the man who pursues science, but it means that the correction is made because of the universality of the human mind which is capable of seeing the particular approach as particular even when it is engaged in the pursuit of such an approach. The universality of the human mind, however, is never such that it can attain to a *universal and total* knowledge which transcends all abstractness.[3] Thus man has to apply himself to the partial and the abstract for the sake of the universal and the total, but should not lose sight of the partiality and abstractness in question.

Onesided Development and the Integral Special Order. The considerations applying to the development of science are valid also for the evolution of the social order. Here also a universal approach to this development transcends man's capacity, although there is implicitly always a reference to, and an evaluation by a vision embracing an harmonious universal development. For this reason any onesided growth of the technological order "spontaneously" calls forth all kinds of counter forces. If these counter forces are really healthy, they will not attempt to stop the onesided growth as growth—which would be foolish—but they will endeavor to develop aspects which have been hitherto neglected although they are necessary for universal growth. For instance, the attention which in the beginning of the technological order was wholly concentrated upon the control of mat-

---

[3]Although philosophy is universal in its aim and tends to totality, it is unable to consider this totality otherwise than as an aspect of totality.

ter has later resulted in an intense awareness of what is specifically proper to man without, however, causing the attention to techno-logical development itself to diminish.

This is really as it should be, for if man wants to develop himself fully, he has to unfold himself in all respects. In this process develop-ment in one direction should not be stopped for the sake of the other for, considering the nature of man's knowledge and power, it could very well happen that the key to one line of development may unex-pectedly be found in another. For instance, primitive technology par-tially lowered man to the level of a machine because he was able to do certain mechanical manipulations cheaper and better than machines. But a more developed technology appeals precisely to the specifically human element of man—and this not only with respect to inventors and constructors but also more and more with respect to anyone who is concerned with the mechanical process of labor.

Disproportions, therefore, resulting from the onesided develop-ment of certain possibilities cannot always be prevented, and inevita-bly also these disproportions will make victims. For instance, time is needed before modern man will be accustomed to the abundance of material goods. Provisionally it is inevitable that these goods will cause an insatiable thirst for more and more possessions, just as also increasingly larger strata of society will want to partake of them. It is impossible to stop this trend, but it is entirely possible to understand it and to evaluate the situation with the aid of this understanding. The fact that such an understanding is present will change the very situation itself. As Gabriel Marcel expresses it, "Whatever may be the foundations upon which the human condition is based, this con-dition presents itself as somehow dependent in being what it is upon the way in which it views itself."[4] It is not the deadening monotony of the conveyer belt which stupifies man, but a lack of understanding of the meaning which this monotonous labor has.

When a particular human purpose can be reached only through man's mechanical labor and this labor occupies even a considerable part of his life, the purposive and understanding execution of this labor does not at all stupify man. It is not infrequently that man finds himself in situations of this kind, and his spiritual resiliency reveals itself precisely in the fact that his spirit does not perish in them. For this reason it has always been possible for man, even in the most try-

---

[4]*Les hommes contre l'humain,* Paris, 1951, p. 74.

ing situations, to remain fully human. The ancient civilizations bear witness to this fact, for they possessed only a miminal control over matter and had to live within the narrow confines which nature spontaneously places at man's disposal. Now that man knows that he is capable of transcending these narrow boundaries, his task ought to be not merely to realize his human existence within any narrow limits but also to push back the barriers confining him.

Transcending the Onesidedness of the Technological Order. Regarding the onesidedness which reveals itself from time to time in the technological order, man has to accept it, on the one hand, as inevitable with a certain amount of resignation and with understanding in order to be able to transcend it. On the other hand, however, he cannot simply resign himself to unilateral technological developments, but must try to eliminate them. The fusion of these two attitudes of resignation and non-resignation constitutes the basis of the genuine wisdom of life which every individual must endeavor to acquire. Everyone has to appreciate correctly the fact that his possibilities are limited and that his situation restricts his human existence, he has to try to make the best of the given situation as well as to endeavor to overcome the restrictions.

The changes that have taken place in our view of the world and of society have taught us not to be permanently resigned to any situation, but we may not at all conclude that therefore limiting factors will not be a permanent feature of human existence. For this reason wisdom of life, which knows how to combine resignation with non-resignation, will always retain its value with respect to the life of the individual and of society. Man's power is and will always remain limited by the inner potentialities of matter, yet he is capable of gradually unveiling these potentialities in an endless way and thus able to develop technical means and the technological order. For this reason understanding this order in both its potentialities and its limitations is very important for man. One of these limitations is the unharmonious and onesided development of this order, which is a consequence of the fact that man's activity is always essentially of a specialized nature.

The development in question, then, can become harmonious only to a certain extent, because it has to result from the interplay of many onesided activities. For it is impossible that every human being will make all intellectual attitudes and all sciences his own or that he will culturally work in all possible fashions. Some will inevitably devote their energy to activity, while others will concentrate upon reflection. It is true, however, that no genuine culture is possible unless all attitudes and modes of cultural activity make their contribution. Moreover, to be really fruitful, each one must realize that his contribution has a relative value, i.e., it possesses an essential value, but this value does not exclude other values. *A priori* speaking, it is not possible to determine what the value of each of these contributions is, for this value also is an aspect of the experimental character proper to all human progress.

5. *The Universality of the Experimental Attitude*

It is a remarkable phenomenon that the experimental attitude of man has been extended to all realms of life. We are not thinking here only of certain trends which officially make use of the title "experimental' to indicate their character to some extent, as is done by experimental poetry and experimental plays. Modern man appears possessed by a wild urge to experiment with everything, and the uncurbed character of this urge resembles the old alchemists rather than the controlled experiments of the more recent pursuit of physical science.

Man wants to investigate everything and to try all possibilities. Just as physical science investigated the elements of nature and not its concrete forms, so art now appears to be searching for the primordial elements of human existence. The traditional modes of expression and the customary means no longer satisfy man, who suspects that there still exists a veritable treasure of unexplored possibilities in and around himself. This is the reason why literature and art show an intense interest in all kinds of things which formerly were taboo. Such taboos remind man too much of what nature spontaneously allotted him and its control of the old cultures. He knows that by going beyond these boundaries he may make the most interesting discoveries. For this reason he does not believe, at least not *a priori*, in any everlasting value and still less in the everlastingness of its expression.

The philosophy of the new era likewise exhibits experimental aspects. It has an aversion for whatever is systematic and traditional and endeavors to plunge into all kinds of new pathways of thought. Meanwhile it should not surprise us that every rejection of traditional forms is quickly followed by the development of new forms. Here also the species-individual structure makes its influence felt. The non-conformist as such is just as much specifically recognizable as the various kinds of conformists.

The Resulting Loss of Certainty. The experimental attitude existing in all realms of human endeavor give contemporary man a strong feeling of uncertainty, of being unable to find anywhere a secure support. This uncertainty reveals itself in the absence of a clear vision of the future, for no one knows whither the development of man and his world will lead. Yet even here it is not too difficult to discover many hopeful perspectives.

Considered in its essence, the experimental attitude is based upon a very real foundation—namely, man's nature, and the possibilities contained in this nature have to be discovered by man in an experimental fashion. At one time, when in the seventeenth century physical science began to proceed experimentally, this science likewise thought that it was not bound by any of the certainties prevailing in the past. Not a single principle was any longer considered to be certain; nevertheless, its soaring flight was really based upon very definite certainties, which we have spoken of as the presuppositions of physical science. In a similar way man's experimental attitude in other realms is based upon definite and fundamentally sound presuppositions. What inspires this attitude is nothing else but the profound conviction that it is man's real nature which forces him to assume the experimental attitude of life.

The analysis of physical science and its consequences shows that, in spite of all modifications of man's picture of nature and of the world, it is implicitly the same picture which dominates the evolution of this world view. The same may be said with respect to the picture of man: all the experimenting with human possibilities is based upon the desire to know and experience better what man is. Ultimately, therefore it contributes also to reflection upon man. On the other hand, it is not merely subservient to this reflection, but also needs to be supported by it, for man's being human cannot be suspended while the experiment is in progress. Today's man may not be sacrificed for the sake of valuable knowledge which man will perhaps discover in the future. It is in this that lies the essential difference between experimenting in physical science and experimenting with man. Medical science has always been aware of this difference, although this science is usually concerned only with bodily experiments. Convinced as it is of their necessity, medical science assumes a wise attitude of prudence. This same prudence should control also all social and artistic experiments with man, for the sake of the human beings who are involved in them. For this reason grave risks are taken when the experimental attitude which has given physical science and technology their greatness is transferred to the realm of man.

There is an additional peculiar aspect to this experimental attitude. On meeting this attitude in all realms of human life, it is difficult to escape from the thought that this attitude is meant in part as a protest against the physical and technological thinking which controls human society as the technological order. We do not mean that it is a protest against the experimental character of this thinking but against considering man as a part of nature which has to be worked over. The attitude aims at safeguarding what is proper to man's personal being. Yet in some of its manifestations it has a tendency to experiment with man's existence in such a way that man's humanity itself is endangered. Thus it does the very thing against which it protests. The proper character of man as a person demands a reverence which does not permit anyone to experiment with him to see what this character contains, at least not in such a way that the person himself is threatened with extinction. Nevertheless, man cannot do without the experiment if he wants to penetrate more profoundly into his own essence. For this reason the extension of the experimental attitude to all realms of life is a definite gain. Unlike what happens in physical science, however, the limits are not determined here solely by what is possible but also by what is permissible.

CHAPTER SIXTEEN

EPILOGUE

Introductory Remarks. Dangerous as it is, it is always tempting to summarize the results of an extensive investigation in a few conclusions. The temptation exists, because it is hardly possible for man to remember everything without such an epilogue. But it is dangerous also, because what he remembers in this way is a poor and distorted picture of reality. This situation is especially true with respect to philosophical studies, because such studies essentially aim at the totality of reality and thus do not easily lend themselves for summarizing conclusions.

To make matters worse, philosophical formulae are lifeless without the actual inspiration of living and refined thinking. With respect to an extensive experimental investigation in the realm of physical science it may be possible to summarize the results in a single formula, without imposing upon anyone the obligation to follow the man of research on the whole laborious pathway by which he reached his discovery. The brief summarizing formula may be intelligible and useful all by itself. A philosophical summary, however, becomes intelligible only if it succeeeds in presenting at the same time also the entire problematic background from which the conclusion has arisen.

Experience illustrates this point very clearly when one reads brief introductions into the history of philosophy. They condense the thoughts of great thinkers into a few sentences and sketch the structure of important philosophical systems with a few deft strokes. The unsuspecting reader often wonders how it is possible that anyone could ever propose such ideas and even more why he managed to make a lasting impression upon the history of thought. He does not realize that he has hardly understood anything at all of the philosopher in question and that he was not even given an opportunity to understand anything of the ideas. Philosophical language has to make use of analogous terms, and these terms receive a meaningful content only when their concrete use is considered together with the problems to which they refer.

For this reason it is meaningless to summarize here by way of conclusion the results obtained through our reflection upon the nature of physical science and technology, their function and influence upon society and culture. All we will do here is to indicate once more a few ideas which manifested themselves constantly throughout our considerations. At the same time we will have an opportunity to make a few general remarks for which it was difficult to find a suitable place within the specialized contents of the preceding chapters.

1. *The Inner Logic of the Development of Physical Science*

Natural Development and Historical Facticity. One of the leading ideas of this book was that the evolution of physical science and technology, as it reveals itself to us in history, was above all a development that was determined from within.

When we considered the various aspects of the method proper to physical science in the first part of this work, it became clear how closely this science harmonizes with man's natural cognitive situation, despite the fact that its method and language have become so abstract and refined that only insiders can understand them. In the second part we reached the same conclusion with respect to technology, partly because of the inner interconnection and interdependence of physical science and technology.

Of course, accidental historical elements also have played a role in the evolution of science and technology, but this role did not determine the nature of this evolution. They initiated, accelerated and retarded developmental processes, they caused secondary results, but they did not determine the line of development. For instance, the question may be asked why it was that precisely in Greece in the sixth to the fourth centuries B.C. philosophical reflection assumed the form which created the spiritual climate required for the pursuit of physical science.

Although a certain reply may be given to this question, it cannot dispense itself from ultimately referring to the mystery of history and its facticity. Nevertheless, the fact that only a climate such as that of Greek thought could give rise to physical science is not facticity but a result of the inner structure proper to this science. For there is only one way in which physical science can be pursued: rational thinking, sensitive experiencing, and technical intervention in material reality have to go hand in hand.

Even in Greek thought this triad was not present from its very inception, and in all probability such a simultaneous rise of all three elements would not have been possible. Several stages had to be passed before they could meet. Although in prescientific thought science and technique went together, they had to go their separate ways before they could find each other again and remain inseparably united.

The Greek Impact on All Cultures. If it is true that there is an inner connection between the philosophical vision of the Greeks and the fact that physical science and technology have flourished in the parts of the world whose culture is derived from that of the Greeks, then this situation allows us to draw an important conclusion. For in that case other civilizations which wish to pursue science and technology will have to take over something of the western attitude and the western view of the world and of man from which this science and technology have come forth.

The problems which this necessity creates are sufficiently well known. At first when science and technology are introduced into other cultures, they will undermine these civilizations, especially if these offer resistance and do not want to grow toward these western achievements. The result will be a "struggle between world views," and the end of it is not difficult to predict. No matter what the cultural past of a people or nation may be, it will be unable to resist the desire to pursue science and technology, for the simple reason that these two demonstrate with all possible clarity how much they are man's destiny. As Hocking expresses it, they are "universals"—once discovered, they become ingredients of every form of culture.[1]

A different question, however, is whether the entire western mentality has to be taken over together with physical science and technology. Here the reply is definitely in the negative, for the way in which the inner growth of science and technology has influenced the West contains not only necessary factors but also facticitous elements. An example is the secularizing influence exercised by physical science. This influence was partially necessary, insofar as it revealed greater possibilities for man's life on earth, but it was also partially of a purely accidental nature, caused by the way in which seventeenth century theology reacted to the new science. Although for a time it seemed that physical science would gradually replace theology and philosophy, *de facto* this substitution did not occur. On the contrary, precisely in our technological age there is reason to speak of an important renewal of theology in both Catholic and Protestant circles.

---

[1] W. E. Hocking, *The Coming World Civilization*, New York, 1956, pp. 52 ff.

Faith and Science. This consideration leads us to another point. In Chapter Nine we spoke of the modification of man's picture of nature, the world, and himself under the influence of physical science and technology. The modification in question is very real. Certain features of the ancient and medieval picture have been definitely lost in the new era, and no one in the twentieth century views the world in the same way as the Greeks and the Middle Ages did.

Nevertheless, this statement needs to be qualified. First of all, it applies only to contemporaries who are to a certain extent familiar with physical science and technology. There are still people on earth who continue to live in the Stone Age, and there are also many others whose life rolls along in the same fashion as prevailed in past centuries, even though they have incidental contact with modern technology. On the other hand, it is true that this situation will end in a relatively short time. By their very nature physical science and technology tend to spread with lightning speed, not only because they are essentially universal, but also because they have at their disposal the necessary means of communication to make this universality effective.

There is, however, also another and more fundamental reason for qualifying the above-mentioned statement. While it is true that there are many bonds which unite men in the twentieth century, there are also other factors which separate them. In certain respects modern man differs from medieval man by virtue of the development of science and technology, but there is nothing in this development which prevents the man of the twentieth century to feel closer in other respects to the Middle Ages than to some of his contemporaries. Even if he pursues science and technology to the fullest extent, the Christian of the twentieth century sees nature as God's creation, just as medieval man did. This agreement, of course, does not exclude differences. For the man of the twentieth century viewing nature as God's creation does not imply that the natural order is an immutable order which is beyond human control. This difference, however, is concerned with a subordinate point and does not exclude essential agreement. As God's creation, nature possesses a sacred character, even for modern man. It is a gift of God. Although this gift constitutes now more of a task than it did in the Middle Ages, it still remains a gift.

True, many people of the twentieth century no longer see and experience nature as a gift of God, but they cannot appeal to the development of physical science to justify their departure from the view of medieval man. For even twentieth century physical science and technology have to start with what is given and have to rely constantly on the givenness of nature.

Are Non-Western Cultures Doomed to Disappear? There are many divergent interpretations of physical science which this science itself cannot solve. Although physical science knows that it is bound by what is *given,* by data in the literal sense of the term, the implications of this situation lie beyond the boundaries of this science. Here too the non-reflective and abstract character of physical science, spoken of in the first chapters, manifests itself. Because of this abstract character and because of the actually existing divergence of interpretation which is connected with it, it is impossible to reply *a priori* to the question to what extent physical science can be harmonized with civilizations other than western culture.

Nevertheless, two points are certain. First of all, whatever elements of other cultures contradict the view of nature and of man that is embodied in physical science are doomed to extinction. Secondly, the way in which physical science and technology have actually influenced western civilization contained also many factors which were merely *de facto* present. For this reason the encounter between the mental attitude of science and technology and other civilizations may ultimately prove to enrich general human culture considerably, even though at first such an encounter will almost always undermine the old cultural possessions.

The situation could hardly be different, for every ancient cultural treasure contains elements that cannot be put into harmony with the mental attitude of physical science. In every civilization the relationship of man and nature occupies such a central position that factors which modify this relationship effectively, as is done by physical science and technology, cannot avoid interfering profounding with a cultural pattern that is based upon a prescientific relationship between man and nature.

Even the Greeks were unable to foresee the inner logic governing the development of what they began in their philosophy and science. Like them, we are not capable of forecasting what the spread of western science and technology will do to other cultures, although it may be true that we know a little more about it than the Greeks did. More than just a little, however, this knowledge does not seem to be.

2. *The Relationship of Spirit and Matter*

The Abstract Character of Physical Science and Technology. A second leading idea which guided us throughout our investigation with respect to the evaluation of science and technology was that their pursuit may not be seen separately from the essence of man, who as spirit-in-matter must become fully himself in and through matter. Although physical science may be directly concerned only with material nature, indirectly the human spirit seeks in physical science also understanding of himself as a spirit which is bound up with matter.

The abstract and non-reflective character of physical science does not contradict this fundamental orientation of this science. For it shows how much physical science, as an abstract science, is embedded in a realm of problems which extends far beyond its own abstract concern. In his self-reflection man always finds himself in this broader realm— a sign of the sovereign nature of the human spirit which is never fully absorbed by a certain method but judges also its own activity. Of course, in physical science itself this judgment remains implicit, for it is not a judgment within the realm of physical science but *about* it. Despite its implicitness, it permeates the whole of physical science as the manifestation of the tendency of the human spirit, which is present also in physical science, to greater self-realization through the understanding of its material conditions.

On the other hand, the abstractness of physical science reveals also the deficiency of man's mind. For abstract knowledge is not complete knowledge and, in addition, man is constantly exposed to the danger of disregarding the abstractness in question. If he does so, he literally loses sight of himself by considering the method of physical science as the only valid one and its view of the world and of man as the only objective view.[2]

The Danger of Misestimating Physical Science. This danger reveals itself most clearly when the physicist turns his attention to the phenomena of life and even more when he speaks about specifically human activities. Because of its abstract method, physical science itself does not know what perception is, what memory, anger, thinking, and speaking are. It does not know these things as a matter of principle, because its method allows it to register only externally

---

[2]That there is no question here of a meaningless metaphor when we say that man loses sight of himself appears from the fact that far too often man's spiritual nature has been denied in the name of physical science.

observable phenomena. It knows the specifically human, as it were, only from the outside and is never present to it from within. The *man* who the physicist is, of course, has knowledge of these things from his own inner experience and from his contact with his fellow men. Without realizing it, he projects one realm of experience into the other, thus making the physically registered stimulus perception itself, the clicking of the adding machine (as a model of the brain) thinking, and the punching of slots in the punch strip remembering. The result is that the physicist seems to have captured the whole of human reality in his physical and technical concepts.

This misconception contains a twofold fatal danger. On the one hand, it easily leads to materialism and, on the other, it may give rise to the view—which is perhaps even worse—that physical science suffers from a limitless superiority complex because it would occupy itself here with something that supposedly lies entirely outside its method and competence. This view would inevitably lead to a dualistic conception of man with all the fatal consequences inherent in such a conception. The specifically human element would thus be seen as superadded to material being, so that physical science would be entitled to devote itself only to matter but not to studying the spirit.

Once, however, physical science is understood to be an abstract science, there is no objection whatsoever against saying that its object extends to the *whole* of material reality, even where this reality is living and spiritual. Its approach will always remain an *abstract* approach; nevertheless its contributions, incomplete as it may be, will be indispensable for the understanding of man's reality. Just as the approach of physical science cannot absolve us from the necessity to approach human reality psychologically, sociologically, historically, and philosophically, so likewise these other approaches cannot dispense us from the physical approach.

There was a time when physical science was greatly overestimated. Here and there it begins to appear now as if this science is being underestimated. True, all realize that man cannot do without this science, but the reason for it is sought not in its spiritual value but in its practical usefulness. In Europe, for instance, many object against the inclusion of science courses in the gymnasium, because they consider this a kind of surrender to the spirit of the time and apparently also a sin against the cultural heritage of the Greeks. A very strange kind of sin, indeed, at least if Plato and Aristotle may be said to have contributed something to the Greek heritage, not to mention others like Euclid.

The Danger of Misestimating Technology. As could be expected because of its intimate connection with physical science, similar remarks could be made about technology. The pursuit of technology is capable of giving rise to the mistaken idea that technical advances are the only real kind of progress and that the technological solutions of problems facing human society are the only necessary solutions. Just as bad, however, again would be the idea that technology has nothing whatsoever to do with the culture of the mind. Because man is spirit-in-matter, all spiritual culture as human culture has to be realized in and through matter. This is the reason why technology is an indispensable part of all spiritual culture, the reason why everything has also a technical aspect, and why technology extends into all realms of human activities. There is no question here of arrogance and undue interference, at least not necessarily so, if the relative value of the technical approach is kept in mind.

Ideal and Reality. No one can know beforehand what possibilities will still be revealed by physical science and technology. If we look at the past, it may seem that science has already explained many phenomena, but internal critique teaches us that almost nothing has been accomplished. How little we know, for example, of the way in which man's nervous system works and of the spiritual functions depending upon this system!

For technology, likewise, it is true that in comparison with ancient times it has made enormous progress, but also that it is still very crude, at least in comparison with the structures encountered in living nature.

This awareness of the distance between the ideal and reality, between what the relationship of matter and spirit could be and what it really is, contains a permanent motive for man to continue his pursuit of science and technology. What urges him on is the desire to know his human potentialities better and to realize them more perfectly. The ideal before his mind is a matter-spirit relationship in which matter will appear not so much as a hindrance of the spirit than as its natural expression, somewhat in the way in which he experiences his body to some extent as the expression of his spirit.

INDEX OF NAMES

369

INDEX OF SUBJECT MATTER

370

Bradford College Library

Q175-M49   BCHA

Me... ...nolo

Melsen   35291

DISCARDED

Bradford Junior College Library

Bradford, Massachusetts

DATE DUE

NOV 3 '64		
JA 14 '70		
MY 12 '76		
GAYLORD		PRINTED IN U.S.A.